Student Solutions Manual and Supplemental Problems to accompany
GENETICS
ANALYSIS OF GENES AND GENOMES
SIXTH EDITION

DANIEL L. HARTL · ELIZABETH W. JONES
PREPARED BY ELENA R. LOZOVSKY

JONES AND BARTLETT PUBLISHERS

Sudbury, Massachusetts

BOSTON TORONTO LONDON SINGAPORE

World Headquarters
Jones and Bartlett Publishers
40 Tall Pine Drive
Sudbury, MA 01776
978-443-5000
info@jbpub.com
www.jbpub.com

Jones and Bartlett Publishers Canada
2406 Nikanna Road
Mississauga, ON L5C 2W6
CANADA

Jones and Bartlett Publishers International
Barb House, Barb Mews
London W6 7PA
UK

ISBN: 0-7637-2931-0

Printed in the United States of America
08 07 06 05 10 9 8 7 6 5 4 3 2

For my mother Klara and my son Ilya.

Contents

Preface

The Supplemental Problems provided in this book have been designed as learning opportunities rather than exercises to be completed by rote. They were written specifically to accompany *Genetics: Analysis of Genes and Genomes*, Sixth Edition, by Daniel L. Hartl and Elizabeth W. Jones, and have been organized into chapters that parallel those of the book. All of the problems can be solved through application of the concepts and principles explicated in *Genetics*, Sixth Edition.

The objective of this student supplement is to help the student develop skills in problem solving. Many of the problems require the understanding and application of only a single concept, such as Mendelian segregation or polypeptide translation. Other problems require application of several concepts in logical order, for example, problems that combine segregation and recombination or that consider the consequences of a mutation on the amino acid sequence of a polypeptide.

Most chapters include one or more questions that call for definitions of some of the key terms from the main text. Some chapters also include a few multiple-choice questions as practice in the genre. However, the vast majority or problems emphasize reasoning skills. Some call only for verbal proficiency, asking for a very short essay explaining how relevant concepts can be used alone or in combination to account for biological observations. Other questions are quantitative and require a precise numerical answer. Problems requiring calculation make use of only simple arithmetic or algebra and draw upon the generally relevant laws of probability and statistics explained in the text. Students should be encouraged not only to give a numerical answer but also to think a problem through, in terms of "order of magnitude," in order to verify their approach and method of solution as well as to catch any howling mistakes caused by miscalculation.

The answers to the Chapter-End Problems from the main text as well as the answers to all Supplemental Problems included here have been worked in full and the reasoning explained in detail. You, the student, are strongly urged to try to work a problem before giving up and consulting the answer. If the method of solution is not immediately apparent, do not go to the answer immediately. Think about it for a while, consult the corresponding chapter in the text, or perhaps come back to it later. Look up the answer only after a few tries. With this approach, you will be pleased to learn that problems that at first look very difficult are often within your capability. A willingness to be patient, to let your mind work quietly and subconsciously on a problem before looking at the answer, pays rewards of positive feedback and increased self-confidence. Even when you are unable to solve a problem after several attempts, a delay in looking at the answer will give the problem more impact, and the method of solution will be less likely to be forgotten.

The problems are graded in difficulty. Although some chapters contain a few problems that are admittedly difficult, they nevertheless do not require any concepts or principles beyond those discussed in the main text. Some problems are intended to be challenging, and even if you are unsuccessful in solving them, you will gain additional understanding of genetics when you look at the answer.

I will be glad to have any feedback from students or instructors who make use of these problems. I welcome comments and suggestions, corrections, and especially additional problems for inclusion in later renditions of this collection. I can be contacted by electronic mail at elozovsk@oeb.harvard.edu.

I am grateful to my colleagues Justin Blumenstiel, Erica Pantages, and Colin Meiklejohn for valuable ideas and helpful discussions. I also wish to acknowledge Rebecca Seastrong, Stephen L. Weaver, and Anne Spencer of Jones and Bartlett for their support and assistance. Special thanks go to Dan Hartl for his effort in editing, correcting errors, and suggesting problems. I am grateful for his encouragement and support that were absolutely vital for this project.

Elena R. Lozovsky
Harvard University

Chapter 1: Introduction to Molecular Genetics and Genomics
Answers to Chapter-end problems

Fill-ins

1. cytosine (C)
2. proteome
3. bacteriophage or phage
4. pleiotropy or pleiotropic effect
5. enzyme
6. genetic code
7. metabolic pathway or biochemical pathway
8. inborn error of metabolism
9. transcription
10. translation

Analysis and Applications

ANS 1.1. a. false; **b.** true; **c.** true; **d.** false.

ANS 1.2. The structure of DNA suggested the following copying mechanism: the strands of the parent duplex could separate and each individual strand could serve as a template for the formation of a new daughter strand with a complementary sequence of bases. Watson and Crick also noted that genetic information could be coded by the sequence of bases along the DNA molecule, analogous to letters of the alphabet printed on a strip of paper. Finally, they noted that changes in genetic information could result from errors in replication, and the altered nucleotide sequence could be then perpetuated.

ANS 1.3. Polarity means that the strand has a directionality, a "left" and "right" or equivalently a "top" and "bottom." One end is the 5' end (conventionally written at the upper left) and the other is the 3' end. To say that the strands in a duplex have opposite polarity is to say that they run in reverse directions: the 5' end of one strand is paired with the 3' end of the other, and the other way around.

ANS 1.4. Replication results in two daughter DNA duplexes, each identical in base sequence with the parental molecule (except for possible mutations). Each of the daughter molecules contains one of the original intact parental strands.

ANS 1.5. The messenger RNA carries the genetic information from DNA to the ribosome and is used as a template for protein synthesis. The ribosome is the physical structure in the cell on which a popypeptide chain is formed. The transfer RNA molecules are adapters that allow each codon in the messenger RNA to specify the presence of a particular amino acid at the corresponding position in the polypeptide chain. There is only one type of ribosome, but many different types of transfer RNA (typically, more than one for each amino acid).

ANS 1.6. A mixture of heat-killed S cells and living R cells causes pneumonia in mice, but neither heat-killed S cells nor living R cells alone will do so.

ANS 1.7. The substance was destroyed by DNA-degrading enzymes but not by protein-degrading enzymes.

ANS 1.8. Phenol would not destroy the transforming activity, strong alkali would.

ANS 1.9. The inside of the head is mainly DNA and the rest of the phage is mainly protein. When a bacterial cell is infected, the head contents are transferred into the cell, but the outer "ghost" of the phage remains attached to the external surface of the cell.

ANS 1.10. Because the mature T2 phage contains only DNA and protein; the labeled RNA was left behind in material released by the burst cells.

ANS 1.11. A small amount of protein was also transferred into the bacterial cell during infection, and some of this was even recovered in the progeny phage. A die-hard advocate of protein as the genetic material could claim that the transmitted protein, though small in amount, was the critical in the hereditary process.

ANS 1.12. Because the amount of A equals that of T, and the amount of G equals that of C, it can be inferred that the DNA in this bacteriophage is double-stranded; 56 percent of the base pairs are A–T pairs and 44 percent are G–C pairs.

ANS 1.13. Because, in this case, that amount of A does not equal that of T, and the amount of G does not equal that of C, it can be concluded that the DNA molecule is single stranded, not double stranded.

ANS 1.14. Because A pairs with T and G pairs with C, the base composition of the other strand must be 24 percent T, 28 percent A, 22 percent C, and 26 percent G.

ANS 1.15. Yes, it is possible, because in some viruses the genetic material is RNA.

ANS 1.16. Because of A–T and G–C base pairing, the complementary strand has the sequence 5'-CCGGGTAAAAGTGCATACGAT-3'. Note that the paired strands have opposite 5'–3' polarity.

ANS 1.17. In this region the complementary strand has the sequence 5'-CGACGACGACGACGA-3'.

ANS 1.18. The probability that four particular bases have the sequence 5'-GGCC-3' is $(1/4)^4 =$ 1/256, hence 256 base pairs is the average spacing between consecutive occurrences; similarly, the average spacing for the sequence 5'-GAATTC-3' is 4096 base pairs.

ANS 1.19. The corresponding region of RNA will contain no U (uracil), since U in RNA pairs with A in DNA.

ANS 1.20. The top strand is the RNA because it contains U instead of T; the mismatched base pair is the sixth from the right.

ANS 1.21. The initial part of the RNA transcript matches the DNA template starting at the 10th nucleotide, hence the completed transcript has the sequence 5'-UAGCUACGAUCGCGUUGGA-3'.

ANS 1.22. The complementary sequence is 5'-UAUCGUAU-3'.

ANS 1.23. The codon for phenylalanine must be 5'-UUU-3'.

ANS 1.24. The codon for leucine must be 5'-UUA-3'.

ANS 1.25. Three with *in vitro* translation, namely, 5'-CGC/UUA/CCA/CAU/GUC/GCG/AAC/UCG-3', 5'-C/GCU/UAC/CAC/AUG/UCG/CGA/ACU/CG-3', and 5'-CG/CUU/ACC/ACA/UGU/CGC/GAA/CUC/G-3'. With *in vivo* translation there is only one, namely, 5'-CGCUUACCAC>AUG/UCG/CGA/ACU/CG-3', where the symbol ">" means "start translation with next codon."

ANS 1.26. Six. Either DNA strand could be transcribed, and each transcript could be translated in any one of three reading frames.

ANS 1.27. The amino acids alternate because, with a triplet code, the codons alternate, namely 5'-UCU/CUC/UCU/CUC/UCU/CUC-3'. From this result we can conclude that the Ser is and Leu are encoded by 5'-UCU-3' and 5'-CUC-3', because we cannot specify which codon corresponds to which amino acid because *in vitro* translation can begin with either 5'-UCU-3' or 5'-CUC-3'.

ANS 1.28. The result means that an mRNA is translated in nonoverlapping groups of three nucleotides: the genetic code is a triplet code.

ANS 1.29. There are 64 possible codons and only 20 amino acids, hence some amino acids (most, in fact) are specified by two or more codons. A mutation that changes a codon for a particular amino acid into a synonymous codon for the same amino acid does not change the amino acid sequence.

ANS 1.30. The codon 5'–UGG–3' codes for Trp, and in this random polymer the Trp codon is expected with a frequency of $1/4 \times 3/4 \times 3/4 = 9/64$. The amino acid Val could be specified by either 5'–GUU–3' or 5'–GUG–3'; the former has an expected frequency of $3/4 \times 1/4 \times 1/4 = 3/64$ and the latter of $3/4 \times 1/4 \times 3/4 = 9/64$, totaling 12/64 or 3/16. The amino acid Phe could be specified only by 5'–UUU–3' in this random polymer, and so Phe would have an expected frequency of $(1/4)^3 = 1/64$.

Challenge Problems

ANS 1.31. a. Met–Ser–Thr–Ala–Val–Leu–Glu–Asn–Pro–Gly. **b.** The mutation changes the initiation codon into a noninitiation codon, and so translation will not start with the first AUG; translation will start either with the next AUG farther along the mRNA or, if this is too distant, not at all. **c.** Met–Ser–Thr–Ala–Val–Leu–Glu–Asn–Pro–Gly; there is no change, because both 5'–UCC–3' and 5'–UCG–3' code for serine. **d.** Met–Ser–Thr–Ala–Ala–Leu–Glu–Asn–Pro–Gly; there is a Val →

Ala amino acid replacement because 5'–GUC–3' codes for Val whereas 5'–GCC–3' codes for Ala. **e.** Met–Ser–Thr–Ala–Val–Leu; translation is terminated at the UAA because 5'–UAA–3' is a "stop" (termination) codon.

ANS 1.32. a. The amino acid sequence is Met–Val–His–Leu–Thr–Pro–Gln–Gln–Lys–Ser. . .. **b.** The amino acid sequence is Met–Val–His–Leu–Thr–Pro–Arg–Arg–Ser–Leu. . .; all codons coming after the deletion are changed because the reading frame shifts, relative to the nonmutant RNA, by –1. **c.** The amino acid sequence is Met–Val–His–Leu–Thr–Pro; In this case translation terminates after the Pro codon because the frameshift mutation creates the termination codon 5' –UGA–3'.

ANS 1.33.

```
a.
3'-TACCACGTGGACTGAGGACTCCTCTTCAGA-5'
5'-ATGGTGCACCTGACTCCTGAGGAGAAGTCT-3'
b.
3'-TACCACGTGGACTGAGGCTCCTCTTCAGA-5'
5'-ATGGTGCACCTGACTCCGAGGAGAAGTCT-3'
c.
3'-TACCACGTGGACTGAGGCACTCCTCTTCAGA-5'
5'-ATGGTGCACCTGACTCCTTGAGGAGAAGTCT-3'
```

Supplemental problems with answers.

S1.2. When a human trait is genetic in origin (for example, a disorder caused by an inborn error of metabolism), does this mean that the trait cannot be influenced by the environment?
ANS S1.2. No, there are numerous cases in which physical therapy, surgery, special diets, drugs or other medications can be used to minimize or eliminate the effects of a "genetic" disorder. The statement that a trait is "genetic" in origin merely means that, within the normal range of environments to which people are exposed, genotype is the main determining factor in the presence of the condition.

S1.3. What is meant by the term "pleiotropy" and what is a "pleiotropic effect"? What is the relevance of sickle-cell anemia to this phenomenon?
ANS S1.3. Pleiotropy is the phenomenon in which a single mutant gene affects multiple, seemingly unrelated traits. The effect on a trait due to pleiotropy is called a pleiotropic effect. Sickle-cell anemia is relevant because a single amino acid replacement in the beta-globin gene results in pleiotropic effects on circulation, function of the major organs, growth rate, susceptibility to infections, and many other traits.

S1.4. What special genetic relationship is there between the cells within a single colony of bacteria growing on nutrient medium on a petri dish?
ANS S1.4. Because they arise from repeated divisions of a single cell, they are all genetically identical, except for possible new mutations that may have occurred during the growth of the colony.

S1.5. What facts known prior to Avery, MacLeod, and McCarty's experiment indirectly suggested that DNA might play a role in the genetic material?

ANS S1.5. The importance of the nucleus in inheritance was implied by its role in fertilization. The discovery of chromosomes inside the nucleus, their behavior during the cell division, and the observation that each species has a characteristic chromosome number, made it likely that chromosomes were the carriers of the genes. Microscopic studies showed that DNA and proteins are both present in chromosomes. Furthermore, almost all cells of a given species contain a constant amount of DNA, whereas the amount and kinds of proteins differ greatly in different cell types.

S1.6. Prior to the experiments of Avery, MacLeod, and McCarty and of Hershey and Chase, why did most biologists and biochemists believe that proteins were probably the genetic material?
ANS S1.6. It was generally believed that the genetic material must be a very complex molecule. Proteins were chemically the most complex macromolecules known at the time. DNA was thought to be a monotonous polymer composed of a simple repeating unit of four nucleotides.

S1.7. Each of the following statements pertains to the experiments of Avery, MacLeod, and McCarty on *Streptococcus pneumoniae*. Classify each statement as true or false. Which single statement is a conclusion that can be drawn from the experiments themselves?
 a. The polysaccharide capsule is required for virulence (the ability to infect and kill mice).
 b. The polysaccharide capsule is not important for virulence.
 c. DNA encodes the sequence of sugars in the polysaccharide capsule.
 d. DNA is the polysaccharide capsule.
 e. Proteins are not the molecules that carry the hereditary information for synthesis of the polysaccharide capsule.
ANS S1.7. a. and **e.** are true, the rest are false. Statement **e.** is one conclusion from the experiments. Although **a.** is also true, it was known prior to the experiments.

S1.8. In the Hershey-Chase experiment, why was it necessary to use a technique that would strip virtually all of the phage heads and tails from the infected cells?
ANS S1.8. Because the heads and tails are labeled with radioactive sulfur in their proteins and any radioactive phosphorous in their DNA that was not injected into the cell.

S1.9. What critical finding in Hershey and Chase's experiment enabled them to interpret the results as a proof that the genetic material in bacteriophage T2 is DNA?
ANS S1.9. The critical finding was that most of the transferred ^{32}P-labeled DNA, but very small amounts of the transferred ^{35}S-labeled protein, was inherited by the progeny phage particles.

S1.10. Define the following terms: replication, transcription, translation, mutation, natural selection.
ANS S1.10. Replication is the process of copying a DNA molecule to create two identical daughter molecules. Transcription is the process by which the information contained in a template strand of DNA is copied into a single-stranded RNA molecule of complementary base sequence. Translation is the process by which an mRNA molecule is used to specify the amino acid sequence of a polypeptide chain on a ribosome. Mutation is any heritable alteration in a gene. Natural selection is the process of evolutionary adaptation in which genotypes genetically best suited to survive and reproduce in a particular environment give rise to a disproportionate share of the offspring and, over many generations, gradually increase the overall ability of the population to survive and reproduce in that environment.

S1.11. What can we infer about the function of DNA from its structure?

ANS S1.11. Three major features of DNA function can be postulated on the basis of its structure. (1) The nucleotide sequence of the DNA molecule can be duplicated if each of the strands is used as a template for the formation of a new strand with a complementary sequence of bases; the resulting daughter duplexes could be then distributed to the progeny cells in the process of cell division. (2). Genetic information could be coded by the sequence of bases along the DNA molecule, analogous to letters of the alphabet printed on a strip of paper. (3). Changes in genetic information could result from errors in copying; the altered nucleotide sequence could be then perpetuated in the process of replication.

S1.12. Is it correct to say that DNA is always the genetic material?

ANS S1.12. No. Certain viruses lack DNA and instead utilize RNA as the genetic material. However, it is true to say that, in cells, DNA is always the genetic material.

S1.13. One of the early models for the structure of DNA was the so-called tetranucleotide hypothesis. According to this hypothesis, one of each of the four nucleotides containing adenine, thymine, guanine, and cytosine joined together to form a covalently linked planar unit (the "tetranucleotide"); these units were, in turn, linked together to yield a repeating polymer of the tetranucleotide. Why could a molecule with this structure never serve as the genetic material?

ANS S1.13. As a simple repeating polymer with identical tetranucleotide subunits, it could not carry genetic information specifying an amino acid sequence.

S1.14. What are the major chemical components found in DNA?

ANS S1.14. DNA is a polymer composed of a five-carbon sugar (2' deoxyribose), phosphoric acid, and four nitrogen-containing bases. The bases are adenine, guanine, thymine, and cytosine.

S1.15. The repeating unit of DNA is:

 a. A ribonucleotide.
 b. An amino acid.
 c. A nitrogenous base.
 d. A sugar, deoxyribose.
 e. None of the above.

ANS S1.15. e; the repeating unit is a deoxyribonucleotide, consisting of a deoxyribose sugar, a phosphate group, and one of the four bases.

S1.16. The two strands of a duplex DNA molecule are said to be complementary in base sequence. Which of the following statements are implied by the complementary nature of the strands?

 a. The two strands have the same sequence of bases.
 b. The base A in one strand is paired with a T in the other strand.
 c. One strand consists of A's paired with T's; the other strand consists of G's paired with C's.
 d. The base G in one strand is paired with a C in the other strand.
 e. The two strands have the same sequence of bases when read in opposite directions.

ANS S1.16. b and **d.**

S.1.17. One strand of a DNA duplex has the base sequence 5'-TGCACTTTACGCCAT-3'. What is the base sequence of the complementary strand?

ANS S1.17. 5'-ATGGCGTAAAGTGCA-3'

S1.18. In the following statements about double-stranded DNA, square brackets indicate the number of molecules. For example, [A] means the number of molecules of the base ade nine, and [deoxyribose] means the number of molecules of 2' deoxyribose. Classify each of the statements as true or false.

 a. [A] = [G]
 b. [A] = [C]
 c. [A] = [T]
 d. [A] + [G] = [T] + [C]
 e. [deoxyribose] = [phosphate]

ANS S1.18. **a.** and **b.** are false; **c.** and **d.** are true because A pairs with T and G pairs with C; **e.** is true because each deoxyribose is attached to one phosphate group.

S1.19. When the base composition of double-stranded DNA from *Micrococcus luteus* was determined, 37.5 percent of the bases were found to be cytosine. What is the percentage of adenine in the DNA of this organism?

ANS S1.19. Because [G] = [C], the amount of C + G = 37.5 + 37.5 = 75 percent. The percent A + T = 100 - 75 = 25 percent. Because [A] = [T], the percent A = 25/2 = 12.5 percent.

S1.20. How many different sequences of length 2 can be created from the letters A, T, G, and C, allowing for repetition of any of the letters? How many sequences of length 3? 4? 5? 10? Of length *n*?

ANS S1.20. $4 \times 4 = 16$ for sequences of length 2; $4 \times 4 \times 4 = 64$ for sequences of length 3; $4^4 = 256$ for sequences of length 4. The other answers are $4^5 = 1024$, $4^{10} = 1,048,576$, and 4^n.

S1.21. Which nucleic acid base is found only in DNA? Which is found only in RNA?

ANS S1.21. Thymine is normally found only in DNA, uracil only in RNA.

S1.22. What are three principal structural differences between RNA and DNA?

ANS S1.22. RNA differs from DNA in three principal ways: (1) the sugar phosphate backbone contains ribose rather than deoxyribose; (2) RNA contains the base uracil (U) instead of thymine (T); (3) RNA usually exists as a single strand, although any particular molecule of RNA may contain short regions of complementary base pairs that can come together to form duplexes.

S1.23. What is the most likely reason for the participation of RNA intermediates in the process of information flow from DNA to protein?

ANS S1.23. The most widely accepted reason is that the participation of RNA is a relic of the earliest stages of evolution. Several observations support the hypothesis that the first forms of life used RNA both for carrying information and catalysis. Later in evolution, additional complexity was incorporated as the informational component was transferred to DNA and as the catalytic functions were transferred to proteins. Nevertheless, because RNA played such a central role in the earliest forms of life, it became locked into the processes of information transfer and protein synthesis, and so it remains today.

S1.24. In ordinary English, the term "palindrome" refers to a word or phrase that reads the same forward and backward, like "madam." Certain short base sequences in duplex DNA are also called palindromes. Two examples are 5'-AGCT-3' and 5'-GGACTT-3'. What feature of these sequences justifies the term?

ANS S1.24. The read the same backward as forward, but on opposite strands.

S.1.25. Which of the following sequences are palindromes?

 a. 5'-ACGCGT-3'
 b. 5'-ATAT-3'
 c. 5'-ACAACA-3'

ANS S.1.25. a and **b.**

S1.26. A duplex DNA molecule contains a random sequence of the four nucleotides with equal proportions of each. What is the average spacing between consecutive occurrences of the sequence 5'-TAAGTTC-3'?

ANS S1.26. The probability that four particular bases have the sequence 5'-TAAGC-3' is $(1/4)^5$ = 1/1024, hence 1024 base pairs is the average spacing between consecutive occurrences.

S1.27. A polymer is made that has a random sequence consisting of 40 percent C's, 30 percent A's, 10 percent G's and 20 percent U's. Among the amino acids in the polypeptide chains resulting from *in vitro* translation, what is the expected frequency of Met? of His?

ANS S1.27. The codon 5'–AUG–3' codes for Met, and in this random polymer the Met codon is expected with a frequency of $0.3 \times 0.2 \times 0.1 = 0.009$. The amino acid His could be specified by either 5'–CAU–3' or 5'–CAC–3'; the former has an expected frequency of $0.4 \times 0.3 \times 0.2 = 0.024$ and the latter of $0.4 \times 0.3 \times 0.4 = 0.048$, totaling 0.072.

S1.28. How many different DNA sequences can encode the amino acid sequence Met–His-Leu?

ANS S1.28. There is one codon for Met, two for His, and six for Leu. Therefore, the total number of different sequences is 1 x 2 x 6 = 12.

S1.29. Can all the existing diversity of life be explained as a result of adaptive evolution brought about by natural selection?

ANS S1.29. Not all of the biological diversity. Natural selection is the key process in bringing about the genetic adaptation of organisms to their environment. However, some evolutionary changes are not necessarily adaptive. For instance, slightly harmful mutations can become incorporated into populations by pure chance. Furthermore, some traits exist not because they are selectively advantageous in themselves but because they are pleiotropic effects of genes selected for other reasons. Furthermore, some of the major extinction events in Earth history do not result from natural selection (for example, the mass extinction of dinosaurs as a result of an asteroid collision with earth).

Chapter 2: DNA Structure and DNA Manipulation
Answers to Chapter-end problems

Fill-ins

1. oligonucleotide or primer
2. denaturation
3. restriction fragment length polymorphism (RFLP)
4. amplification
5. gel electrophoresis
6. restriction endonuclease or restriction enzyme
7. codominant
8. Southern blot
9. DNA polymorphism
10. nucleic acid hybridization or renaturation

Analysis and Applications

ANS 2.1. Each fragment terminates with a single-stranded overhang whose base sequence is complementary to that of any other fragment.

ANS 2.2. A DNA palindrome reads the same forward and backward, but along opposite strands. **a.** Yes, partner strand reads 3'-TTAA-5'; **b.** No, partner strand reads 3'-TTTT-5'; **c.** Yes, partner strand reads 3'-TTNAA-5', where the two N's must be Watson-Crick base paired; **d.** No, partner strand reads 3'-TT(T/A)TT-5'; **e.** Yes, partner strand reads 3'-TT(C/G)AA-5'.

ANS 2.3. a. 5'-AATT-3'; **b.** 5'-ATGCAT-3'; **c.** 5'-GGNCC-3'; **d.** 5'-ATNNAT-3'.

ANS 2.4. a. *Hae*III produces blunt ends; **b.** *Mae*I produces a 5' overhang; **c.** *Cfo*I produces a 3' overhang.

ANS 2.5. The fragment sizes, from top to bottom, are 12 kb, 9 kb, 6 kb, and 3 kb.

ANS 2.6.

ANS 2.7.

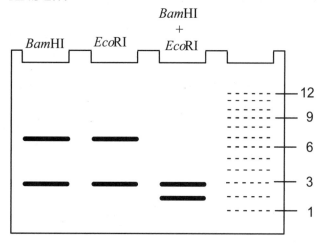

ANS 2.8. a. $B_5 = T$; **b.** $B_6 = G$; **c.** $B_7 = $ pyrimidine; **d.** $B_8 = T$ or A.

ANS 2.9. 1 with B_1, 2 with B_2, 3 with B_3, 4 with B_4.

ANS 2.10. The probability of a restriction site is $1/4^n$, where n is the number of nucleotides in the site. **a.** $1/4^4 = 0.0039$; **b.** $1/4^6 = 0.00024$; **c.** $1/4^8 = 0.000015$.

ANS 2.11. The probability of a restriction site is $1/4^n$, where n is the number of nucleotides in the site, and the average distance between sites is the reciprocal of this. **a.** $4^4 = 256$ bp ≈ 0.25 kb; **b.** $4^6 = 4096$ bp ≈ 4 kb; **c.** $4^8 = 65536$ bp ≈ 66 kb.

ANS 2.12. a. $3 \times 10^9/256 \approx 12$ million; $3 \times 10^9/4096 \approx 730,000$; $3 \times 10^9/65536 \approx 46,000$.

ANS 2.13. Every *Bam*HI site is a *Sau*3A site because the *Bam*HI site includes a *Sau*3A site. However, not every *Sau*3A site is necessarily a *Bam*HI site, because the nucleotides at opposite ends of the site may not be 5'-G and C-3'.

ANS 2.14. There are two BamHI sites in the original molecule. Cleavage produces the fragments:
```
5'-ATTG-3'
3'-TAACCTAG-5'
5'-GATCCAAACCCCAAAG-3'
   3'-GTTTGGGGTTTCCTAG-5'
5'-GATCCTTA-3'
   3'-GAAT-5'
```
If the fragments come back together and are sealed, the middle fragment can be present in either the original orientation or reversed, since the ends are complementary. Hence, the possible products are
```
5'-ATTGGATCCAAACCCCAAAGGATCCTTA-3'
3'-TAACCTAGGTTTGGGGTTTCCTAGGAAT-5'
```
or
```
5'-ATTGGATCCTTTGGGGTTTGGATCCTTA-3'
3'-TAACCTAGGAAACCCCAAACCTAGGAAT-5'.
```

ANS 2.15.

a. 5'-ATGCCCTGCA-3'
 3'-TACGGG-5'

 5'-GTACCATGACGCGTTACGCAGCTGATCGAAACGCGTATATATGCC-3'
 3'-ACGTCATGGTACTGCGCAATGCGTCGACTAGCTTTGCGCATATATACGG-5'

b. 5'-ATGCCCTGCAGTACCATGACGCGTTACGCAG-3'
 3'-TACGGGACGTCATGGTACTGCGCAATGCGTC-5'

 5'-CTGATCGAAACGCGTATATATGCC-3'
 3'-GACTAGCTTTGCGCATATATACGG-5'

c. 5'-ATGCCCTGCAGTACCATGA-3'
 3'-TACGGGACGTCATGGTACTGCGC-5'
 5'-CGCGTTACGCAGCTGATCGAAA-3'
 3'-AATGCGTCGACTAGCTTTGCGC-5'
 5'-CGCGTATATATGCC-3'
 3'-ATATATACGG-5'

ANS 2.16.

a. 5'-ATGCCCTGCA-3'
 3'-TACGGG-5'
 5'-GTACCATGA-3'
 3'-ACGTCATGGTACTGCGC-5'

 5'-CGCGTTACGCAGCTGATCGAAA-3'
 3'-AATGCGTCGACTAGCTTTGCGC-5'
 5'-CGCGTATATATGCC-3'
 3'-ATATATACGG-5'

b. 5'-ATGCCCTGCAGTACCATGA-3'
 3'-TACGGGACGTCATGGTACTGCGC-5'
 5'-CGCGTTACGCAG-3'
 3'-AATGCGTC-5'
 5'-CTGATCGAAA-3'
 3'-GACTAGCTTTGCGC-5'
 5'-CGCGTATATATGCC-3'
 3'-ATATATACGG-5'

ANS 2.17.
Cleavage with *Pst*I destroys the *Pvu*II site, but cleavage with *Pvu*II leaves the *Pst*I site intact.

ANS 2.18. The results imply that the circle contains one *Bam*HI site and one *Eco*RI site separated by a distance of 3 kb. Either of the diagrams below fulfills this requirements. The numbers are the coordinates in kb, arbitrarily assigning the *Bam*HI site to position 0.

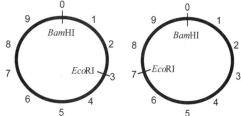

ANS 2.19. Probe A yields bands of 5 and 12 kb, probe B yields bands of 7 and 12 kb.

ANS 2.20. There are three possible genotypes: A_1A_1 (homozygous), A_1A_2 (heterozygous), and A_2A_2 (homozygous). Genomic DNA from homozygous A_1A_1 yields a single band of 4 kb, that from heterozygous A_1A_2 yields bands of 4 kb and 6 kb, and that from A_2A_2 yields a single band of 6 kb.

ANS 2.21. This RFLP has two alleles, one (call it A_1) identified by a 4-kb band and the other (call it A_2) identified by a 12-kb band. The possible genotypes are A_1A_1 (homozygous), A_1A_2 (heterozygous), and A_2A_2 (homozygous), whose phenotypes are, for A_1A_1, one band of 4 kb; for A_1A_2, bands of 4 kb and 12 kb; and, for A_2A_2, one band of 12 kb.

ANS 2.22. Two alleles and three genotypes. The top two DNA molecules are indistinguishable using the probe shown, since both yield a 3 kb restriction fragment that hybridizes with the probe. The bottom molecule yields a 6 kb fragment. Thus the possible genotypes are "*3 / 3*" (homozygous), "*3 / 6*" (heterozygous), and "*6 / 6*" (homozygous).

ANS 2.23. Three alleles. Let A_1 represent the allele that yields the DNA molecule at the top, A_2 that in the middle, and A_3 that at the bottom. They differ in the size of the restriction fragment that hybridizes with the probe. A_1 yields a 3 kb fragment, A_2 a 5 kb fragment, and A_3 a 6 kb fragment. There are 6 possible genotypes. The genotypes and phenotypes (bands observed) are as follows: A_1A_1 (3 kb band only), A_1A_2 (3 kb + 5 kb), A_2A_2 (5 kb only), A_1A_3 (3 kb + 6 kb), A_2A_3 (5 kb + 6 kb), and A_3A_3 (6 kb only).

ANS 2.24. The priming sites are shown in red
5'-GATTACCGGTAAATGCCGGATTAACCCGGGTTATCAGGCCACGTACAACTGGAGTCC-3'
3'-CTAATGGCCATTTACGGCCTAATTGGGCCCAATAGTCCGGTGCATGTTGACCTCAGG-5'
Hence, the amplified fragment has the sequence
5'-AATGCCGGATTAACCCGGGTTATCAGGCCACGTACA-3'
3'-TTACGGCCTAATTGGGCCCAATAGTCCGGTGCATGT-5'

ANS 2.25. No, because the primers have the wrong polarity. They will not pair with any regions of the target DNA strands.

ANS 2.26. a. $3 \text{ kb}/3 \times 10^6 \text{ kb} = 0.0001$ percent. **b.** $(3 \times 2^{10} \text{ kb})/(3 \times 2^{10} \text{ kb} + 3 \times 10^6 \text{ kb}) = 0.1$ percent. **c.** $(3 \times 2^{20} \text{ kb})/(3 \times 2^{20} \text{ kb} + 3 \times 10^6 \text{ kb}) = 51.2$ percent. **d.** $(3 \times 2^{30} \text{ kb})/(3 \times 2^{30} \text{ kb} + 3 \times 10^6 \text{ kb}) = 99.9$ percent.

ANS 2.27. A band that appears in some, but not all, samples is a RAPD polymorphism, hence bands 2, 6, 8, and 11 are RAPD polymorphisms.

ANS 2.28. Since the evidence is based on total genomic DNA from an individual, all bands found in the evidence must match bands in the perpetrator. Anyone with one or more bands that do not match those in the evidence can be excluded. To find the matching bands in the suspects, for each locus draw straight horizontal lines through the bands of X. For locus 1, suspects A, C, D, and G are excluded but B, E, and F not excluded; for locus 2, suspects A, B, C, D, and G are excluded but E and F not excluded; and for locus 3, suspects A, C, D, F, and G are excluded but B and E not excluded. Taking all three probes together, all can be excluded except for suspect E. This does not necessarily imply that E is the robber, only that E cannot be excluded. Nevertheless, a match of three highly polymorphic DNA markers is highly suggestive.

ANS 2.29. For each locus, the child must share one band with the mother and one with the father. For locus 1, the smaller band is shared with the mother, and the allele yielding the larger band could have come from either A or B. For locus 2, the larger band in the child is shared with the mother, and the allele for the smaller band could not have come from A. Hence the evidence from these loci excludes A but does not exclude B.

ANS 2.30. After cleavage, phosphate 2 goes with B1, and phosphate 4 goes with B3, so the B1 and B3 mononucleotides will be radioactive.

Challenge Problems

ANS 2.31. Solve $(1.8 \times 2^n \text{ kb})/(1.8 \times 2^n \text{ kb} + 180 \times 10^3 \text{ kb}) \geq 0.99$, where n is the number of cycles of PCR. The ratio evaluates to 0.988 for $n = 23$ and to 0.994 for $n = 24$. The desired answer is therefore $n = 24$.

ANS 2.32. Evidently there are so many alleles in the population the most genotypes at each locus are heterozygous for two different alleles. For a couple to be the parents of X, the father must have a band that matches one of those from X, and the mother must have a band that matches the remaining band from X. X must inherit one allele from the father and the other allele from the mother. To find the matching bands in the putative parents, for each locus draw straight horizontal lines through the bands of X. For locus 1, the possible parents are A, C, and E; and for locus 2 they are B and C. Hence, based on both loci together, all parents can be excluded except couple C. (Note that, for locus 2, could A has bands that match those in X, but both matching bands are from the male.)

ANS 2.33. a. The phosphate that was originally at the 5' end of the labeled nucleotide becomes attached to the 3' hydroxyl of the next nucleotide in line, and it remains with the 3' hydroxyl after cleavage. Thus the "nearest neighbor" of the labeled nucleotide becomes radioactive. **b.** The "nearest neighbor" that becomes labeled is on the 5' side of the labeled nucleotide.

Supplemental problems with answers.

S2.1 A trinucleotide can be labeled with a single radioactive phosphorous atom in either the innermost position (called the α position), the middle position (β), or the outermost position (γ).

Which of the three labeled trinucleotides should be used to incorporate the radioactive phosphorous into newly synthesized DNA, and why?

ANS S2.1. Use the α-labeled trinucleotide, because the α-phosphate becomes attached to the 3' hydroxyl of the growing nucleotide chain, and the β–γ diphosphate (*pyrophosphate*) is released.

S2.2. The 165 kb genome of the phage T4 is a linear double-stranded DNA molecule.

 a. How many complete turns of the two polynucleotide chains are present in such a double helix?

 b. How long (in μm) is such molecule?

ANS S2.2. a. There are ten nucleotide pairs per turn of the helix, so the total number of complete turns equals 1.65×10^4. **b**. The distance between nucleotide pairs is 0.34 nm, therefore, the length of T4 genome is $165 \times 10^3 \times 0.34$ nm $= 56.1 \times 10^3$ nm, or 56.1 μm.

S2.3. The haploid genome of the wall cress, *Arabidopsis thaliana,* contains 100,000 kb and has five chromosomes. If a particular chromosome contains 10 percent of the DNA in the haploid genome, what is the approximate length of its DNA molecule in micrometers?

ANS S2.3. 10 percent of the haploid genome is 10,000 kb, or 10^7 base pairs. Each base pair in the double helix extends 3.4 angstrom units, and so 10^7 base pairs equals 3.4×10^7 angstrom units. Because there are 10^{-4} micrometers per angstrom unit, the required length is 3.4×10^3 micrometers or, dropping the scientific notation, 3400 micrometers. This length is 3.4 mm, which, if the molecule were not so thin, would be long enough to see with the naked eye.

S2.4. There are 15 different "alleles" of a particular STRP in a population of flowering plant Phlox roemariana. How many different genotypes can exist in this population?

ANS S2.4. There are 15 homozygous genotypes and $(15 \times 14)/2 = 105$ heterozygous genotypes, hence the total number equals 120.

S2.5. The temperature required for denaturation of a DNA sample depends on its C+G composition. Which of the following DNA sequences would require higher temperature for denaturation? Explain.

 a. 5′-TTATAAAATATATTTTTATAT-3′
 3′-AATATTTTATATAAAAATATA-5′
 b. 5′-CCCCCGCGCGGCCGGGCGCGCG-3′
 3′-GGGGGCGCGCCGGCCCGCGCGC-5′

ANS S2.5. The temperature required for denaturation increases with the C+G content, because connection between C and G, which are joined by three hydrogen bond, is stronger than between A and T, which are joined by two hydrogen bonds. Therefore sequence **a** will denature ant lower temperature than sequence **b**.

S2.6. The genome of the protozoan parasite *Plasmodium falciparum,* which causes malaria, has a high A + T content: about 70 percent of the base pairs are A–T base pairs. Compared with a sequence with 50 percent A + T, how would the high A + T content of *P. falciparum* affect the number of fragments obtained by digestion of genomic DNA with:

 a. *Hind*III (restriction site 5'-AAGCTT-3')
 b. *Pvu*II (restriction site 5'-CAGCTG-3')
 c. *Apa*I (restriction site 5'-GGGCCC-3')
 d. *Dra*I (restriction site 5'-TTTAAA-3')

ANS S2.6. a. More than would be expected from a random sequence, since the restriction site is itself A + T rich. **b.** Fewer than would be expected, since the restriction site is A + T poor. **c.** Many fewer than would be expected. **d.** Many more than would be expected.

S2.7. The restriction site of *Hin*dIII is 5'-AAGCTT-3'. Is 3'-AAGCTT-5' also a *Hin*dIII restriction site? Why or why not?
ANS S2.7. 3'-AAGCTT-5' is not a *Hin*dIII restriction site because it is a different sequence. It has the wrong polarity and is not recognized or cleaved by the enzyme.

S2.8. What common feature is shared by restriction fragments produced by the restriction enzymes *Bam*HI (5'-G↓GATCC-3) and *Sau*3A (5'-↓GATC-3')? (The downward arrow denotes the site of cleavage in each strand.)
ANS S2.8. They both leave the same 4-base overhang at the 5' end, namely 5'-GATC-3'.

S2.9. When a new strand of DNA is being synthesized, to which end (3' or 5') is each new nucleotide added? What does this imply about the direction (3' → 5' or 5' → 3') in which the DNA polymerase complex moves along the template strand?
ANS S2.9. New nucleotides are added to the 3' end of the growing strand; because the new strand and the template strand are antiparallel, this means that the polymerase moves along the template strand in a 3' → 5' direction

S2.10. Design hexamer primers that would amplify the entire DNA sequence shown here.
```
5'-GATTACATCGGCATTACCGATTTAAAGCCCTGCTGCTGCGAGTCC-3'
3'-CTAATGTAGCCGTAATGGCTAAATTTCGGGACGACGACGCTCAGG-5'
```
ANS S2.10. Forward primer 5'-GATTAC-3' and reverse primer 3'-CTCAGG-5'.

S2.11. You are given a plasmid containing part of a gene of *D. melanogaster*. The gene fragment is 303 base pairs long. You would like to amplify it using the polymerase chain reaction (PCR). You design oligonucleotide primers 19 nucleotides in length that are complementary to the plasmid sequences immediately adjacent to both ends of the cloning site. What would be the exact size of the resulting PCR product?
ANS S2.11. The primer sequences are included in the PCR product at both ends of the gene fragment. The total length of the amplified piece of DNA is therefore 19 + 303 + 19 = 341 base pairs.

S2.12. A friend brings you three samples of nucleic acid and asks you to determine each sample's chemical identity (whether DNA or RNA) and whether the molecules are double-stranded or single-stranded. You use powerful nucleases to degrade each sample to its constituent nucleotides, and then you determine the approximate relative proportions of nucleotides. The results of your assays are presented below. What can you tell your friend about the nature of these samples?
Assay results
 Sample 1: dGTP 14% dCTP 15% dATP 36% dTTP 35%
 Sample 2: dGTP 12% dCTP 36% dATP 47% dTTP 5%
 Sample 3: GTP 22% CTP 47% ATP 17% UTP 14%
ANS S2.12. Samples 1 and 2 are made up of deoxyribonucleotides and therefore are DNA samples. Sample 3 is composed of ribonucleotides and is therefore a sample of RNA. Double stranded DNA

must have equal proportions of dATP and dTTP as well as of dGTP and dCTP (make sure you understand why!). Only sample 1 has this feature and is therefore likely to be double-stranded DNA. Sample 2 is single-stranded DNA and sample 3 is single-stranded RNA.

S2.13. The genome of bacteriophage λ, which infects cells of *E. coli*, is a double-stranded DNA molecule 50 kb in length. A 1 kb region is to be amplified by PCR.

 a. Prior to amplification, what fraction of the total DNA does the target sequence constitute?

 b. What fraction does it constitute after 5 cycles of PCR?

 c. After 10 cycles of PCR?

 d. After 15 cycles of PCR?

ANS S2.13. a. 1 kb/50 kb = 2 percent. **b.** 2^5 kb/(2^5 kb + 50 kb) = 39 percent. **c.** 2^{10} kb/(2^{10} kb + 50 kb) = 95 percent. **d.** 2^{15} kb/(2^{15} kb + 50 kb) = 99.8 percent.

S2.14. A DNA fragment of 3 kb is to be amplified by PCR from genomic DNA of the European mountain grasshopper *Podisma pedestris*, which has a total genome size of 18×10^9 bp (6 times the size of the human genome).

 a. Prior to amplification, what fraction of the total DNA does the target sequence constitute?

 b. What fraction does it constitute after 10 cycles of PCR?

 c. After 20 cycles of PCR?

 d. After 30 cycles of PCR?

ANS S2.14. a. 3 kb/18×10^6 kb = 0.000016 percent. **b.** $(3 \times 2^{10}$ kb)/(3×2^{10} kb + 18×10^6 kb) = 0.017 percent. **c.** $(3 \times 2^{20}$ kb)/(3×2^{20} kb + 18×10^6 kb) = 14.9 percent. **d.** $(3 \times 2^{30}$ kb)/(3×2^{30} kb + 18×10^6 kb) = 99.4 percent.

S2.15. You wish to amplify a unique 100-bp sequence from the human genome (3×10^9 bp) using the polymerase chain reaction. At the end of the amplification, you want the amount of amplified DNA to represent not less than 99 percent of all the DNA present. Assume that the amplification is exponential.

 a. How many cycles of amplification are necessary to achieve the 99 percent goal?

 b. How would the number of cycles change if you were to amplify a fragment of 1000 bp?

ANS S2.15. a. Let *x* be the amount of amplified DNA in base pairs, then $x/(x + 3 \times 10^9) = 0.99$ represents the minimum quantity for the 99 percent goal. Hence $x = 2.97 \times 10^{11}$ bp. This total amount of DNA represents $(2.97 \times 10^{11})/100 = 2.97 \times 10^9$ fragments, each of 100 base pairs. Because a PCR of *n* cycles yields 2^n amplified fragments, we set $2^n = 2.97 \times 10^9$. Hence, *n* = 31.5 cycles, so not less than 32 cycles are needed. **b.** In the case of a 1000 base pair target sequence, the number of amplified fragments is $(2.97 \times 10^{11})/1000$, from which *n* = 28.1; in this case, you would need at least 29 cycles to obtain the desired amount of product. (Because of the exponential amplification, the same relative quantity of a tenfold shorter fragment requires only ten percent more cycles.)

S2.16. The accompanying gel shows two RAPD polymorphisms detected in individuals A and B taken from a natural population of green frogs. When the animals A and B were mated, all of the progeny exhibited the 2-kb band present in A and all exhibited the 6-kb band present in B. How can this result be explained?

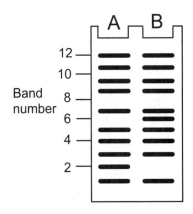

ANS S2.16. Evidently individual A was homozygous for the DNA sequence which, when amplified, yields a RAPD fragment of 2 kb, and individual B was homozygous for the DNA sequence which, when amplified, yields a RAPD fragment of 6 kb, hence all of the progeny must inherit one of both DNA sequences, yielding both the 2-kb and the 6-kb band.

S2.17. The genomic DNA of an organism has a base composition of 40 percent A–T base pairs and 60 percent G–C base pairs. Assuming a random sequence of bases (a dubious assumption for most organisms), what is the expected frequency of the following restriction sites:

 a. 5'-AATT-3'

 b. 5'-AGCT-3'

 c. 5'-GGCC-3'

ANS S2.17. The random sequence has base frequencies of 0.2 A, 0.2 T, 0.3 G, and 0.3 C, hence the expected frequencies of the restriction sites are as follows: **a.** $(0.2)(0.2)(0.2)(0.2) = 0.0016$, or one every 625 bp; **b.** $(0.2)(0.3)(0.3)(0.2) = 0.0036$, or about one every 278 bp; **c.** $(0.3)(0.3)(0.3)(0.3) = 0.0081$, or about one every 123 bp.

S2.18. With reference to the "nearest-neighbor" procedure outlined in Problem **2.33** in the text, suppose that DNA were synthesized in the presence of radioactive cytosine 5' triphosphate. After cleavage with snake venom phosphodiesterase, the label was distributed as follows: adenosine 3' monophosphate, 25%, guanosine 3' monophosphate 20%, thymidine 3' monophosphate 30%, and cytosine 3' monophosphate.

 a. Interpret these results in terms of the dinucleotide frequencies present in the newly synthesized DNA strand.

 b. What dinucleotide frequencies are implied in the complementary strand?

ANS S2.18. a. The interpretation is that, among all dinucleotides of the form 5'–NC–3', where N is any base, 25% are 5'–AC–3', 20% are 5'–GC–3', 30% 5'–TC–3', and 25% are 5'–CC–3'. **b.** In the complementary strand the dinucleotides are of the form 3'–NG–5', and they are 25% 5'–TG–3', 20% 5'–CG–3', 30% 5'–AG–3', and 25% 5'–GG–3'.

S2.19. For the following restriction endonucleases, calculate the average distance between restriction sites in an organism whose DNA has a random sequence and equal proportions of all four nucleotides. The symbol R means any purine (A or G) and Y means any pyrimidine (T or C), but an R—Y pair must be either A—T or G—C.

*Taq*I 5′-TCGA-3′

 3′-AGCT-5′

17

BamHI 5'-GGATCC-3'
 3'-CCTAGG-5'
HaeII 5'-RGCGCY-3'
 3'-YCGCGR-5'

ANS S2.19. For each site, the probability equals the product of the probability of each of the nucleotide pairs in turn, 1/4 for any of the specified pairs and 1/2 for R–Y. The average spacing is the reciprocal of the probability, hence, for $TaqI$, the average distance between sites is $4^4 = 256$ base pairs; for $BamHI$, it is $4^6 = 4096$ base pairs; and for $HaeII$, it is $4^4 \, 2^2 = 1024$ base pairs.

S2.20. For each of the restriction enzymes in Problem **S2.16**, calculate the expected number of restriction sites in the genome of a nematode *Caenorhabditis elegans,* assuming the sequence is approximately random. The genome size of this organism is 100,000 kb.

ANS S2.20. The expected number of sites is the genome size, which in this case is 10^8, divided by the average spacing between sites. Hence, for $TaqI$, the expected number of sites is 390,625; for $BamHI$, 24,414; and for $HaeII$, 97,656.

S2.21. A duplex DNA molecule contains a random sequence of the four nucleotides with equal proportions of each. What is the average spacing between consecutive occurrences of the following 6-bp sequences.

 a. 5′-GAATTC-3′
 b. 5′-CCNNGG-3′ (where N is A, C, T, or G)
 c. 5′-CCWWGG-3′ (where W is A or T)

ANS S2.21. a. The probability of this particular sequence is $(1/4)^6$ and the average spacing between sites is a reciprocal of this and equals 4096 bp; **b.** The probability of this sequence is $(1/4)^4 \times 1^2$, hence, the average distance is 256 bp; **c.** By the same logic, the probability is $(1/4)^4 \times (1/2)^2$ and the average distance equals 1024 bp.

S2.22. Aliquots of a 7.8-kilobase (kb) linear piece of DNA are digested with the restriction enzymes *PvuII, HincII, ClaI,* and *BanII,* alone and in pairs. The digestion products are separated by gel electrophoresis, and the size of each fragment is determined by comparison to size standards. The fragment sizes obtained, in kilobase pairs, are given below. Draw a diagram of the 7.8-kb fragment, showing the location of the restriction sites for each enzyme.

 a. Digestion with *PvuII*: 1.3 kb, 6.5 kb
 b. Digestion with *HincII*: 0.5 kb, 3.3 kb, 4 kb
 c. Digestion with *ClaI*: 1 kb, 6.8 kb
 d. Digestion with *BanII*: 1.3 kb, 6.5 kb
 e. Digestion with *PvuII* and *ClaI*: 1 kb, 5.5 kb, 1.3 kb
 f. Digestion with *PvuII* and *HincII*: 0.5 kb, 0.8 kb, 2.5 kb, 4 kb
 g. Digestion with *HincII* and *ClaI*: 0.5 kb, 1 kb, 3 kb, 3.3 kb
 h. Digestion with *HincII* and *BanII*: 0.5 kb, 0.8 kb, 2.5 kb, 4 kb
 i. Digestion with *ClaI* and *BanII*: 1 kb, 1.3 kb, 5.5 kb

ANS S2.22. The restriction map is as shown below. The map is equivalent to one in which the orientation is reversed.

S2.23. A 3.3-kb size fragment created after the *Hinc*II digestion in the previous problem is inserted into a unique *Hinc*II site of the plasmid pUC18 and transformed into *E. coli*. Individual transformed colonies are isolated, and the recombinant plasmids from each colony are purified and mapped with the restriction enzyme *Pvu*II. To the surprise of a novice molecular geneticist, the plasmids do not all give the same pattern of restriction fragments on a gel. The plasmids fall into two distinct groups. Both groups yield the same number of bands in the gel, the aggregate size of which is the same, but two of the fragment sizes are different. Explain the reason for this difference.

ANS S2.23. The *Hinc*II fragment, which contains a *Pvu*II restriction site, is inserted in opposite orientations in the two types of clones.

S2.24. Suppose that you digest the genomic DNA of a particular organism with *Sau*3A (↓GATC). Then you ligate the resulting fragments into a unique *Bam*HI (G↓GATCC) cloning site of a plasmid vector. Would it be possible to isolate the cloned fragments from the vector using *Bam*HI? From what proportion of clones would it be possible?

ANS S2.24. Although the sticky ends of *Sau*3A and *Bam*HI are compatible, the *Bam*HI restriction site is reconstituted only if the genomic fragment has C next to the *Sau*3A site. The probability of a C at this position is 0.25, assuming equal amounts of four bases and their random distribution in the genome. The probability of recreating *Bam*HI sites at both ends of the cloned fragment (and, therefore, of being able to isolate the cloned fragment from the vector with *Bam*HI) is $0.25^2 = 0.0625$. Hence, only 6.25 percent of the cloned fragments would be flanked by *Bam*HI sites.

S2.25. A particular STRP consisting of 5'-ATAT...ATAT-3', varies in a population probably from six to twenty repeats of the AT dinucleotide. Two individuals, Jan and Fred, have been chosen at random from the large population, and their DNA analyzed. What is the probability that the two restriction fragments containing this STRP from Jan are identical in length to the two fragments from Fred?

ANS S2.25. The chance that any pair of randomly chosen STRPs of this nature are identical in length is $15 \times (1/15)^2 = 1/15$ The probability that Jan's fragment #1 is identical to Fred's fragment #1 is 1/15, as is the probability that Jan's fragment #2 is identical to Fred's fragment #2. These independent events occur with a probability of $(1/15) \times (1/15)$, or 1/225. However, another possibility is that Jan's fragment #1 is identical in length to Fred's fragment #2 (probability 1/15), and Jan's fragment #2 is identical to Fred's fragment #1 (probability 1/15), which yields a separate 1/225 probability, for a net probability of Jan and Fred being identical at this STRP of 2/225, or about 0.89%. Formally, this isn't quite finished, because the two possibilities listed above are not entirely mutually exclusive; if Jan and Fred's STRPs were all of the same length, that would satisfy both of the above possibilities. Thus, to compute the true probability, one must subtract the probability of all four being identical once for each of the fifteen potential alleles, since in the original computation it has been counted twice. This yields $2/225 - [15 \times (1/15)^4] = 29/3375$, or 0.86%.

Chapter 3: Transmission Genetics: The Principle of Segregation
Answers to Chapter-end problems

Fill-ins

1. segregation
2. epistasis
3. multiplication rule
4. codominance
5. independent assortment
6. penetrance
7. complementation test
8. incomplete dominance
9. testcross
10. noncomplementation

Analysis and Applications

ANS 3.1. *Aa* yields *A* and *a* gametes, *Bb* yields *B* and *b* gametes, and *Aa Bb* yields *A B, A b, a B,* and *a b* gametes.

ANS 3.2. Multiply the number of possible gametes formed for each gene (one for each homozygous gene and two for each heterozygous gene). In the case of *AA Bb Cc Dd Ee,* there are a total of $1 \times 2 \times 2 \times 2 \times 2 = 16$ possible gametes. With n homozygous genes and m heterozygous genes, the number of possible gametes is $1^n \times 2^m$, which equals 2^m.

ANS 3.3. The round seeds in the F_2 generation consist of 1/3 *AA* and 2/3 *Aa*. Only the latter produce *a*-bearing pollen, and so the fraction of *aa* seeds expected is $2/3 \times 1/2 = 1/3$

ANS 3.4 For the child to be affected, both III-1 and III-2 must be heterozygous *Aa*. For III-1 to be *Aa,* individual II-2 must be *Aa* and must transmit the recessive allele to III-1. The probability that II-2 is *Aa* equals 2/3, and then the probability of transmitting the *a* allele to III-1 is 1/2. Altogether, the probability that III-1 is a carrier equals $(2/3) \times (1/2) = 1/3$. This is also the probability that III-2 is a carrier. Given that both III-1 and III-2 have genotype *Aa*, the probability of an *aa* offspring is 1/4. Overall, the probability that both III-1 and III-2 are carriers and that they have an *aa* child is $(1/3) \times (1/3) \times (1/4) = 1/36$. The numbers are multiplied because each of the events is independent. (The reason for the 2/3 is as follows: because II-3 is affected, the genotypes of I-1 and I-2 must be *Aa*. Among nonaffected individuals from this mating (individuals II-2 and II-4), the ratios of *AA* and *Aa* are 1/4 : 2/4, and so the probability of *Aa* is 2/3.)

ANS 3.5. Evidently the 4 kb bands is a marker for the recessive allele. **a.** The expected phenotype of II-3 is a single band of 4 kb. **b.** Because II-4 is not affected, the possible molecular phenotypes are a single band of 8 kb or two bands of 4 kb and 8 kb.

ANS 3.6. 1/2; 1/2. The probability argument is that each birth is independent of all the previous ones, and so the number of girls and boys already born has no influence on the sexes of future children.

ANS 3.7. The probability of all boys is $(1/2)^4 = 1/16$. The probability of all girls is also 1/16, and so the probability of either all boys or all girls equals $1/16 + 1/16 = 1/8$. The probability of equal numbers of the two sexes is $6 \times (1/2)^4 = 3/8$. The factor of 6 is the number of possible birth orders of two boys and two girls (i.e., BBGG, BGBG, BGGB, GGBB, GBGB, GBBG).

ANS 3.8. a. The parent with the dominant phenotype must carry one copy of the recessive allele and hence must be heterozygous. **b.** Because some of the progeny are homozygous recessive, both parents must be heterozygous. **c.** The parent with the dominant phenotype could be either homozygous dominant or heterozygous; the occurrence of no homozygous recessive offspring encourages the suspicion that the parent may be homozygous dominant but, because there are only two offspring, heterozygosity cannot be ruled out.

ANS 3.9. An *A b* gamete can be formed only if the parent is *AA Bb,* which has probability 1/2, and in this case, 1/2 of the gametes are *A b*; overall, the probability of an *A b* gamete is $(1/2) \times (1/2) = 1/4$. *A B* gametes derive from *AA BB* parents with probability 1 and from *AA Bb* parents with probability 1/2; overall, the probability of an *A B* gamete is $(1/2) \times 1 + (1/2) \times (1/2) = 3/4$. (Alternatively, the probability of an *A B* gamete may be calculated as $1 - 1/4 = 3/4$, because *A b* and *A B* are the only possibilities.)

ANS 3.10. a. Two phenotypic classes are expected for the *A–a* pair of alleles (*A–* and *aa*), two for the *B–b* pair (*B–* and *bb*), and three for the *R–r* pair (*RR, Rr,* and *rr*), yielding a total number of phenotypic classes of $2 \times 2 \times 3 = 12$. **b.** The probability of an *aa bb RR* offspring is 1/4 (*aa*) $\times$ 1/4 (*bb*) $\times$ 1/4 (*RR*) = 1/64. **c.** Homozygosity may occur for either allele of each of the three genes, yielding such combinations as *AA BB rr, aa bb RR, AA bb rr,* and so forth. Because the probability of homozygosity for either allele is 1/2 for each gene, the proportion expected to be homozygous for all three genes is $(1/2) \times (1/2) \times (1/2) = 1/8$.

ANS 3.11. The probability of a heterozygous genotype for any one of the genes is 1/2, and so for all four together the probability is $(1/2)^4 = 1/16$.

ANS 3.12. Because both parents have solid coats but produce some spotted offspring, they must be *Ss*. With respect to the *A–a* pair of alleles, the female parent (tan) is *aa* and, because there are some tan offspring, the genotype of the black male parent must be *Aa*. Thus, the parental genotypes are *Ss aa* (solid tan female) and *Ss Aa* (solid black male).

ANS 3.13. Because one of the children is deaf (genotype *dd*, in which *d* is the recessive allele), both parents must be heterozygous *Dd*. The progeny genotypes expected from the mating *Dd* $\times$ *Dd* are 1/4 *DD*, 2/4 *Dd*, and 1/4 *dd*. The son is not deaf and hence cannot be *dd*. Among the nondeaf offspring, the genotypes *DD* and *Dd* are in the proportions 1 : 2, and so their relative probabilities are 1/3 *DD* and 2/3 *Dd*. Therefore, the probability that the normal son is heterozygous is 2/3.

ANS 3.14. a. Because the trait is rare, it is reasonable to assume that the affected father is heterozygous *HD / hd,* in which *hd* represents the normal allele. Half of his gametes contain the *HD* allele, and so the probability is 1/2 that the son received the allele and will later develop the disorder. **b.** We do not know whether the son is heterozygous *HD / hd,* but the probability is 1/2 that he is; if he is heterozygous, half of his gametes will contain the *HD* allele. Therefore, the overall probability that his child has the *HD* allele is (1/2) x (1/2) = 1/4.

ANS 3.15. a. The trait is most likely to be due to a recessive allele because there is consanguinity (mating between relatives) in the pedigree. **b.** The double line indicates consanguineous mating. **c.** III-1 and III-2 are first cousins. **d.** Either I-1 or I-2 is most likely *Aa,* as are II-2, II-3, III-1, and III-2. Individuals II-1 and II-4 most likely *AA.*

ANS 3.16. Both parents must be heterozygous (*Aa*) because each had an albino (*aa*) parent. Therefore, the probability of an albino child is 1/4, and the probability of two homozygous recessive children is (1/4) x (1/4) = 1/16. The probability that at least one child is an albino is the probability that exactly one is albino plus the probability that both are albinos. The probability that exactly one is an albino is 2 x (3/4) x (1/4) = 6/16, in which the factor of 2 comes from the fact that there may be two birth orders: normal-albino or albino-normal. Therefore, the overall probability of at least one albino child equals 1/16 + 6/16 = 7/16. Alternatively, the probability of at least one albino child may be calculated as 1 minus the probability that both are nonalbino, or $1 - (3/4)^2 = 7/16$.

ANS 3.17. a. Most likely due to a dominant allele because it is expressed in every generation, occurs equally in females and males, affected parents have approximately 50% affected offspring, and nonaffected parents do not have affected offspring. **b.** All affected persons are *Aa,* all nonaffected persons are *aa.*

ANS 3.18. The mother is heterozygous for alleles yielding bands of 6 and 9 kb, and the father is heterozygous for alleles yielding bands of 3 and 12 kb. Four genotypes of progeny are possible ('*6/3*", "*6/12*", "*9/3*", and "*9/12*") and the phenotypes are, respectively, bands of 3 and 6 kb, bands of 6 and 12 kb, bands of 3 and 9 kb, and bands of 9 and 12 kb.

ANS 3.19. a. The cross *RR BB* x *rr bb* yields F_1 progeny of genotype *Rr Bb,* which have red kernels. **b.** Because there is independent segregation (independent assortment), the F_2 genotypes are *R– B–, R– bb, rr B–,* and *rr bb.* These genotypes are in the proportions 9 : 3 : 3 : 1, respectively, and they produce kernels that are red, brown, brown, and white, respectively. Therefore, the F_2 plants have red, brown, or white seeds in the proportions 9/16 : 6/16 : 1/16.

ANS 3.20. Because the genes segregate independently, they can be considered separately. For the *Cr, cr* pair of alleles, the genotypes of the zygotes are *Cp Cp, Cp cp,* and *cp cp* in the proportions 1/4, 1/2, and 1/4, respectively. However, the *Cp Cp* zygotes do not survive, and so among the survivors the genotypes are *Cp cp* (creeper) and *cp cp* (noncreeper), in the proportions 2/3 and 1/3, respectively. For the *W, w* pair of alleles, the progeny genotypes are *W–* (white) and *ww* (yellow), in the proportions 3/4 and 1/4, respectively. Altogether, the phenotypes and proportions of the surviving offspring can be obtained by multiplying (2/3 creeper + 1/3 noncreeper) x (3/4 white + 1/4 yellow),

which yields 6/12 creeper, white + 2/12 creeper, yellow + 3/12 noncreeper, white + 1/12 noncreeper, yellow. Note that the proportions sum to 12/12 = 1, which serves as a check.

ANS 3.21. Colored offspring must have the genotype C– ii; otherwise, color could not be produced (as in cc) or would be suppressed (as in I–). Among the F_2 progeny, 3/4 of the offspring have the C– genotype and 1/4 of the offspring have the ii genotype. Because the genes undergo independent assortment, the overall expected proportion of colored offspring is (3/4) x (1/4) = 3/16.

ANS 3.22. The 9 : 3 : 3 : 1 ratio is that of the genotypes A– B–, A– bb, aa B–, and aa bb. The modified 9 : 7 ratio implies that all of the last three genotypes have the same phenotype. The F_1 testcross is between the genotypes Aa Bb x aa bb, and the progeny are expected in the proportions 1/4 Aa Bb, 1/4 Aa bb, 1/4 aa Bb, and 1/4 aa bb. Again, the last three genotypes have the same phenotype, and so the ratio of phenotypes among progeny of the testcross is 1 : 3.

ANS 3.23. For any individual offspring, the probabilities of black B– and white bb are 3/4 and 1/4, respectively. **a.** The order white-black-white occurs with probability (1/4) x (3/4) x (1/4) = 3/64. The order black-white-black occurs with probability (3/4) x (1/4) x (3/4) = 9/64. Therefore, the probability of either the order white-black-white or the order black-white-black equals 3/64 + 9/64 = 3/16. The probabilities are summed because the events are mutually exclusive. **b.** The probability of exactly two white and one black equals $3 \times (1/4)^2 \times (3/4)^1 = 9/64$. The factor of 3 is the number of birth orders of two white and one black (there are three, because the black offspring must be either the first, second, or third), and the rest of the expression is the probability that any one of the birth orders occurs (in this case, 3/64).

ANS 3.24. a. $(1/2)^6 = 1/64$. **b.** $6 \times (1/2)^6 = 6/64$. **c.** $15 \times (1/2)^6 = 15/64$. **d.** $20 \times (1/2)^6 = 20/64$. **e.** $1 - 1/64 - 6/64 - 15/64 = 42/64$.

ANS 3.25. Black and splashed white are the homozygous genotypes and slate blue the heterozygote. The probabilities of each of these phenotypes from the mating between two heterozygotes are 1/4 black, 1/2 slate blue, and 1/4 splashed white. The probability of occurrence of the particular birth order black-slate blue-splashed white is (1/4) x (1/2) x (1/4) = 1/32, but altogether there are six different orders in which exactly one of each type could be produced. (The black offspring could be first, second, or third and, in each case, the remaining phenotypes could occur in either of two orders.) Consequently, the overall probability of one of each phenotype, in any order, is 6 x (1/32) = 3/16.

ANS 3.26. The probability that one or more offspring are aa equals 1 minus the probability that all are A–. In the mating Aa x Aa, the probability that all of n offspring will be Aa equals $(3/4)^n$, and the question asks for the value of n such that $1 - (3/4)^n > 0.95$. Solving this inequality yields $n > \log(1 - 0.95)/\log(3/4) = 10.4$. Therefore, 11 is the smallest number of offspring for which there is a greater than 95 percent chance that at least one will be aa. As a check, note that $(3/4)^{10} = 0.056$ and $(3/4)^{11} = 0.042$, and so with 10 offspring the chance of one or more aa equals 0.944 and with 11 offspring the chance of one or more aa equals 0.958.

ANS 3.27. The ratio of probabilities that the sire is $AA : Aa$ is $1/3 : 2/3$. The ratio of the probabilities of producing n pups, all $A-$, for $AA : Aa$ sires is $1 : (1/2)^n$. Hence, for n $A-$ pups, the ratio of probabilities of $AA : Aa$ sires is $1/3 : (2/3)(1/2)^n$. Therefore, the probability that the sire is AA, given that he had a litter of n $A-$ pups, equals $(1/3)/[(1/3) + (2/3)(1/2)^n]$. This is the degree of confidence you can have that the sire is AA. For $n = 1$ to 15, the answer is shown in the accompanying table. It is interesting that 6 progeny are required for 95 percent confidence and 8 for 99 percent confidence.

1	0.5
2	0.666
3	0.8
4	0.888
5	0.941
6	0.969
7	0.984
8	0.992
9	0.996
10	0.998
11	0.999
12	0.9995
13	0.9997
14	0.9998
15	0.9999

ANS 3.28. Let A be the allele associated with the 6 kb band and B that associated with the 9 kb band. The alternative alleles (which yield no amplification with PCR) may be denoted a and b. The genotype of parent A is therefore $AA\ bb$ and that of parent B is $aa\ BB$. Each RAPD polymorphisms is dominant, so the F$_1$ progeny ($Aa\ Bb$) have both bands. With independent assortment, the F$_2$ progeny are 9/16 $A-\ B-$ (bands of 6 and 9 kb), 3/16 $A-\ bb$ (band of 6 kb), 3/16 $aa\ B-$ (band of 9 kb), and 1/16 $aa\ bb$ (no bands).

ANS 3.29. The F$_1$ progeny ($A_1A_2\ B_1B_2$) has four bands of 2, 3, 8, and 10 kb. The F$_2$ progeny consist of 1/16 $A_1A_1\ B_1B_1$ (bands of 2 and 8 kb), 2/16 $A_1A_1\ B_1B_2$ (bands of 2, 8, and 10 kb), 1/16 A_1A_1 B_2B_2 (bands of 2 and 10 kb), 2/16 $A_1A_2\ B_1B_1$ (bands of 2, 3, and 8 kb), 4/16 $A_1A_2\ B_1B_2$ (bands of 2, 3, 8, and 10 kb), 2/16 $A_1A_2\ B_2B_2$ (bands of 2, 3, and 8 kb), 1/16 $A_2A_2\ B_1B_1$ (bands of 3 and 8 kb), 2/16 $A_2A_2\ B_1B_2$ (bands of 3, 8, and 10 kb), and 2/16 $A_2A_2\ B_2B_2$ (bands of 3 and 10 kb).

ANS: 3.30. The existing data allows the mutants to be grouped into three complementation groups as follows: {a, c, d}, {b, f}, and {e}. The missing entries are shown in the accompanying table.

	a	b	c	d	e	f
a	(−)	+	−	(−)	+	(+)
b		(−)	(+)	(+)	(+)	−
c			(−)	−	(+)	(+)
d				(−)	(+)	(+)
e					(−)	+
f						(−)

24

Challenge Problems

ANS 3.31. Probe A would be unsuitable with either restriction enzyme because both DNA molecules would yield a single large fragment that hybridizes with the probe. Probe C would not be useful because it would hybridize with each of the multiple copies of the transposable element throughout the genome. Probe B with *Eco*RI would not work because it would not hybridize to an *Eco*RI fragment from either allele. Probe B with *Bam*HI would work, yielding a single fragment of 4 kb from the wildtype allele and a single fragment of 5 kb from the mutant allele.

ANS 3.32. Make a Punnett square with the ratio of *D* : *d* along each margin as 3/4 : 1/4. (a) The progeny genotypes *D/D, D/d,* and *d/d* therefore occur in the proportions 9/16 : 6/16 : 1/16. (b) If *D* is dominant, the ratio of dominant: recessive phenotypes is 15 : 1. (c) Among the *D*– genotypes, the ratio *D/D* : *D/d* is 9 : 6 or 3 : 2. (d) If meiotic drive happens in only one sex, the Punnett square has 3/4 : 1/4 along one margin and 1/2 : 1/2 along the other. The progeny genotypes *D/D, D/d,* and *d/d* are in the ratio 3/8 : 1/2 : 1/8. The ratio of dominant : recessive phenotypes is 7 : 1. Among *D*– genotypes, the ratio *D/D* : *D/d* is 3 : 4.

ANS 3.33. a. 0. **b.** 0. **c.** 0. **d.** 0. **e.** 1. **f.** 1. **g.** 1/4. **h.** 1/4. **i.** 3/4. **j.** 3/4. **k.** 1/2. **l.** 1.

Supplemental problems with answers.

S3.1. Define the following terms: genotype, phenotype, allele, dominant, recessive.
ANS S3.1. The genotype is a genetic constitution of an individual virus, cell, or organism. The phenotype refers to the observable properties of a virus, cell, or organism, which result from the interaction of the genotype and the environment. An allele is any of a set of alternative forms of a particular gene. A dominant allele results in the same phenotype regardless of whether it is in heterozygous or homozygous condition. A recessive allele produces its phenotype only when homozygous. (The terms dominant and recessive are sometimes used to refer to the trait itself, such as in the phrase "phenylketonuria is a recessive trait.")

S3.2. How many different alleles of a particular gene may exist in a population of organisms? How many alleles of a particular gene can be present in an individual organism?
ANS S3.2. A population of organisms may include any number of different alleles of a particular gene. An individual organism can have no more than two alleles of the same gene, one inherited from the mother and the other from the father.

S3.3. A breeder of Irish setters has a particularly valuable male show dog descended from a famous female named Rheona Didona, which was known to carry a harmful recessive gene for blindness caused by atrophy of the retina. Before she breeds the dog, she wants some assurance that it does not carry this harmful allele. How would you advise her to test the dog?
ANS S3.3. The breeder should testcross the male to a female with retinal atrophy. The appearance of mutant pups would indicate the dog was a heterozygous carrier. If no mutant pups appear in several litters, it is unlikely that the male carries the harmful allele.

S3.4. Any of a large number of different recessive mutations cause profound hereditary deafness. Children homozygous for such mutations are often found in small, isolated communities in which matings tend to be within the group. In these instances, a mutation that originates in one person can

be transmitted to several members of the population in future generations and become homozygous through a marriage between group members who are carriers. A deaf man from one community marries a deaf woman from a different, unrelated community. Both of them have deaf parents. The marriage produces three children, all with normal hearing. How can you explain this result?

ANS S3.4. Each parent is homozygous for a recessive allele of a different gene. Said in another way, the mutations in the parents show complementation.

S3.5. Consider a human family with four children, and remember that each birth is equally likely to result in a boy or a girl.

 a. What proportion of sibships will include at least one boy?

 b. What fraction of sibships will have the gender order GBGB?

ANS S3.5. a. In approaching this kind of problem, note first that the sibships with at least one boy include all sibships except those with all girls. Therefore, the simplest way to obtain the answer is to calculate the proportion of sibships with four girls and then subtract this from 1. The probability of four girls is $(1/2)^4 = 1/16$, which equals 0.0625; the rest of the sibships account for the proportion $1 - 0.0625 = 0.9375$, which is the with at least one boy. **b.** Because a particular birth order is specified, the answer is $(1/2)^4 = 1/16$. To approach the problem in another way, note that 6/16 of all sibships with four children include two boys and two girls, but only 1/6 of such sibships have the specific birth order FMFM; hence, the answer is $(6/16)(1/6) = 1/16$.

S3.6. Mendel's cross of homozygous round yellow with homozygous wrinkled green peas yielded the phenotypes 9/16 round yellow, 3/16 round green, 3/16 wrinkled yellow, and 1/16 wrinkled green progeny in the F_2 generation. If he had testcrossed the round green progeny individually, what proportion of them would have yielded some progeny with round yellow seeds?

 a. 1/4

 b. 1/3

 c. 1/2

 d. 3/4

 e. 0

ANS S3.6. e: the testcross would be round green x wrinkled green, and green is the phenotype of the homozygous recessive.

S3.7. A man and a woman each have a 50% chance of being a carrier (heterozygous) for a recessive allele associated with a genetic disease. If they have one child, what is the chance that the child will be homozygous recessive?

ANS S3.7. 1/2 x 1/2 x 1/4 = 1/16.

S3.8. Intestinal lactase deficiency (ILD) is a common inborn error of metabolism in humans; affected persons are homozygous for a recessive allele of a gene on chromosome 2. A woman and her husband, both phenotypically normal, had a daughter with ILD. She married a normal man and had three sons. One had ILD and two were normal. Determine the probability that the couple's next child will have ILD.

 a. 0.25

 b. 0.50

 c. 0.75

 d. 1.00

e. 0.0625

ANS S3.8. b; the mother is affected and so must be homozygous; because the mating produced a homozygous recessive child, the father must be heterozygous.

S3.9. A man and a woman are both heterozygous for a recessive allele for an inborn error of metabolism.

 a. If they have one child, what is the probability that it will be affected?

 b. If they have two children, what is the probability that at least one will be affected?

 c. If they have three children, what is the probability that at least one will be affected?

ANS S3.9. a. $1/4$. **b.** $1 - (3/4)^2 = 7/16$. **c.** $1 - (3/4)^3 = 37/64$.

S3.10. Seborrheic keratosis is a rare hereditary skin condition due to an autosomal dominant mutation. Affected people have skin marked with numerous small, sharply margined, yellowish or brownish areas covered with a thin, greasy scale. A man with keratosis marries a normal woman, and they have three children. What is the chance that all three are normal? What is the chance that all three are affected?

ANS S3.10. Since a dominant allele of this gene is rare, it may be assumed that the man is heterozygous. The chance for any child to receive the dominant allele (or not to receive it) is $1/2$. Therefore, the probability that all three children are normal is $(1/2)^3 = 1/8$. The probability that all three are affected is the same.

S3.11. In plants, certain mutant genes are known that affect the ability of gametes to participate in fertilization. Suppose an allele A is such a mutant, and that pollen cells bearing the A allele are only half as likely to survive and participate in fertilization as pollen cells bearing the a allele. What is the expected ratio of $AA : Aa : aa$ plants in the F_2 generation in a monohybrid cross?

ANS S3.11. In the functional female gametes, the ratio of $A : a$ is $1/2 : 1/2$; in the functional male gametes, the ratio of $A : a$ is $1/4 : 3/4$ (because only half of the A-bearing products of meiosis are functional). The F_2 ratio of $AA : Aa : aa$ is therefore $1/8 : 1/2 : 3/8$.

S3.12. In *Drosophila,* the dominant allele Cy (*Curly*) results in curly wings. The cross $Cy/+$ x $Cy/+$ (where $+$ represents the wildtype allele of Cy) results in a ratio of 2 curly : 1 wildtype F_1 progeny. The cross between the curly F_1 progeny also gives a ratio of 2 curly : 1 wildtype F_2 progeny. How can this result be explained?

ANS S3.12. When two heterozygotes are crossed, we expect a $1 : 2 : 1$ ratio of homozygous dominant : heterozygous : homozygous recessive genotypes. In this case, the expectation would be a genotypic ratio of 1 Cy/Cy : 2 $Cy/+$: 1 $+/+$. Because we do see a ratio of 2 curly-winged flies to 1 wildtype, the $2 : 1$ part of the expectation seems to be correct. The simplest explanation for the missing Cy/Cy class of progeny is that the Cy/Cy homozygous genotype is lethal; these flies die before adulthood. What this observation means is that Cy is dominant with respect to wing phenotype but recessive with respect to lethality.

S3.13. White Leghorn chickens are homozygous for a dominant allele, *C,* of a gene responsible for colored feathers, and also for a dominant allele, *I,* of an independently segregating gene that prevents the expression of *C.* The White Wyandotte breed is homozygous recessive for both genes *cc ii.* What

proportion of the F_2 progeny obtained from mating White Leghorn x White Wyandotte F_1 hybrids would be expected to have colored feathers?

ANS S3.13. $(1/4)(3/4) = 3/16$; the 1/4 is the probability of *ii* and the 3/4 is the probability of *C–*.

S3.14. The tailless trait in the Manx cat is determined by the alleles of a single gene. In the cross Manx _ Manx, both tailless and tailed progeny are produced, in a ratio of 2 tailless : 1 tailed. All tailless progeny from this cross, when mated with tailed, produce a 1 : 1 ratio of tailless to tailed progeny.

 a. Is the allele for the tailless trait dominant or recessive?

 b. What genetic hypothesis can account for the 2 : 1 ratio of tailless : tailed and the result of the testcrosses with the tailless cats?

ANS S3.14. a. If the tailless phenotype were homozygous recessive, then the cross tailless with tailless should produce only tailless progeny. This is not the case, and so the tailless phenotype must result from a dominant allele, let us call it *T*. **b.** Because the cross tailless with tailless produces both tailless and tailed progeny, both parents must be heterozygous *Tt*. The expected ratio of genotypes among the zygotes is 1/4 *TT*, 1/2 *Tt,* and 1/4 *tt*. Because *T* is dominant, the *Tt* animals are tailless and the *tt* animals are tailed. The 2 : 1 ratio can be explained if the *TT* zygotes do not survive (the homozygous dominant genotype is lethal). Because all surviving tailless animals must be *Tt*, this genetic hypothesis would also explain why all of the tailless animals from the cross, when mated with *tt*, give a 1 : 1 ratio of tailless (*Tt*) to wildtype (*tt*). (Developmental studies confirm that about 25 percent of the embryos do not survive.)

S3.15. Absence of the enzyme alpha-1-antitrypsin is associated with a very high risk of developing emphysema and early death due to damaged lungs. Enzyme deficiency is usually due to homozygosity for an allele denoted *PI-Z*. A phenotypically normal man whose father died of the emphysema associated with homozygosity for *PI-Z* marries a phenotypically normal woman with a negative family history for the trait. They consider having a child.

 a. Draw the pedigree as described above.

 b. If the frequency of heterozygous *PI-Z* in the population is 1 in 30, what is the chance that the first child will be homozygous *PI-Z*?

 c. If the first child is homozygous *PI-Z,* what is the probability that the second child will be either homozygous or heterozygous for the normal allele?

ANS S3.15. a. The pedigree is shown below. The diamond shape represents the hypothetical child, whose sex is undetermined.

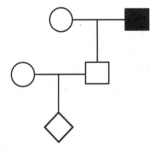

b. The man has a probability of 1 of being heterozygous for the *PI-Z* allele. His wife, who is from the general population, has a 1/30 chance of being heterozygous for this allele. If both of them carry the *PI-Z* allele, then 1/4 of their children will be affected with the disease. Therefore, the probability of

their first child being homozygous *PI-Z* is 1 x 1/30 x 1/4 = 0.0083 **c.** If their first child is affected by the disease, then the woman is definitely a carrier. In this case, the next child will be either homozygous or heterozygous for the normal allele with the probability 1/4 + 1/2 = 3/4.

S3.16. In the accompanying pedigree, the affected male II-5 is affected with a genetic condition due to a rare recessive allele. Use the symbols *A* and *a* to denote the dominant and recessive alleles.
 a. What is the genotype of II-5?
 b. What are the genotypes of I-1 and I-2?
 c. What is the probability that II-2 is heterozygous?
 d. Assuming that II-1 has genotype *AA,* what is the probability that III-1 is heterozygous?

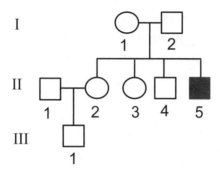

ANS S3.16. a. *aa.* **b.** Both *Aa.* **c.** 2/3. **d.** 1/3.

S3.17. Plants of the genotypes *Aa Bb cc* and *aa Bb Cc* are crossed. The three genes are on different chromosomes. What proportion of the progeny will have the phenotype *A– B– C–,* and what fraction of the *A– B– C–* plants will have the genotype *Aa Bb Cc*?
 a. 1/16; all
 b. 3/8; 2/3
 c. 3/16; 2/3
 d. 1/2; 1/2
 e. 1/2; all

ANS S3.17. c, because the fraction of *A–* plants is 1/2, that of *B–* plants is 3/4, and that of *C–* plants is 1/2, and the genes are unlinked; among these, all must be *Aa,* all must be *Cc,* and the proportions of *BB* and *Bb* are 1/3 : 2/3, hence 2/3 of the *A– B– C–* plants have the genotype *Aa Bb Cc.*

S3.18. In the cross *Aa Bb Cc Dd* x *Aa Bb Cc Dd,* in which all four genes undergo independent assortment, what proportion of offspring are expected to be heterozygous for all four genes? What is the answer if the cross is *Aa Bb Cc Dd* x *Aa Bb cc dd*?
ANS S3.18. $(1/2)^4$ = 1/16 in both cases.

S3.19. In the cross *AA Bb Cc* x *Aa Bb cc,* where all three genes assort independently and each uppercase allele is dominant, what proportion of the progeny are expected to have the phenotype *A_ bb cc*?
 a. 1/64
 b. 1/32
 c. 1/16

d. 1/8

e. 1/4

ANS S3.19. d, because the fractions of *A–*, *bb*, and *cc* are 1, 1/4, and 1/2, respectively, and the genes undergo independent assortment.

S3.20. In the cross *Aa Bb* x *Aa Bb,* what fraction of the progeny will be homozygous for one gene and heterozygous for the other if the two genes assort independently?

 a. 1/16

 b. 1/8

 c. 1/2

 d. 1/4

 e. 3/4

ANS S3.20. c, because, for each gene, the proportions of homozygous : heterozygous progeny equal 1/2; hence, 1/2 x 1/2 = 1/4 of the progeny are homozygous for either *AA* or *aa* and heterozygous *Bb*, and 1/4 of the progeny are heterozygous *Aa* and homozygous for either *BB* or *bb*. Altogether, the chance is 1/4 + 1/4 = 1/2.

S3.21. With *n* alleles:

 a. How many homozygous genotypes are possible?

 b. How many heterozygous genotypes?

 c. How many genotypes altogether?

ANS S3.21. a. *n*; **b.** $n(n-1)/2$; **c.** $n + n(n-1)/2 = n(n+1)/2$.

S3.22. The pedigree in the accompanying illustration shows the inheritance of coat color in a group of cocker spaniels. The coat colors and genotypes are indicated in the key.

 a. Specify in as much detail as possible the genotype of each dog in the pedigree.

 b. What are the possible genotypes of animal III-4, and what is the probability of each genotype?

 c. If a single pup is produced from the mating of III-4 x III-3, what is the probability that the pup will be lemon?

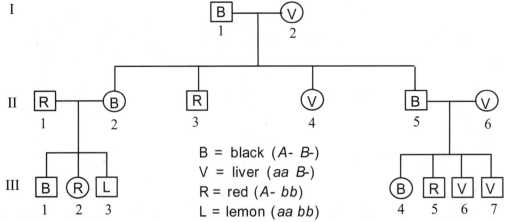

ANS S3.22. a. Mating I-1 x I-2 produces both A– bb and aa B– progeny, so the parents must be: I-1, Aa Bb and I-2, aa Bb. Mating II-1 x II-2 produces a lemon pup, so the parental genotypes must be II-1, Aa bb and II-2, Aa Bb. Mating II-5 x II-6 produces both A– bb and aa B– progeny, so the parental

genotypes must be II-5, Aa Bb and II-6, aa Bb. The other genotypes, as completely as they can be specified, are: II-3, Aa bb; II-4, aa B– , III-1, A– Bb; III-2, A– bb; III-3, aa bb; III-4, Aa B–; III-5, Aa bb; III-6, aa B–; III-7, aa B–. **b.** The female III-4 is known to be Aa B– and a progeny of the mating Aa Bb x aa Bb. The female III-4 could be Aa BB or Aa Bb, with respective probabilities 1/3 and 2/3. **c.** Because III-3 is aa bb, only the mating Aa Bb x aa bb could produce a lemon-colored pup. The probability that III-4 is Aa Bb equals 2/3 and, given this genotype, the probability of a lemon-colored pup is (1/2)(1/2) = 1/4, and so the overall probability of a lemon-colored pup is (2/3)(1/4) = 1/6.

S3.23. In terms of the type of epistasis indicated, would you say that a 27 : 37 ratio has more in common with a 9 : 7 ratio or with a 15 : 1 ratio? Explain your argument.
ANS S3.23. A 27 : 37 ratio has more in common with a 9 : 7 ratio for the following reason. In a dihybrid cross in which phenotypes of the offspring homozygous for at least one *recessive* allele are indistinguishable, a 9 : 3 : 3 : 1 ratio becomes transformed into a 9 : 7 ratio. Note that $9/16 = (3/4)^2$. If another pair of alleles with the same effect is added, the F_2 ratio becomes 27 : 37 because $27/64 = (3/4)^3$. The type of gene interaction that results in a 15 : 1 ratio takes place when in a dihybrid cross all progeny with at least one *dominant* allele have the same phenotype.

S3.24. A trihybrid cross *AA BB rr _ aa bb RR* is made in a plant species in which *A* and *B* are dominant to their respective alleles but there is no dominance between *R* and *r*. Assuming independent assortment, consider the F_2 progeny from this cross.

 a. How many phenotypic classes are expected?
 b. What is the probability of the parental *aa bb RR* genotype?
 c. What proportion of the progeny would be expected to be homozygous for all three genes?
ANS S3.24. a. Two phenotypic classes are expected for each of the *A, a* and *B, b* pairs of alleles, and three for the *R, r* pair, yielding a total number of 12. **b.** 1/64. **c.** 1/8.

S3.25. Four babies accidentally become mixed up in a maternity ward. The ABO types of the four babies are known to be O, A, B, and AB, and those of the four sets of parents are shown below. One of the attendants insists that DNA typing will be necessary to straighten out the mess, but another claims that the ABO blood types alone are sufficient. To determine who is correct, try to match each baby with its correct set of parents.
 a. AB x O
 b. A x O
 c. A x AB
 d. O x O
ANS S3.25. Since we have only four sets of parents and four babies, we can try to match them according to the ABO types alone. If there is more than one way to match them up, then DNA typing will be necessary. Note that the parents **d** can only have the baby with blood type O. The baby with the blood type AB could be born only to the parents **c**. The parents **b** could not give a birth to a baby with blood type B, therefore, their baby must be the remaining one with blood type A. This leaves the baby with blood type B and, luckily, this blood type is consistent with the parents **a**. Since this is the only way to make the matches consistent with the genetics of the ABO blood groups, DNA typing is unnecessary.

S3.26. For each of the following F_2 ratios, some indicating epistasis, what phenotypic ratio would you expect in a testcross of the F_1 dihybrid?

 a. 15 : 1
 b. 13 : 3
 c. 9 : 4 : 3
 d. 9 : 6 : 1
 e. 12 : 3 : 1
 f. 9 : 3 : 3 : 1
 g. 3 : 6 : 3 : 1 : 2 : 1
 h. 1 : 2 : 1 : 2 : 4 : 2 : 1 : 2 : 1

ANS S3.26. All ratios are possibilities resulting from independent segregation in a dihybrid cross, all except **g** and **h** indicating that each gene has one allele showing complete dominance. The ratio **f** is the standard 9 : 3 : 3 : 1 ratio. Letting *A, a* and *B, b* represent the alleles of the segregating genes, the testcross of the dihybrid yields the genotypes *Aa Bb* : *aa Bb* : *Aa bb* : *aa bb* in the proportions 1 : 1 : 1 : 1. **a.** 15 : 1 indicates that all genotypes except *aa bb* have the same phenotype, so the ratio of phenotypes in the testcross will be 3 : 1. **b.** 13 : 3 means that all genotypes except *aa B–* have the same phenotype, hence the testcross yields the phenotypic ratio 3 : 1. **c.** 9 : 3 : 4 means that *A– B–* and *aa B–* have different phenotypes and that *A– bb* and *aa bb* have a different phenotype but are identical to one another; in this case, the testcross yields the phenotypic ratio 1 : 1 : 2. **d.** Here, *aa B–* and *A– bb* yield the same phenotype, so the testcross ratio of phenotypes is 1 : 2 : 1. **e.** In this case, the *aa B–* genotype has the same phenotype as the *A– B–* genotype. The phenotypic ratio in the testcross is 2 : 1 : 1. **f.** Testcross phenotypes 1 : 1 : 1 : 1. **g.** This F_2 ratio means that each of the three genotypes of the *B* gene yield two different phenotypes, one in the *AA* and *Aa* genotype and the other in the *aa* genotype. The phenotypic ratio in the testcross is therefore 1 : 1 : 1 : 1. **h.** In this case, each genotype yields a unique phenotype, so the testcross ratio is again 1 : 1 : 1 : 1.

S3.27. In plants of the genus *Primula,* the *K* locus controls synthesis of a compound called malvidin. Two plants heterozygous at the *K* locus were crossed, producing the following distribution of progeny:

 1010 Make malvidin
 345 Do not make malvidin

You wish to determine if the *D* locus (located on a different chromosome from *K*), affects production of malvidin as well. True-breeding plants that make malvidin (*KK dd*) were crossed to true-breeding plants that do not make malvidin (*kk DD*). All F_1 plants failed to produce malvidin. F_1 heterozygotes were self-fertilized, and the F_2 progeny, assayed for malvidin synthesis, yielded the following distribution:

 522 Make malvidin
 2270 Do not make malvidin

Complementation Data

	a1	*a2*	*a3*	*a4*	*a5*	*a6*	*a7*	*a8*	*a9*	*a10*
a1	–	–	–	–	–	–	–	–	?	–
a2		–	–	?	–	–	–	–	?	–
a3			–	–	–	–	?	–	–	–
a4				–	–	–	?	–	–	–

a5	–	–	–	–	–	–
a6		–	–	–	–	–
a7			–	–	–	–
a8				–	–	–
a9					–	–
a10						–

a. Write the genotypes and the corresponding phenotypes of all the F_2 progeny obtained.

b. Does the *D* locus affect malvidin synthesis? What is the basis of your conclusion?

ANS S3.27. a. The 3 : 1 ratio in the first cross tells us that making malvidin (*K*) is dominant to not making malvidin (*k*). In the dihybrid cross, the proportion of malvidin-producing plants is 18.7 percent, yet 3/4 of the progeny should be *K*–. Because 0.187/0.750 = 24.9 percent, the result of the dihybrid cross suggests that a malvidin-producing plant must, in addition to the genotype *K*–, have the genotype *dd*. The genotypes and phenotypes in the F_2 progeny are therefore:

9 *K*– *D*–	Does not make malvidin
3 *K*– *dd*	Makes malvidin
3 *kk D*–	Does not make malvidin
1 *kk dd*	Does not make malvidin

(With this type of epistasis the ratio of F_2 phenotypes is 13 : 3.)

b. The *D* locus does affect malvidin synthesis. We could say that "*D* is a dominant suppressor of *K*"; in other words, *K*– is necessary for malvidin synthesis, but the presence of *D*– suppresses this phenotype.

S3.28. From the complementation data in the table below, assign the ten mutations *a1* through *a10* to complementation groups. Use the complementation groups to deduce the expected results of the complementation tests indicated as missing data (denoted by the question marks).

	a1	a2	a3	a4	a5	a6	a7	a8	a9	a10
a1	-									
a2	+	-								
a3	+	+	-							
a4	+	?	+	-						
a5	-	+	+	+	-					
a6	+	+	-	+	+	-				
a7	+	+	?	?	+	-	-			
a8	+	-	+	-	+	+	+	-		
a9	?	?	+	+	-	+	+	+	-	
a10	+	+	+	+	+	+	+	+	+	-

ANS S3.28. The data indicate four complementation groups, as shown in the accompanying diagram. Grouping the alleles in the same complementation group in parentheses, the four complementation groups can be represented as: (*a1, a5, a9*); (*a2, a4, a8*); (*a3, a6, a7*); and (*a10*).

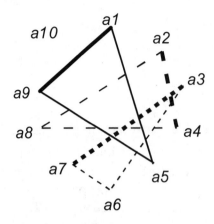

The thickened lines correspond to question marks that should be replaced by – signs because the mutations are in the same complementation group. Specifically, the expected results of the missing crosses are as follows: *a1* x *a9*, –; *a2* x *a4*, –; *a2* x *a9*, +; *a3* x *a7*, –; and *a4* x *a7*, +.

Chapter 4: Chromosomes and Sex-Chromosome Inheritance
Answers to Chapter-end problems.

Fill-ins

1. S phase
2. anaphase I
3. nondisjunction
4. chiasma
5. heterogametic
6. centromere or kinetochore
7. bivalent
8. statistically significant
9. degrees of freedom
10. Pascal's triangle

Analysis and Applications

ANS 4.1. Chromosome replication takes place in the S period, which is in the interphase stage of mitosis and the interphase I stage of meiosis. (Note that chromosome replication does *not* take place in interphase II of meiosis.) Chromosomes condense and first become visible in the light microscope in prophase of mitosis and prophase I of meiosis.

ANS 4.2. Illustration C is anaphase of mitosis. Illustration A is anaphase I of meiosis. Illustration B is anaphase II of meiosis.

ANS 4.3. Each chromosome present in telophase of mitosis is identical with one of a pair of chromatids present in the preceding metaphase that were held together at the centromere. In this example, there are 23 pairs of chromosomes present after telophase, which implies $23 \times 2 = 46$ chromosomes altogether. Therefore, at the preceding metaphase, there were $46 \times 2 = 92$ chromatids

ANS 4.4. In leptotene, the chromosomes first become visible as *thin threads*. In zygotene, they become *paired threads* because of synapsis. The chromosomes continue to condense to become *thick threads* in pachytene. In diplotene, the sister chromatids become evident and each chromosome is seen to be a *paired thread* consisting of the sister chromatids. (Early signs of the bipartite nature of each chromosome are evident in pachytene.) In diakinesis, the homologous chromosomes repulse each other and *move apart,* and they would fall apart entirely were they not held together by the chiasmas.

ANS 4.5. The number of chromosomes. Each centromere defines a single chromosome; two chromatids are considered as part of a single chromosome as long as they share a single centromere. As soon as the centromere splits in anaphase, each chromatid is considered to be a chromosome in its own right. Meiosis I reduces the chromosome number from diploid to haploid because the daughter nuclei contain the haploid number of chromosomes (each chromosome consisting of a single centromere connecting two chromatids.) In meiosis II, the centromeres split, and so the number of chromosomes is kept equal.

ANS 4.6. a. 20 chromosomes and 40 chromatids; **b.** 20 chromosomes and 40 chromatids; **c.** 10 chromosomes and 20 chromatids

ANS 4.7. a. For each centromere, there are two possibilities (for example, A or a); so altogether there are $2^7 = 128$ possible gametes. **b.** The probability of a gamete's receiving a particular centromere desigated by a capital letter is 1/2 for each centromere, and each centromere segregates independently of the others; hence, the probability for all seven simultaneously is $(1/2)^7 = 1/128$.

ANS 4.8. The wheat parent produces gametes with 14 chromosomes and the rye parent gametes with 7, and so the hybrid plants have 21 chromosomes.

ANS 4.9. The crisscross occurs because the X chromosome in a male is transmitted only to his daughters. The expression is misleading because any X chromosome in a female can be transmitted to a son or a daughter.

ANS 4.10. Because there is an affected son, the phenotypically normal mother must be heterozygous. This implies that the daughter has a probability of 1/2 of being heterozygous.

ANS: 4.11. In the father, in the second meiotic division.

ANS 4.12. The *Bar* mutation is an X-linked dominant. Because the sexes are affected unequally, some association with the sex chromosomes is suggested. Mating **a.** provides an important clue. Because a male receives his X chromosome from his mother, the wildtype phenotype of the sons suggests that the *Bar* gene is on the X chromosome. The fact that all daughters are affected is also consistent with X-linkage, provided that the *Bar* mutation is dominant. Mating **b.** confirms the hypothesis, because the females from mating **a.** would have the genotype *Bar* / + and so would produce the indicated progeny

ANS 4.13. a. Cross is *v* / Y × + / +, in which Y represents the Y chromosome; progeny are 1/2 + / Y males (wildtype) and 1/2 *v* / + females (phenotypically wildtype, but heterozygous). **b.** Mating is *v* / *v* × + / Y; progeny are 1/2 *v* / Y males (vermilion) and 1/2 *v* / + females (phenotypically wildtype, but heterozygous). **c.** Mating is *v* / + × + / Y; progeny are 1/4 *v* / + females (phenotypically wildtype), 1/4 + / + females (wildtype), 1/4 *v* / Y males (vermilion), and 1/4 + / Y males (wildtype). **d.** Mating is *v* / + × *v* / Y; progeny are 1/4 *v* / *v* females (vermilion), 1/4 *v* / + females (wildtype), 1/4 *v* / Y males (vermilion), and 1/4 + / Y males (wildtype).

ANS 4.14. All the females will be *v* / *v*⁺ ; *bw* / *bw* and will have brown eyes; all the males will be *v* / Y ; *bw* / *bw* and will have white eyes

ANS 4.15. Because the sex-chromosome situation is the reverse of that in mammals, female chickens are ZW and males ZZ, and females receive their Z chromosome from their father. Therefore, the answer is to mate a gold male (*ss*) with a silver female (*S*). The male progeny will all be *Ss* (silver plumage) and the female progeny will be *s* (gold plumage), and these are easily distinguished

ANS 4.16. a. The mother is a heterozygous carrier of the mutation, and therefore the probability that a daughter is a carrier is 1/2. The probability that both daughters are carriers is $(1/2)^2 = 1/4$. **b.** If the daughter is not heterozygous, the probability of an affected son is 0 and, if the daughter is heterozygous the probability of an affected son is 1/2; the overall probability is therefore 1/2 (that is, the chance that the daughter is a carrier) × 1/2 (that is, the probability of an affected son if the daughter is a carrier) = 1/4.

ANS 4.17. Let A and a represent the normal and mutant X-linked alleles. Y represents the Y chromosome. The genotypes are as follows: I-1 is Aa (because there is an affected son), I-2 is AY, II-1 is AY, II-2 is aY, II-3 is Aa (because there is an affected son), II-4 is AY, and III-1 is aY.

ANS 4.18. 20, because, in females, there are five homozygous and ten heterozygous genotypes, and in males there are five hemizygous genotypes.

ANS 4.19. The accompanying Punnett square shows the outcome of the cross. The X and Y chromosomes from the male are denoted in red, the attached-X chromosomes (yoked Xs) and Y from the female in black. The red X chromosome also contains the w mutation. The zygotes in the upper left and lower right corners (shaded) fail to survive because they have three X chromosomes or none. The surviving progeny consist of white-eyed males (XY) and red-eyed females (XXY) in equal proportions. Attached-X inheritance differs from the typical situation in that the sons, rather than the daughters, receive their fathers' X chromosome.

	X	Y
$\widehat{XX}$	$\widehat{XX}X$	$\widehat{XX}Y$
Y	XY	YY

ANS 4.20. The genotype of the female is Cc, where c denotes the allele for color blindness. In meiosis, the c-bearing chromatids undergo nondisjunction and produce an XX-bearing egg of genotype cc. Fertilization by a normal Y-bearing sperm results in an XXY zygote with genotype cc, which results in color blindness.

ANS 4.21. The female produces 1/2 X-bearing eggs and 1/2 O-bearing eggs ("O" means no X chromosome), and the male produces 1/2 X-bearing sperm and 1/2 Y-bearing sperm. Random combinations result in 1/4 XX, 1/4 XO, 1/4 XY, and 1/4 YO, and the last class dies because no X chromosome is present. Among the survivors, the expected progeny are 1/3 XX females, 1/3 XO females, and 1/3 XY males.

ANS 4.22 a. II-2 must be heterozygous, because she has an affected son, which means that half of her sons will be affected. The probability of a nonaffected child is therefore 3/4, and the probability of two nonaffected children is $(3/4)^2 = 9/16$. **b.** Because the mother of II-4 is heterozygous, the

probability that II-4 is heterozygous is 1/2. If she is heterozygous, half of her sons will be affected. Therefore, the overall probability of an affected child is $1/2 \times 1/4 = 1/8$.

ANS 4.23. a. This question is like asking for the probability of the sex distribution GGGBBB (in that order), which equals $(1/2)^6 = 1/64$. **b.** This question is like asking for the probability of the sex distribution either GGGBBB or BBBGGG, which equals $2(1/2)^6 = 1/32$.

ANS 4.24: $[(8!/0!8!\,) + (8!/2!6!\,) + (8!/4!4!\,) + (8!/6!2!\,) + (8!/8!0!\,)](1/2)^8 = 128/2^8 = 0.500$.

ANS 4.25: $[7!/4!3!](1/2)^7 + [7!/3!4!](1/2)^7 = 70/128 = 0.547$.

ANS: 4.26. 1/2; 1/4.

ANS: 4.27. X-linked inheritance is suggested by the fact that each male has only one band, which is transmitted to his daughters but not his sons. The deduced genotypes are: I-1 (A_2A_2), I-2 (A_1), II-1 (A_2), II-2 (A_1A_2), II-3 (A_2), II-4 (A_2), II-5 (A_1A_2), II-6 (A_1), III-1 (A_1), II-2 (A_1A_2), III-3 (A_1A_2), and III-4 (A_2).

ANS 4.28. With 1:1 segregation, the expected numbers are 125 in each class, and so the χ^2 equals $(140 - 125)^2/125 + (110 - 125)^2/125 = 3.6$, and there is one degree of freedom because there are two classes of data. The associated P value is approximately 6 percent, which means that a fit at least as bad would be expected 6 percent of the time even with Mendelian segregation. Therefore, based on these data, there is no justification for rejecting the hypothesis of 1:1 segregation. (On the other hand, the observed P value is close to 5 percent, which is the conventional level for rejecting the hypothesis, and so the result should not inspire great confidence.)

ANS 4.29. The total number of progeny equals 800, and on the assumption of a 9:3:3:1 ratio, the expected numbers equal 450, 150, 150, and 50, respectively. The χ^2 equals $(462 - 450)^2/450 + (167 - 150)^2/150 + (127 - 150)^2/150 + (44 - 50)^2/50 = 6.49$, and there are three degrees of freedom (because there are four classes of data). The P value is approximately 0.09, which is well above the conventional rejection level of 0.05. Consequently, the observed numbers provide no basis for rejecting the hypothesis of a 9:3:3:1 ratio.

ANS 4.30. The χ^2 value equals $(234 - 200)^2/200 + (203 - 200)^2/200 + (175 - 200)^2/200 + (188 - 200)^2/200 = 9.67$. It has 3 degrees of freedom (four classes of data), and the P value is about 0.025. We therefore conclude that these data are not in satisfactory agreement with the hypothesis of 1:1:1:1 segregation.

Challenge Problems

ANS 4.31. X-linked inheritance for the morphological trait, because the affected male I-2 has normal sons and carrier daughters. Y-linkage for the molecular trait, because females have no DNA for the RFLP and because males receive the allele present in the father.

ANS 4.32. The surviving offspring are expected to be 2/3 tailless and 1/3 tailed. In a litter of five pups, the expected distribution is $(1/3)^5 = 0.0041$ with all 5 tailed, $5(1/3)^4(2/3)^1 = 0.0411$ with 4 tailed, $10(1/3)^3(2/3)^2 = 0.1646$ with 3 tailed, $10(1/3)^2(2/3)^3 = 0.3292$ with 2 tailed, $5(1/3)^1(2/3)^4 = 0.3292$ with 1 tailed, and $1(2/3)^5 = 0.1317$ with 0 tailed. The two most probable outcomes are equally probable because any particular litter with 2 tailed and 3 tailless is half as likely as any particular litter with a tailed and 4 tailless (8/243 versus 16/243), but there are twice as many possible arrangements of the former (10 versus 5).

ANS 4.33. $(1/2)^2(1/2)/[(1/2)^2(1/2) + 1^2(1/2)] = 1/5; \ 1/5 \times 1/2 = 1/10$.

Supplemental problems with answers

S4.1. Classify each statement as true or false as it applies to mitosis.
 a. DNA synthesis takes place in prophase; chromosome distribution to daughter cells takes place in metaphase.
 b. DNA synthesis takes place in metaphase; chromosome distribution to daughter cells takes place in anaphase.
 c. Chromosome condensation takes place in prophase; chromosome distribution to daughter cells takes place in anaphase.
 d. Chromosomes pair in metaphase.
ANS S4.1: a. False. **b.** False. **c.** True. **d** False.

S4.2. Which of the following statements are true?
 a. A bivalent contains one centromere, two sister chromatids, and one homolog.
 b. A bivalent contains two centromeres, four sister chromatids, and two homologs.
 c. A bivalent contains two linear, duplex DNA molecules.
 d. A bivalent contains four linear, duplex DNA molecules.
 e. A bivalent contains eight linear, duplex DNA molecules.
ANS S4.2: a. false. **b.** True. **c.** False. **d.** True. **e.** False.

S4.3. Which of the following statements correctly describes a difference between mitosis and meiosis?
 a. Meiosis includes two nuclear divisions, mitosis only one.
 b. Bivalents appear in mitosis but not in meiosis.
 c. Sister chromatids appear in meiosis but not in mitosis.
 d. Centromeres do not divide in meiosis; they do in mitosis.
ANS S4.3: a. True. **b** False. **c.** False. **d.** False.

S4.4. Classify each of the following statements as true or false as it applies to the segregation of alleles for a genetic trait in a diploid organism.
 a. There is a 1 : 1 ratio of meiotic products.
 b. There is a 3 : 1 ratio of meiotic products.
 c. There is a 1 : 2 : 1 ratio of meiotic products.
 d. There is a 3 : 1 ratio of F_2 genotypes.

e. All of the above.

ANS S4.4: a is true and all the others are false. Statement **d** is false because, while it is true sometimes, it is not always true; segregation implies a 3 : 1 ratio in the F_2 generation only in a cross between heterozygous genotypes when one of the alleles is dominant.

S4.5. What is a chiasma? In what stage of meiosis are chiasmata observed?

ANS S4.5: A chiasma is a cross-shaped connection between chromatids that results from a physical exchange between two chromatids of homologous chromosomes; chiasmata are observed late in pachytene and subsequent stages of meiosis until anaphase I.

S4.6. When in meiosis does the physical manifestation of independent assortment take place?

ANS S4.6: At metaphase I when nonhomologous chromosomes align independently on the metaphase plate.

S4.7. In the life cycle of corn, *Zea mays,* how many haploid chromosome sets are there in cells of the following tissues?

 a. Megasporocyte

 b. Megaspore

 c. Root tip

 d. Endosperm

 e. Embryo

 f. Microspore

ANS S4.7: a. 2. **b.** 1. **c.** 2. **d.** 3. **e.** 2. **f.** 1.

S4.8. A cytogeneticist examining cells in *Tradescantia* stamen hairs is trying to determine the length of the various stages in mitosis and the cell cycle. She examines 2000 cells and finds 320 cells in prophase, 150 cells in metaphase, 80 cells in anaphase, and 120 cells in telophase. What conclusion can be made regarding the relative length of each stage of the cell cycle including the time spent in interphase? Express each answer as a percentage of the total cell-cycle time.

ANS S4.8: Assuming that she happens upon cells in each stage according to the length of time that an average cell spends in that stage, prophase takes up 320/2000 = 16.0% of the total time, metaphase 150/2000 = 7.5%, anaphase 4.0%, and telophase 120/2000 = 6.0%. The remaining time (66.5%) must be spent in interphase.

S4.9. Somatic cells of the red fox, *Vulpes vulpes,* normally have 38 chromosomes. What is the number of chromosomes present in the nucleus in a cell of this organism in each of the following stages? (For purposes of this problem, count each chromatid as a chromosome in its own right.)

 a. Metaphase of mitosis

 b. Metaphase I of meiosis

 c. Telophase I of meiosis

 d. Telophase II of meiosis

ANS S4.9: a. 76. **b.** 76. **c.** 38. **d.** 19.

S4.10. A woman who is homozygous for normal color vision mates with a colorblind male. They produce a female child who has only one X chromosome and who is also color blind. In which parent did the nondisjunction take place? Can you specify which meiotic division?

ANS S4.10: The mother, but one cannot specify which meiotic division.

S4.11. One of the characteristics of rare X-linked recessive conditions is that the great majority of affected persons are males. Explain why this is expected.
ANS S4.11: It requires two rare recessive together to yield an affected, homozygous female, but only one rare recessive is needed to yield an affected male.

S4.12. The most common form of color blindness in human beings results from X-linked recessive alleles. One type of allele, call it cb^r, results in defective red perception, whereas another type of allele, call it cb^g, results in defective green perception. A woman who is heterozygous cb^r/cb^g mates with a normal male, and they produce a son whose chromosome constitution is XXY. What are the possible genotypes of this boy if:

 a. The nondisjunction took place in meiosis I?

 b. The nondisjunction took place in the cb^r-bearing chromosome in meiosis II?

 c. The nondisjunction took place in the cb^g-bearing chromosome in meiosis II?

ANS S4.12: **a.** $cb^r\ cb^g$; if nondisjunction occured in meiosis I in the father, possible genotypes could also be $cb^r\ +$ or $cb^g\ +$. **b.** $cb^r\ cb^r$ **c.** $cb^g\ cb^g$.

S4.13. The terms "reductional division" and "equational division" are literally correct in describing the two meiotic divisions with respect to division of the centromeres. To assess the applicability of the terms to alleles along a chromosome, consider a chromosome arm in which exactly one exchange event takes place in prophase I. Denote as *A* the region between the centromere and the position of the exchange and as *B* the region between the position of the exchange and the tip of the chromosome arm. If "reductional" is defined as resulting in products that are genetically different and "equational" is defined as resulting in products that are genetically identical, what can you say about the "reductional" or "equational" nature of the two meiotic divisions with respect to the regions *A* and *B*?
ANS S4.13: Because sister chromatids are genetically identical, the first meiotic division is "reductional" for *A* and "equational" for *B* whereas the second meiotic division is "equational" for *A* and "reductional" for *B*.

S4.14. What differences are there between the sexes in the pattern of transmission of genes located on the autosomes versus those on the sex chromosomes? (Assume that females are the homogametic sex and males the heterogametic sex.)
ANS S4.14: Males and females transmit autosomal genes in the same manner owing to segregation. In females, X-linked genes are transmitted to both sons and daughters, but in males, X-linked genes are transmitted only to daughters. Genes on the Y chromosome are transmitted from father to son to grandson and so forth.

S4.15. What observations about *Drosophila* provided proof of the chromosomal theory of heredity?
ANS S4.15: Rare exceptions to the expected pattern of inheritance of X-linked genes were found by Calvin Bridges and correctly interpreted in terms of chromosome behavior. Bridges showed that the exceptions could be explained by occasional failure of the two X chromosomes in the mother to separate from each other in meiosis, which is called nondisjunction.

S4.16. In *Drosophila*, sex is determined by the ratio of X chromosomes to autosomes. Below are several X/A combinations, in which A indicates one complete haploid set of autosomes. What is the expected sex of each of the following flies?

 a. X/AA
 b. XX/AA
 c. XXX/AA
 d. XX/AAA

ANS S4.16: a. Ratio X/A = 0.5, phenotype male. **b.** Ratio X/A = 1.0, phenotype female. **c.** Ratio X/A > 1.0, phenotype female. **d.** Ratio X/A = 0.66, phenotype intersex.

S4.17. People with the chromosome constitution 47, XXY are phenotypically males. A normal woman whose father had hemophilia mates with a normal man and produces an XXY son who also has hemophilia. What kind of nondisjunction can explain this result?

ANS S4.17: The mother must be heterozygous, since her father was affected, hence her genotype is *Hh*, where *h* denotes the recessive hemophilia mutation. In meiosis, the *h*-bearing chromatids undergo nondisjunction and produce an XX-bearing egg with genotype *hh*. Fertilization by a normal Y-bearing sperm results in an 47, XXY zygote of genotype *hh*, whence the hemophilia.

S4.18. A recessive mutation of an X-linked gene in human beings results in hemophilia, marked by a prolonged increase in the time needed for blood clotting. Suppose that a phenotypically normal couple produces two normal daughters and a son affected with hemophilia.

 a. What is the probability that both of the daughters are heterozygous carriers?
 b. If one of the daughters mates with a normal man and produces a son, what is the probability that the son will be affected?

ANS S4.18: a. The mother must be a heterozygous carrier of the mutation, and therefore the probability that any particular daughter is a carrier is 1/2. The probability that both daughters are carriers is $(1/2)^2 = 1/4$. **b.** If the daughter is not heterozygous, the probability of an affected son is 0 and, if the daughter is heterozygous, the probability of an affected son is 1/2; the overall probability is therefore 1/2 (that is, the chance that the daughter is a carrier) × 1/2 (that is, the probability of an affected son if the daughter is a carrier) = 1/4.

S4.19. In the mouse, an organism with a single X chromosome ("XO") is a fertile female. What sex-chromosome constitutions are expected, and in what frequencies, from mating an "XO" female with a normal male?

ANS S4.19: Because the "YO" zygotes do not survive, the progeny are expected to be 1/3 normal female (XX), 1/3 normal male (XY), and 1/3 "XO" female.

S4.20. Which of the following types of inheritance have the feature that an affected male has all affected daughters but no affected sons?

 a. Autosomal recessive
 b. Autosomal dominant
 c. Y-linked
 d. X-linked recessive
 e. X-linked dominant

ANS S4.20: e, because all daughters, but none of the sons, receive the father's X chromosome.

S4.21. Mendel studied the inheritance of phenotypic characters determined by seven pairs of alleles. It is an interesting coincidence that the pea plant also has seven pairs of chromosomes. What is the probability that, if seven loci are chosen at random in an organism that has seven chromosomes, each locus is in a different chromosome? (*Note*: Mendel's seven genes are actually located in only four chromosomes, but only two of the genes—tall versus short plant and smooth versus constricted pod—are close enough together that independent assortment would not be observed; he apparently never examined these two traits for independent assortment.)

ANS S4.21: No matter which chromosome the first locus is in, the chance that the second will be in a different chromosome is 6/7; the chance that the third locus will be in a different chromosome from either of the first two is 5/7. Continuing this argument, we finally obtain 6/7 x 5/7 x 4/7 x 3/7 x 2/7 x 1/7 = 0.00612, or less than 1 percent. The likelihood of having every gene on different chromosome is quit small, and for this reason Mendel has been accused of deliberately choosing unlikned genes. In fact, it is now known that not all of Mendel's genes are on different chromosomes. Three of the genes (*fa*, determining axial versus terminal flowers; *le*, determining tall versus short plants; and *v*, determining smooth versus constricted pods) are all located in chromosome 4. The *le* and *v* genes undergo recombination at the rate of about 12 percent, but Mendel apparently did not study this particular combination for independent assortment. The *fa* gene is very distant from the other two and shows independent assortment with them.

S4.22. *Drosophila montana* has a somatic chromosome number of 12. Say the centromeres of the six homologous pairs are designated as A/a, B/b, C/c, D/d, E/e , and F/f.

 a. How many different combinations of centromeres can be produced in meiosis?

 b. What is the probability that a gamete will contain only centromeres designated by capital letters?

ANS S4.22: a. $(2)^6 = 64$. **b.** $(1/2)^6 = 0.016$.

S4.23. How many different genotypes are possible for

 a. An autosomal gene with four alleles?

 b. An X-linked gene with four alleles?

ANS S4.23: a. 10, because there are 4 homozygous and 6 heterozygous genotypes. **b.** 14, because, there are 4 homozygous female genotypes, 4 hemizygous male genotypes, and 6 heterozygous female genotypes.

S4.24. Among sibships of size 6 that include three or more girls, what is the ratio of girls:boys? Assume an overall sex distribution of 1:1.

ANS S4.24: Among sibships of size 6, the sex distribution is 1/64 with 0 girls, 6/64 with 1, 15/64 with 2, 20/64 with 3, 15/64 with 4, 6/64 with 5, and 1/674 with 6. Among those with three of more girls, the sex distribution is 20/42 with 3, 15/42 with 4, 6/42 with 5, and 1/42 with 6. Among these sibships the average proportion of girls is (20/42)(3/6) + (15/42)(4/6) + (6/42)(5/6) + (1/42)(6/6) = 0.619, and so the ratio of girls : boys is 0.619 : 0.381 or 1.625 : 1.

S4.25. Duchenne-type muscular dystrophy is an inherited disease of muscle due to a mutant form of a proetin called dystrophin. The pattern of inheritance of the disease has these characteristics: (1) affected males have unaffected children, (2) the unaffected sisters of affected males often have affected sons, and (3) the unaffected brothers of affected males have unaffected children. What type of inheritance is suggested by these findings? Explain your reasoning.

ANS S4.25: These are typical characteristics of X-linked inheritance. Affected males transmit the mutant X chromosome only to their daughters. A carrier female will have both affected and unaffected sons as well as both carrier and noncarrier daughters. The carrier daughters (sisters of the affected sons) will transmit the mutant gene, but the unaffected sons (brothers of the affected sons) will not.

S4.26. For an autosomal gene with m alleles, how many different genotypes are there?
ANS S4.26: There are m homozygous genotypes and $m(m - 1)/2$ heterozygous genotypes, for a total of
$m(m + 1)/2$.

S4.27. Consider the mating Aa x Aa.
 a. What is the probability that a sibship of size 8 will contain no aa offspring?
 b. What is the probability that a sibship of size 8 will contain a perfect Mendelian ratio of 3 A-:1 aa?
ANS S4.27: a. An absence of aa means that all progeny are $A-$, each of which has a probability of $3/4$; hence, the probability of all $A-$ offspring is $(3/4)^8 = 0.10$. **b.** From the binomial formula, $[8!/6!2!](3/4)^6(1/4)^2 = 0.31$.

S4.28. Tall, red-flowered hibiscus is mated with short, white-flowered hibiscus. Both varieties are true breeding. All the F_1 plants are backcrossed with the short, white-flowered variety. This backcross yielded 188 tall red, 203 tall white, 175 short red, and 178 short white plants. Does the observed result fit the genetic hypothesis of 1:1:1:1 segregation as assessed by a χ^2 test?
ANS S4.28: The χ^2 value equals $(188 - 186)^2/186 + (203 - 186)^2/186 + (175 - 186)^2/186 + (178 - 186)^2/186 = 2.56$. It has 3 degrees of freedom (four classes of data), and the P value is about 0.5. We therefore conclude that there is no reason, from these data, to reject the hypothesis of 1:1:1:1 segregation.

S4.29. What are the values of chi-square that yield P values of 5% (statistically significant) when there are 1, 2, 3, 4, and 5 degrees of freedom? For the types of chi-square tests illustrated in this chapter, how many classes of data do these degrees of freedom represent? Because the significant chi-square values increase with the number of degrees of freedom, does this mean that it becomes increasingly "harder" (less likely) to obtain a statistically significant chi-square value when the genetic hypothesis is true?
ANS S4.29: 3.84 for 1 df, 5.99 for 2 df, 7.82 for 3 df, 9.49 for 4 df, 11.07 for 5 df (these values are from statistical tables, values read from the graph will not be as accurate). These values correspond to 2, 3, 4, 5, and 6 classes of data, respectively, for the type of chi-square tests in this chapter. Perhaps surprisingly, the increasing chi-square value needed for significance does not imply that one is less likely to obtain a statistically significant chi-square with increasing degrees of freedom. The probability of obtaining a statistically significant chi-square value, given that the genetic hypothesis is true, is 5%, no matter what the number of degrees of freedom.

S4.30. Matings between two types of guinea pigs with normal phenotypes produce 64 offspring, 11 of which showed a hyperactive behavioral abnormality. The other 53 offspring were behaviorally normal. Assume that the parents were heterozygous.

a. Do these data fit the model that hyperactivity is caused by a recessive allele of a single gene?

b. Do they fit the model that hyperactivity is caused by simultaneous homozygosity for recessive alleles of each of two unlinked genes?

ANS S4.30: Hypothesis **a** predicts a 3:1 ratio of normal : hyperactive, hence the expected numbers are 3/4 x 64 = 48 and 1/4 x 64 = 16. The $\chi^2 = (53 - 48)^2/48 + (11 - 16)^2/16 = 2.1$. With one degree of freedom, the P value from the χ^2 chart is 0.15, so there is no reason in these data to reject the single-gene hypothesis. On the other hand, hypothesis **b** predicts a ratio of 15:1, hence the expected values are 60 and 4 and the $\chi^2 = (53 - 60)^2/60 + (11 - 4)^2/4 = 13.1$. With one degree of freedom, $P = 0.0003$, and so the two-gene hypothesis can be rejected.

S4.31. Are the observed progeny numbers of 11, 11, 22, and 22 consistent with a genetic hypothesis that predicts a 1:1:1:1 ratio?

ANS S4.31: $\chi^2 = (16.5 - 11)^2/16.5 + (16.5 - 11)^2/16.5 + (22 - 16.5)^2/16.5 + (22 - 16.5)^2/16.5 = 7.33$ with 3 df, which yields a P value of about 0.08. The difference from expectation is not statistically significant, so the genetic hypothesis cannot be rejected even though the discrepancies from the expected numbers may seem to be large.

S4.32. A dihybrid cross yielded four classes of phenotypes in the percentages 59%, 18%, 17%, and 6%, among a total of 1000 progeny. Are these data consistent with the independent segregation of two genes?

ANS S4.33: Remember that chi-square values must be calculated based on the observed numbers, not the observed percentages. In this case, the chi-square = 3.38 with 3 df, for which the P value is approximately 0.30. The fit is satisfactory.

S4.33. Are the observed progeny numbers of 230, 135, and 35 consistent with a model of epistasis between two unlinked genes yielding an expected ratio of phenotypes of 9:6:1?

ANS S4.33: The $\chi^2 = (230 - 225)^2/225 + (135 - 150)^2/150 + (35 - 25)^2/25 = 5.5$ with 2 df, for which the P value is approximately 0.07. These data would not lead to the rejection of the hypothesis.

S4.34. In a χ^2 test with 1 degree of freedom, the value of χ^2 that results in significance at the 5 percent level ($P = 0.05$) is approximately 4. If a genetic hypothesis predicts a 1:1 ratio of two progeny types, calculate what deviations from the expected 1:1 ratio yield $P = 0.05$ (and rejection of the genetic hypothesis) when

 a. The total number of progeny equals 50

 b. The total number of progeny equals 100

ANS S4.34: a. Let x be the observed number in one class of progeny and $(50 - x)$ be the number of progeny in the other. The expected numbers are 25 each. The χ^2 equals $(x - 25)^2/25 + (50 - x - 25)^2/25 = 2(x - 25)^2/25$. Setting this equal to 4 yields $(x - 25)^2 = 50$, or $x - 25 = 7$ is the deviation that yields statistical significance at the 5 percent level. In other words, a ratio of progeny of 18:32 (or of 32:18) or worse leads to rejection of the hypothesis. **b.** Solve as in part **a** but use 100 instead of 50 as the total progeny and 50 as the expected numbers. The result is $2(x - 50)^2/50 = 4$, or $x - 50 = 10$. Therefore, an observed ratio of 40:60 (or of 60:40) or worse leads to rejection of the genetic hypothesis.

Chapter 5: Genetic Linkage and Chromosome Mapping
Answers to Chapter-end problems

Fill-ins

1. linkage
2. repulsion configuration
3. centimorgan or map unit
4. map distance
5. coincidence
6. frequency of recombination
7. chromosome interference
8. syntenic genes
9. tetratype (TT) tetrad
10. nonparental ditype (NPD) tetrad

Analysis and Applications

ANS 5.1. In the genotype $A\ B/\ a\ b$, the two wildtype alleles are in the same chromosome, in the genotype $A\ b/\ a\ B$, they are in different chromosomes. The slash separates the alleles present in one chromosome from those present in the homologous chromosome. The $A\ B/\ a\ b$ genotype is in coupling (*cis*), the $A\ b/\ a\ B$ genotype in repulsion (*trans*).

ANS 5.2. There is no crossing-over in male *Drosophila,* and so the gametes will be $A\ B$ and $a\ b$ in equal proportions. In the female, each of the nonrecombinant gametes $A\ B$ and $a\ b$ is expected with a frequency of $(1 - 0.05)/2 = 0.475$, and each of the recombinant gametes $A\ b$ and $a\ B$ is expected with a frequency of $0.05/2 = 0.025$.

ANS 5.3. a. 17; **b.** 1; **c.** in diploids there is one linkage group per pair of homologous chromosomes, and so the number of linkage groups is $42/2 = 21$.

ANS 5.4. Independent assortment takes place when the genes always have one or more crossovers between them, provided the chromatids participate in the crossovers at random.

ANS 5.5. Recombination at a rate of 6.2 percent implies that double crossovers (and other multiple crossovers) occur at a negligible frequency; in such a case the distance in map units equals the frequency of recombination, and so the map distance between the genes is 6.2 map units.

ANS 5.6. Each meiotic cell produces four products, namely, $A\ B$ and $a\ b,$ which contain the chromatids that do not participate in the crossover, and $A\ b$ and $a\ B,$ which contain the chromatids that do take part in the crossover. Therefore, the frequency of recombinant gametes is 50 percent. Because one crossover occurs in the region between the genes in every cell, the occurrence of multiple crossing-over will not affect the recombination frequency as long as the chromatids participating in each crossover are chosen at random

ANS 5.7. The *aa bb* genotype requires an *a b* gamete from each parent. From the *A b / a B* parent, the probability of an *a b* gamete is 0.16 / 2 = 0.08 and, from the *A B / a b* parent, the probability of an *a b* gamete is (1 − 0.16)/2 = 0.42; therefore, the probability of an *aa bb* progeny is 0.08 × 0.42 = 0.034, or 3.4 percent.

ANS 5.8. a. With the exception of the persons who carry recombinant chromosomes listed in part **d** of the answer, all affected people are *HD A_2/ hd A_1*, and all unaffected persons are *hd A_1/ hd A_1*. **b.** Evidently, the A_2 allele is rare enough that, by chance, a homozygous A_2A_2 person does not occur in this sample. (Alternatively, the A_2 allele could be very strongly associated with *HD*.) **c.** There is evidence for linkage between the genes, because most persons who inherit *HD* also inherit the A_2 allele associated with the dominant allele in this pedigree. **d.** The recombinant chromosomes appear in sample numbers 8, 10, 16, 24, and 30. **e.** There are 25 persons in whom a recombinant chromosome could have been detected, of whom 5 are carry a recombinant chromosome, hence the estimated frequency of recombination from this pedigree is 5/25 = 20%.

ANS 5.9. We are given the information that II-2 through II-5 are not affected, but told nothing about the affected or nonaffected status of II-1 or II-6. **a.** The gel diagram indicates that II-6 homozygous *a/a* for the RFLP. For II-6 to be affected, his genotype would have to be *cf a/cf a*, so both chromosomes would be non-recombinant. The probability of a nonrecombinant *cf a* chromosome from the mother is (1-0.16)/2 = 0.42 and from the father is (1-0.10)/2 = 0.45. The relative frequencies of the cystic fibrosis genotypes among the RFLP *a/a* homozygotes are

```
cf   a / cf   a   =   0.42 x 0.45 = 0.189
CF   a / CF   a   =   0.08 x 0.05 = 0.004
cf   a / CF   a   =   0.42 x 0.05 = 0.021
CF   a / cf   a   =   0.08 x 0.45 = 0.036
```

These total 0.250. Among these, the fraction that are *cf/cf* equals 0.189. Hence, the probability that II-6 is affected is 0.189 / 0.250 = 0.756. **b.** The gel diagram indicates that II-1 is heterozygous for the RFLP. The relative frequencies of the cystic fibrosis genotypes among the RFLP heterozygotes are

```
CF   A / CF   a   =   0.42 x 0.05 = 0.021
CF   a / CF   A   =   0.08 x 0.45 = 0.036
CF   A / cf   a   =   0.42 x 0.45 = 0.189
CF   a / cf   A   =   0.08 x 0.05 = 0.004
cf   A / CF   a   =   0.08 x 0.05 = 0.004
cf   a / CF   A   =   0.42 x 0.45 = 0.189
cf   A / cf   a   =   0.08 x 0.45 = 0.036
cf   a / cf   A   =   0.42 x 0.05 = 0.021
```

These total 0.500. Among these, the fraction that are *CF/cf* equals 0.189 + 0.004 + 0.114 + 0.189 = 0.386. Hence, the probability that II-1 is a carrier is 0.386/0.500 = 0.772.

ANS 5.10. a. The coat-color gene cannot be linked to the gene with alleles A_1 and A_2, because this gene is autosomal and the coat-color gene is X-linked. (One indication that the A_1, A_2 allele pair is autosomal is that some males exhibit two both bands and so are heterozygous.) **b.** The coat-color gene is linked to the gene with alleles B_3, and B_4, because most progeny from a doubly heterozygous mother carry a nonrecombinant X chromosome. **c.** There are six recombinant genotypes, namely, numbers 2, 6, 11, 16, 32 and 34. **d.** There are a total of 30 offspring in whom

47

recombination in the mother could be detected, and so the estimated frequency of recombination is 6/30 = 20%.

ANS 5.11. a. The three-allele hypothesis predicts that the matings will be $FS \times FS$ and should yield $FF : FS : SS$ offspring in a ratio of 1:2:1. **b.** These ratios are not observed and, furthermore, some of the progeny show the "null" pattern. **c.** One possibility is that the F and S bands are from unlinked loci and that there is a "null" allele of each, say, f and s. Because f and s are common, and F and S rare, most persons with two bands would have the genotype $Ff\,Ss$. The cross should therefore yield 9/16 F– S– (two bands), 3/16 F– ss (fast band only), 3/16 $ff\,S$– (slow band only), and 1/16 $ff\,ss$ (no bands). (d) The data are consistent with this hypothesis (chi-square = 2.67 with three degress of freedom, P value approximately 0.50).

ANS: 5.12. a. No, they are not alleles. If they were alleles, they would undergo segregation, and the progeny would consist equally of either DDT-resistant or Dieldrin-resistant animals. There would be no progeny resistant to both insecticides and no progeny sensitive to both insecticides. **b.** The test for linkage is whether the parental and nonparental chromosomes occur in equal proportions, and so the reciprocal classes must be pooled. This yields 177 parental and 205 nonparental. The chi-square = 2.05 with 1 df, for which P is approximately 0.15. The genes are therefore unlinked (they show independent assortment), even though they are in the same chromosome. **c.** The conclusion is that DDT and Dl are so far apart in the chromosome that one or more crossovers always occurs between them.

ANS 5.13. All the female gametes are $bz\ m$. The male gametes are $bz^+\ M$ with frequency (1 – 0.06)/2 = 47 percent, $bz\ m$ with frequency 47 percent, $bz^+\ m$ with frequency 0.06/2 = 3 percent, and $bz\ M$ with frequency 3 percent. The progeny are therefore black males ($bz^+\ M\ /\ bz\ m$) with frequency 47 percent, bronze females ($bz\ m\ /\ bz\ m$) with frequency 47 percent, black females ($bz^+\ m./\ bz\ m$) with frequency 3 percent, and bronze males ($bz\ M\ /\ bz\ m$) with frequency 3 percent).

ANS 5.14. The most frequent gametes from the double heterozygous parent are the nonrecombinant gametes, in this case $Gl\ ra$ and $gl\ Ra$. The genotype of the parent was therefore $Gl\ ra\ /\ gl\ Ra$. The recombinant gametes are $Gl\ Ra$ and $gl\ ra,$ and the frequency of recombination is (6 + 3)/(88 + 103 + 6 + 3) = 4.5 percent.

ANS 5.15. There is no recombination in the male, and so the male gametes are + + and $b\ cn,$ each with a probability of 0.5. A map distance of 8 units means that the recombination frequency between the genes is 0.08. The female gametes are + +, $b\ cn$ [the nonrecombinants, each of which occurs at a frequency of (1 – 0.08)/2 = 0.46] and + cn and b + [the recombinants, each of which occurs at a frequency of 0.08/2 = 0.04]. When the male and female gametes are combined at random, their frequencies are multiplied, and the progeny and their frequencies are as follows:

DISPLAY:

+ + / + +	0.23		+ + / b cn	0.23
b cn / + +	0.23		b cn / b cn	0.23
b + / + +	0.02		b + / b cn	0.02
+ cn / + +	0.02		+ cn / b cn	0.02

Note that *b cn / + +* is the same as *+ + / b cn,* and so the overall frequency of this genotype is 0.46. With regard to phenotypes, the progeny are wildtype (73 percent), black cinnabar (23 percent), black (2 percent), and cinnabar (2 percent).

ANS 5.16. The most-frequent classes of gametes are the nonrecombinants, and so the parental genotype was *A B c / a b C.* The least-frequent gametes are the double recombinants, and the allele that distinguishes them from the nonrecombinants (in this case, *C* and *c*) is in the middle. Therefore, the gene order is *A–C–B*

ANS 5.17. Comparison of the first three numbers implies that *r* lies between *c* and *p,* and the last two numbers imply that *s* is closer to *r* than to *c.* The map is therefore *c–10–r–3–p–5–s.* From this map, you would expect the recombination frequency between *c* and *p* to be 13 percent and that between *c* and *s* to be 18 percent. The observed values are a little smaller because of double crossovers.

ANS 5.18. a. The nonrecombinant gametes (the most frequent classes) are $y\ v^+\ sn$ and $y^+\ v\ sn^+$, and the double recombinants (the least-frequent classes) indicate that *sn* is in the middle. Therefore, the correct order of the genes is *y–sn–v,* and the parental genotype was $y\ sn\ v^+ / y^+\ sn^+\ v$. The total progeny is 1000. The recombination frequency in the *y–sn* interval is $(108 + 5 + 95 + 3)/1000 = 21.1$ percent, and the recombination frequency in the *sn–v* interval is $(53 + 5 + 63 + 3)/1000 = 12.4$ percent. The genetic map is *y–21.1–sn–12.4–v.* **b.** On the assumption of independence, the expected frequency of double crossovers is $0.211 \times 0.124 = 0.0262$, whereas the observed is $(5 + 3)/1000 = 0.008$. The coincidence is the ratio $0.008/0.0262 = 0.31$, and so the interference is $1 - 0.31 = 0.69$, or 69 percent.

ANS 5.19. The nonrecombinant gametes are *c wx Sh* and *C Wx sh,* and the double recombinants indicate that *sh* is in the middle. The parental genotype was therefore *c Sh wx / C sh Wx.* The frequency of recombination in the *c–sh* region is $(84 + 20 + 99 + 15)/6708 = 3.25$ percent, and that in the *sh–wx* region is $(974 + 20 + 951 + 15)/6708 = 29.2$ percent. The genetic map is therefore *c–3.25–sh–29.2–wx.*

ANS 5.20. Let *x* be the observed frequency of double crossovers. Then, single crossovers in the *a–b* interval occur with frequency $0.15 - x$ and single crossovers in the *b–c* interval occur with frequency $0.20 - x$. The observed recombination frequency between *a* and *c* equals the sum of the single crossover frequencies (because double crossovers are undetected), which implies that $0.15 - x + 0.20 - x = 0.31$, or $x = 0.02$. The expected frequency of double crossovers equals $0.15 \times 0.20 = 0.03$, and the coincidence is therefore $0.02/0.03 = 0.67$. The interference equals $1 - 0.67 = 33$ percent.

ANS 5.21. *b* and *st* are unlinked, as are *hk* and *st.* The evidence is the 1:1:1:1 segregation observed. For *b* and *st,* the comparisons are $243 + 10$ (black, scarlet) versus $241 + 15$ (black, nonscarlet) versus $226 + 12$ (nonblack, scarlet) versus $235 + 18$ (nonblack, nonscarlet). For *hk* and *st,* the comparisons are $226 + 10$ (hook, scarlet) versus $235 + 15$ (hook, nonscarlet) versus $243 + 12$ (nonhook, scarlet) versus $241 + 18$ (nonhook, nonscarlet). On the other hand, *b* and *hk* are linked, and the frequency of recombination between them is $(15 + 10 + 12 + 18)/1000 = 5.5$ percent.

ANS 5.22. The frequency of *dpy-21 unc-34* recombinants is expected to be 0.24/2 = 0.12 among both eggs and sperm, and so the expected frequency of *dpy-21 unc-34 / dpy-21 unc-34* zygotes is $0.12^2 = 1.44$ percent

ANS 5.23. The genes must be linked because, with independent assortment, the frequency of dark eyes (*R– P–*) would be 9/16 in both experiments. The first experiment is a mating of *R P / r p × r p / r p*. The dark-eyed progeny represent half the nonrecombinants, and so the recombination frequency *r* can be estimated as $(1 - r)/2 = 628/(628 + 889)$, or $r = 0.172$. The second experiment is a mating of *R p / r P × r p / r p*. In this case, the dark-eyed progeny represent half the recombinants, and so *r* can be estimated as $r/2 = 86/(86 + 771)$, or $r = 0.201$. It is not uncommon for repeated experiments or crosses carried out in different ways to yield somewhat different estimates of the recombination frequency–in this problem, 0.17 and 0.20. The most-reliable value is obtained by averaging the experimental values, in this case, $(0.171 + 0.201)/2 = 0.186$.

ANS 5.24. Consider row 1: there are – entries for 3 and 7, and so 1, 3, and 7 form one complementation group. Row 2: all +, and so 2 is the only representative of a second complementation group. Row 3: mutation already classified. Row 4: there is a – for 6 only and no other – in column 4, and so 4 and 6 comprise a third complementation group. Row 5: – only for 9 and no other – in column 5, and so 5 and 9 form a fourth complementation group. Rows 6 and 7: mutations already classified. Row 8: all +, and so 8 is the only member of a fifth complementation group. In summary, there are five complementation groups as follows: group 1 (mutations 1, 3, and 7); group 2 (mutation 2); group 3 (mutations 4 and 6); group 4 (mutations 5 and 9); group 5 (mutation 8).

ANS 5.25. Consider each gene in relation to first- and second-division segregation. Gene *a* gives 1766 asci with first-division segregation and 234 with second-division segregation; the frequency of second-division segregation is $234/(1766 + 234) = 0.117$, which implies that the distance between *a* and the centromere is 0.117/2 = 5.85 percent. Gene *b* gives 1780 first-division and 220 second-division segregations, for a frequency of second-division segregation of $220/(1780 + 220) = 0.110$. The distance between *b* and the centromere is therefore 0.110/2 = 5.50 map units. If we consider *a* and *b* together, there are 1986 PD asci, 14 TT asci, and no NPD. Because NPD << PD, genes *a* and *b* are linked. The frequency of recombination between *a* and *b* is $[(1/2) \times 14]/2000 = 0.35$ percent. Comparing this distance with the gene-centromere distances calculated earlier results in the map *a*– 0.35–*b*–5.50–centromere.

ANS 5.26. Considered individually, gene *c* yields 90 first-division segregation asci and 10 (1 + 9) second-division segregation asci, and so the frequency of recombination between *c* and the centromere is $(10/100) \times 1/2 = 5$ percent. Gene *v* yields 79 first-division and 21 (20 + 1) second-division asci, and so the frequency of recombination between *v* and the centromere is $(21/100) \times 1/2 = 10.5$ percent. If the genes are taken together, the asci include 34 PD, 36 NPD, and 30 (20 + 1 + 9) TT. Because NPD = PD, the genes are unlinked. In summary, *c* and *v* are in different chromosomes with *c* 5 map units from the centromere and *v* 10.5 map units from the centromere.

ANS 5.27. Analysis of cross 1. Ascospore arrangements 1, 2, 4 and 5 result when there is a crossover between the gene and the centromere. Types 3 and 6 result when there is no crossing-over

between the gene and the centromere. The map distance between the gene and its centromere is (1/2)(Frequency of second-division segregation) × 100 = (1/2)[(6 + 6 + 6 + 6)/120] × 100 = 10 centimorgans. Analysis of cross 2. There is no crossing-over between the gene and its centromere. Analysis of cross 3. The proportion of second-division segregation (asci types 1, 2, 4, and 5) equals 80/120 = 67 percent. This distribution of asci results when crossing-over is frequent enough to randomize the position of alleles with respect to their centromeres. The gene is said to be "unlinked" with its centromere.

ANS 5.28. For each pair of genes, classify the tetrads as PD, NPD, or TT and tabulate the results as follows:

leu2-trp1	*leu2-met14*	*trp1-met14*
PD 230 + 235 = 465	PD 235 + 220 = 455	PD 235 + 215 + 46 = 496
NPD 215 + 220 = 435	NPD 230 + 215 = 445	NPD 230 + 220 + 54 = 504
TT 54 + 46 = 100	TT 54 + 46 = 100	TT 0

For *leu2 - trp1*, PD = NPD; therefore, *leu2* and *trp1* are unlinked. Similarly, for *leu2 -met14*, PD = NPD; these genes are also unlinked. Likewise, *trp1* and *met14* are unlinked because PD = NPD. However, for the *trp1 - met14* gene pair there are no tetratypes, which means that each gene is closely linked to its own centromere. Because they do not recombine with their centromeres, the segregation of *trp1* and *met14* can be used as genetic markers of centromere segregation; their presence marks the sister spores created by segregation in the first meiotic division. Using the *trp1* and *met14* markers in this fashion allows the remaining *leu2* gene to be mapped with respect to its centromere, because all tetratype tetrads will result from crossing over between *leu2* and its centromere owing to the fact that neither of the other two genes recombines with its centromere. The map distance between leu2 and its centromere is therefore (1/2)(100/1000) × 100 = 5 centimorgans.

ANS 5.29. For the*rad6 - trp5* gene pair, PD = 188 + 206 = 140 + 154 + 154 + 109 = 797, NPD = 0, and TT = 105 + 92 + 3 + 2 + 1 = 203. Because PD >> NPD the genes are linked. In this case, TT > 0 and NPD = 0, so that the map distance is calculated as (1/2)(203/1000) × 100 = 10.15 centimorgans. For the *trp5 - leu1* gene pair, PD = 188 + 206 + 105 + 92 + 109 = 700, NPD = 0, and TT = 140 + 154 +3 + 2 + 1 = 300; here again, PD >> NPD, TT > 0 and NPD = 0, hence the map distance is calculated as (1/2)(300/1000) × 100 = 15 centimorgans. For the *rad6 - leu1* gene pair, PD = 188 + 206 + 109 = 503, NPD = 1, and TT = 105 + 92 + 140 + 154 + 3 + 2 = 496. In this case, PD >> NPD but TT > 0 and NPD > 0. The map distance is calculated as (1/2)[(496 + 6 × 1)/1000] × 100 = 25.1 centimorgans. For the *leu1 - met14* gene pair, PD = 188 + 105 + 140 + 2 = 435, NPD = 206 + 92 + 154 + 3 + 1 = 456, and TT =109. In this case PD = NPD and so *leu1* is not linked to *met14*. However, we already know from the previous problem that *met14* is tightly linked with its centromere, and this information can be used to calculate the map distance between *leu1* and its centromere. Because TT = 109 and also TT < 2/3, the map distance between leu1 and its centromere is (1/2)(109/1000) × 100 = 5.45 centimorgans. For the *rad6-met14* gene pair, PD = 188 + 1 = 189, NPD = 206, and TT = 105 + 92 + 140 + 154 + 109 +3 + 2 = 605. Here again PD = NPD indicating no linkage between the genes. Because *met14* is tightly linked to its centromere, and TT = 605 but TT < 2/3, the map distance between rad6 and its centromere is (1/2)(605/1000) × 100 = 30.25 centimorgans. For the *trp5 - met14* gene pair, PD = 188 + 105 = 293. NPD = 206 + 92 = 298, and TT = 140 + 154 + 109 +3 +2 + 1 = 409. Once again, PD = NPD indicating no linkage between the genes. As before, we use met14 as a centromere marker to calculate the distance between trp5 and its

centromere as $(1/2)(409/1000) \times 100 = 20.5$ centimorgans. The overall conclusion is that *rad6*, *trp5* and *leu1* are all linked to each other; *met14* is tightly linked to its centromere but not to the other three genes. The genetic map based on these data is:

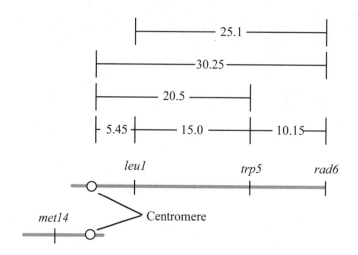

ANS 5.30. a. PD asci contain four *Sk-1 sk-2* and four *sk-1 Sk-2* ascospores, so all eight spores die. NPD asci contain four *Sk-1 Sk-2* and four *sk-1 sk-2* ascospores, and the *sk-1 sk-2* spores die. TT asci contain two ascospore of each genotype, and only the *Sk-1 Sk-2* spores survive, so six spores die. **b.** *Sk-1* and *Sk-2* are unlinked because PD = NPD (in this case, 76 PD and 72 NPD).

Challenge Problems

ANS 5.31. a. Consider the data as a series of two-point crosses and calculate the pairwise frequencies of recombination. In this case it is not necessary to consider all six possible pairs of genes because three of the genes are linked. Considered only as pairwise crosses by ignoring all the other markers, the *cnx–ga3* recombination fraction is 0.10, the *cnx–sex1* recombination fraction is 0.504, and the *cnx–th2* recombination fraction is 0.204. Therefore *cnx, ga3,* and *th2* are linked, and *sex1* is unlinked. **b.** Now pool the data for the *sex1* and *sex1+* classes and carry out a conventional three-point cross linkage analysis. The order of the genes is found to be *cnx–ga3–th2*. The genetic map is as shown here:

(Note that the true map distance between *cnx* and *th2* is greater than the 20.4 calculated by ignoring *ga3*.) **c.** The interference across the region is 0.19.

ANS 5.32. Because the progeny population is expected to consist of the genotypes *A B/ a b, A b/ a b, a B/ a b,* and *a b/ a b,* in the frequencies 0.4, 0.2, 0.2, and 0.4, respectively, the answers are: **a.** 0. **b.** 1. **c.** 0.4. **d.** 1. **e.** 1. **f.** 0.4.

ANS 5.33. a. 7.43 percent, 13.76 percent, 27.6 percent, and 40 percent, respectively. **b.** Rearrange the mapping function to give d in terms of r, which yields $d = \dfrac{100 \ln(1 - r/50)}{\ln(0.2)}$. The answers are 1.26 cM, 6.55 cM, 43.1 cM, and 100 cM, respectively. **c.** The graph appears as illustrated here.

Supplemental problems with answers

S5.1. After a large number of genes have been mapped, how many linkage groups will be found in each of the following?
 a. The bacterial cell *Salmonella typhimurium,* with a single, circular DNA molecule
 b. The haploid yeast *Saccharomyces cerevisiae,* with 16 chromosomes
 c. The common wheat *Triticum vulgare,* with 42 chromosomes per somatic cell
ANS S5.1. a. 1. **b.** 16. **c.** 42/2 = 21.

S5.2. Does physical distance always correlate with map distance?
ANS S5.2. Although there is a general correlation between physical distance and genetic map distance, there are several important exceptions. For instance, the frequency of recombination between genes may differ in males and females, which results in different genetic distances between same genes when measured in the two sexes. (*Drosophila* is a good example, because the map distance between genes in the same chromosome in males is always 0.) Another example: crossing-over is much less frequent in regions of heterochromatin than in regions of euchromatin.

S5.3. In genetic linkage studies, what is the definition of a map unit?
ANS S5.3. One map unit (one centimorgan, cM) between two genetic markers is equal to 1% recombination between the markers as measured among the haploid products of meiosis.

S5.4. Distinguish between the terms "chromosome interference" and "chromatid interference." Which is measured by the coincidence?
ANS S5.4. Chromosome interference is the effect that the occurrence of one crossover in a region has on the occurrence of another crossover in a nearby region. Chromatid interference refers to choice of chromatids that participate in the exchanges when there is double crossing-over or a higher multiple of crossing-over. (Chromatid interference is not observed in most organisms.) The degree of chromosome interference is measured by the coincidence.

S5.5. What experiment in *Drosophila* demonstrated that crossing-over takes place in the four-strand stage? How would the result of the experiment have been different if crossing-over took place in the two-strand stage?

ANS S5.5. Females that are heterozygous for a gene in an attached-X chromosome produce some female progeny that are homozygous for the recessive alleles because of crossing-over between the homologous chromosome arms in the region between the gene and the centromere. A recessive allele can become homozygous only if the recombination takes place at the four-strand stage, after the chromosome has replicated. Crossing-over occurring before replication would result only in a swap of the alleles between the chromosome arms; no homozygous attached-X chromosomes would be observed.

S5.6. In wheat, normal plant height requires the presence of either or both of two dominant alleles, *A* and *B*. Plants homozygous for both recessive alleles (*a b/a b*) are dwarfed but otherwise normal. The two genes are on the same chromosome and recombine with a frequency of 16 percent. From the cross *A b/a B × A B/a b,* what is the expected frequency of dwarfed plants among the progeny?

ANS S5.6. The *a b /a b* genotype requires an *a b* gamete from each parent. From the *A b /a B* parent, the probability of an *a b* gamete is 0.16/2 = 0.08; from the *A B /a b* parent, the probability of an *a b* gamete is (1 - 0.16)/2 = 0.42. Hence, the probability of an *a b /a b* progeny is 0.08 × 0.42 = 0.034, or 3.4 percent.

S5.7. Two yeast strains were mated; one was *red* with mating type **a**; the other was *red*[+] with mating type α. The resulting diploids were induced to undergo meiosis, and the meiotic products of the diploid were as follows (total progeny = 100):

40	*red*[+]	α
44	*red*	**a**
9	*red*[+]	**a**
7	*red*	α

How many map units separate the *red* gene from that for mating type?

ANS S5.7. There are 16 recombinants in 100 progeny, hence the genes are separated by 16 map units.

S5.8. In meiosis, under what conditions does second-division segregation of a pair of alleles take place?

ANS S5.8. Second-division segregation of a pair of alleles takes place when there is a crossover between the gene and the centromere.

S5.9. In the domestic rabbit, the recessive allele *b* (brown) results in brown fur and the recessive allele *f* (furless) results in a reduced amount of fur. Testcrosses of *B f/ b F* animals yielded 19 nonbrown furless, 15 brown nonfurless, 4 brown furless, and 8 nonbrown nonfurless. Estimate the recombination frequency between these genes.

ANS S5.9. 12/46 = 26.1%.

S5.10. The genetic map of an X chromosome of *Drosophila melanogaster* has a length of 73.1 map units. The X chromosome of the related species, *Drosophila virilis,* is even longer—170.5 map units. In view of the fact that the frequency of recombination between two genes cannot exceed 50 percent,

how is it possible for the map distance between genes at opposite ends of a chromosome to exceed 50 map units?

ANS S5.10. The map distance between widely separated genes is determined by summing the distances of shorter intervals between the genes. Hence, the accumulated map distance can (and often does) exceed 50 map units, even though the maximum observed frequency of recombination between any two genetic markers is 50 percent.

S5.11. Explain why the most accurate measurement of map distance between two genes is obtained by summing shorter distances between the genes.

ANS S5.11. The map distance is the frequency of recombination under conditions in which double crossovers (and higher multiples) do not occur. In a two-point cross, when the interval between genes is too large, multiple crossovers can be formed in addition to single crossovers. Some of the double and multiple crossovers do not result in recombination of the genes and hence remain undetected. As a consequence, the observed value of the recombination fraction between the genes is smaller than that obtained by summing the distances among intervals that are short enough that multiple crossovers are nor formed. The latter is the more accurate measure.

S5.12. In a region of chromosome flanked by two genetic markers, 40% of the cells undergoing meiosis have no crossover, 40% of the cells have a single crossover, and 20% of the cells have a double crossover.

 a. What is the frequency of genetic recombination between the genetic markers?

 b. What is the genetic map distance between the markers?

ANS S5.12. a. $r = (0.40 \times 0) + (0.40 \times 0.5) + (0.20 \times 0.5) = 0.30$, or 30%. **b.** $d = (1/2)(0.40 \times 1 + 0.20 \times 2) = 0.40$, or 40 centimorgans.

S5.13. In *D. melanogaster,* the recessive allele *ap* (*apterous*) drastically reduces the size of the wings and halteres (flight balancers), and the recessive allele *cl* (*clot*) produces dark maroon eye color. Both genes are located in the second chromosome. You have a friend taking a genetics laboratory course. To obtain the genetic distance between these genes, she performs a cross of a double-heterozygous female and a maroon-eyed, wingless male. She examines 25 flies in the F_1 generation and calculates that the frequency of recombination is 56 percent. What is wrong with this number? What is a plausible explanation for the results obtained?

ANS S5.13. The maximum value of the frequency of recombination is 50 percent, which is observed for genes that segregate independently, either because they are located in different chromosomes or because they reside sufficiently far apart in the same chromosome. The probable reason for the 56 percent figure is that there were too few F_1 progeny examined. With such a small sample, the results can be quite unreliable. In this example, the actual map distance between the genes is 36 map units. She expected 9 recombinants and observed 14.

S5.14. Your friend in Problem **S5.13** logs onto FlyBase and learns that the *ap-cl* distance is 36 map units. She therefore decides to repeat the cross and to examine more F_1 flies. Because both genes are autosomal, she does not expect any difference between reciprocal crosses. Hence, in setting up the cross this time, she mates a double-heterozygous male with a maroon-eyed, wingless female. To her astonishment, among 1000 F_1 progeny she was unable to find even one recombinant progeny. How can this anomaly be explained?

ANS S5.14. The result is not an anomaly but a consequence of the absence of recombination in the *Drosophila* male. Your friend should have known this (or perhaps asked you), and planned her experiments accordingly.

S5.15. A single crossover occurs in each chromosomal interval in the genotype *A B C/ a b c*, and one of the resulting chromosomes is chosen at random. What is the probability that the chromosome carries *A b C*? Assume that the chromatids participate in the crossovers at random (that is, there is no chromatid interference.)
ANS S5.15. 1/8.

S5.16. A three-strand double crossover takes place in the genotype *A B C/ a b c*, with one crossover in each genetic interval. What proportion of the resulting chromosomes is either *A b C* or *a B c*?
ANS S5.16. 2/8 = 1/4.

S.5.17. A recessive lethal allele, *le*, is known to be linked to the white-eye gene in *Drosophila* with a recombination frequency of 20 percent. Females of genotype *w le$^+$/ w$^+$ s* are crossed with wildtype males, and the sons of the mating are examined. Because of the lethal, all sons that inherit a *le*-bearing chromosome will die. What ratio of white-eyed : red-eyed male progeny are expected?
ANS S5.17. The proportions are 1 – 0.20 = 0.80 white-eyed and 0.20 red-eyed progeny, for a ratio of 80:20 or 4:1.

S5.18. In *D. virilis,* the mutations dusky body color (*dy*), cut wings (*ct*), and white eyes (*w*) are all recessive alleles located in the X chromosome. Females heterozygous for all three mutations were crossed to *dy ct w* males, and the following phenotypes were observed among the offspring.

wildtype	18
dusky	153
cut	6
white	76
cut, white	150
dusky, cut	72
dusky, cut, white	22
dusky, white	3

 a. What are the genotypes of two maternal X chromosomes?
 b. What is the map order of the genes?
 c. What are the two-factor recombination frequencies between each pair of genes?
 d. Are there as many observed double-crossover gametes as would be expected if there were no interference?
 e. What are the coefficient of coincidence and the interference across this region of the X chromosome?
ANS S5.18. In this cross, the phenotypes of the progeny directly reflect the genotype of the chromosome contributed by the mother. **a.**The two most common classes are the nonrecombinant (parental) types, so the mother's genotype was: (*dy + + / + ct w*), where the parentheses mean that the gene order is unknown. **b.** The least common classes indicate the double crossover classes; these are cut and dusky white, which means that *w* is in the middle. The mother's genotype is written with the correct gene order as *dy + + / + w ct*. **c.** The recombination frequency between *dy* and *w* equals (18 + 22 + 6 + 3)/500 = 0.098; that between *w* and *ct* equals (72 + 76 + 6 + 3)/500 = 0.314. **d.** The

observed number of double crossovers = 3 + 6 = 9, whereas the expected number equals 0.098 × 0.314 × 500 = 15.4; there are fewer observed double crossovers than would be expected if the occurrence of one crossover did not decrease the likelihood of a second. **e.** The coefficient of coincidence = 9/15.4 = 0.58 and the interference is 1 - 0.58 = 0.42.

S5.19. The genes considered in Problem **S5.18** are also located on the X chromosome in *D. melanogaster*. However, their order and the distances between them are completely different because of chromosome rearrangements that have happened since the divergence of two species approximately 40 million years ago. In *D. melanogaster*, the genetic map of this region is *dy*—16.2—*ct*—18.5—*w*. If you performed a cross identical to that in Problem S4.14 with *D. melanogaster* and observed 500 progeny, what types of progeny would be expected and in what numbers? Assume that the interference between the genes is the same in *D. melanogaster* as in *D. virilis*, and round the expected number of progeny to the nearest whole number. For convenience, list the progeny types in the same order as in Problem S4.14.

ANS S5.19. In *D. melanogaster*, the gene order is *dy ct w*, and so the mother's genotype is *dy* + + / + *ct w*. The interference of 0.42 implies a coincidence of 0.58. The expected number of double recombinants equals 0.162 × 0.185 × 500 = 15 and, because coincidence = observed doubles/expected doubles, the observed doubles would be 0.58 × 15 = 8.7. The expected number of single recombinants in the *dy –ct* region is 0.162 × 500 - 8.7 = 72.3 and that of single recombinants in the *ct–w* region is 0.185 × 500 - 8.7 = 83.8. The remaining progeny, 500 - 8.7 - 72.3 - 83.8 = 335.2 are nonrecombinants. Within each of these categories of progeny, there are an equal number expected in each of the reciprocal classes. Rounding off to the nearest whole number, the expected numbers of progeny are:

wild type	36
dusky	168
cut	42
white	4
cut, white	168
dusky, cut	4
dusky, cut, white	36
dusky, white	42

S5.20. In corn, the genes *v* (virescent seedlings), *pr* (red aleurone), and *bm* (brown midrib) are all on chromosome 5, but not necessarily in the order given. The cross v^+ *pr m* /*v* pr^+ bm^+ × *v pr bm* / *v pr bm* produces 1000 progeny with the following phenotypes:

v^+	*pr*	*bm*	209
v	pr^+	bm^+	213
v^+	*pr*	bm^+	175
v	pr^+	*bm*	181
v^+	pr^+	*bm*	69
v	*pr*	bm^+	76
v^+	pr^+	bm^+	36
v	*pr*	*bm*	41

a. Determine the gene order, the recombination frequencies between adjacent genes, the coincidence, and the interference.

b. Explain why, in this example, the recombination frequencies are not good estimates of map distance.

ANS S5.20. a. The parental types are evidently $v^+ \ pr \ bm$ and $v \ pr^+ \ bm^+$, and the double recombinant types $v^+ \ pr^+ \ bm^+$ and $v \ pr \ bm$. This puts v in the middle. The pr—v recombination frequency is $(69 + 76 + 36 + 41)/1000 = 22.2$ percent, and the v—bm recombination frequency is $(175 + 181 + 36 + 41)/1000 = 43.3$ percent. The expected number of double crossovers equals $0.222 \times 0.433 \times 1000 = 96.13$, and so the coincidence is $(36 + 41)/96.13 = 0.80$. The interference is therefore $1 - 0.80 = 0.20$. **b.** The true map distances are certainly larger than 22.2 and 43.3 centimorgans. The frequencies of recombination between these genes are so large that there are undoubtedly many undetected double crossovers in each region..

S5.21. The accompanying illustration shows a human pedigree along with the pattern of DNA fragments observed from one region of the genome.

a. Examine the pedigree and the band patterns and suggest a mode of inheritance.

b. This same three-band pattern was found at the scene of a murder in blood samples taken from the fingernails of the victim, who apparently had scratched the perpetrator during their mortal struggle. What does this finding suggest about the supposed murdered?

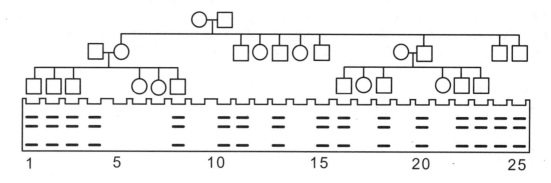

ANS S5.21. a. The inheritance of the three-band pattern is consistent with Y-linked inheritance. **b.** The finding suggests that the perpetrator was a male.

S5.22. A student in a genetics laboratory is assigned to study the linkage relationships between three linked genes in the nematode *Caenorhabditis elegans*. The genes are *daf-2* (*dauer larvae formation-2*, the dauer larva is an optional "resting stage" in the life cycle), *lin-12* (*lineage-12*, which affects the specification of cell lineages in the formation of the vulva), and *dpy-18* (*dumpy-18*, a mutant with a shortened body). Two-point crosses yielded a map distance of 15 centimorgans between *lin-12* and *daf-2*, and 10 centimorgans between *lin-12* and *dpy-18*. A testcross of *daf-2* +/ + *dpy-18* yielded these progeny:

Wildtype	122
Dumpy	379
Dauer larva abnormal	401
Dumpy and dauer larva abnormal	98

a. What is the frequency of recombination between *daf-2* and *dpy-18*?

b. Is this frequency consistent with the map distances between *lin-12* and *daf-2* and between *lin-12* and *dpy-18*?

 c. What is the order of the genes?

 d. Is there evidence of complete chromosome interference in these data?

 e. What is the map distance between *daf-2* and *dpy-18*?

ANS S5.22. a. 22%. **b.** Yes, if *lin-12* is in the middle. **c.** *daf-2 lin-12 dpy-18* (or the other way around). **d.** Chromosome interference must be incomplete because the frequency of recombination (22%) is less than the value that would be expected by summing the map distances between *daf-2* and *lin-12* and between *lin-12* and *dpy-18*. **e.** 15 + 10 = 25 (not 22, which is the frequency of recombination and which underestimates the map distance because of double crossing over).

S5.23. *Neurospora crassa* is a haploid ascomycete fungus. A mutant strain that requires arginine for growth (*arg⁻*) is crossed with a strain that requires tyrosine and phenylalanine (*tyr⁻ phe⁻*). Each requirement results from a single mutation. Tests on 200 randomly collected spores from the cross gave the following results, in which the + in any column indicates the presence of the wildtype allele of the gene.

arg	tyr	phe	Number of spores
+	−	−	43
−	+	+	42
+	−	+	43
−	+	−	42
+	+	−	8
−	−	+	9
+	+	+	6
−	−	−	7

 a. What are the three possible two-gene recombination frequencies?

 b. Is any linkage suggested by these data?

ANS S5.23. a. Consider first *arg* and *tyr*, in which the cross is *arg⁻ tyr⁺* × *arg⁺ tyr⁻*. The recombinant types are *arg⁻ tyr⁻* and *arg⁺ tyr⁺*, of which there are 9 + 7 + 8 + 6 = 30, yielding a recombination frequency of 30/200 = 15 percent. The data for *arg* and *phe* are analyzed similarly, and there are 43 + 7 + 42 + 6 = 98 recombinants, yielding a recombination frequency of 98/200 = 49 percent. For *tyr* and *phe*, the cross is *tyr⁺ phe⁺* × *tyr⁻ phe⁻*; the recombinant progeny are *tyr⁺ phe⁻* and *tyr⁻ phe⁺* = 43 + 42 + 9 + 8 = 102, for a recombination frequency of 102/200 = 51 percent. Both 49 and 51 percent are undoubtedly random statistical deviations from 50 percent, indicating no linkage. **b.** *arg–tyr* are linked but not *arg–phe* or *tyr–phe*.

S.5.24. A small portion of the genetic map of *Neurospora crassa* chromosome III is illustrated here. The *ace-2* mutation prevents acetate utilization, and *his-7* blocks histidine synthesis. In a cross of *ACE-2 his-7* × *ace-2 HIS-7*, and assuming complete chromosome interference, what are the expected frequencies of:

 a. First-division segregation of *ace-2* and first-division segregation of *his-7*?

 b. First-division segregation of *ace-2* and second-division segregation of *his-7*?

 c. Second-division segregation of *ace-2* and first-division segregation of *his-7*?

 d. Second-division segregation of *ace-2* and second-division segregation of *his-7*?

e. Parental ditype (PD), tetratype (TT), and nonparental ditype (NPD) tetrads?

ANS S5.24. Crossing-over is equally likely in either region, and double crossovers cannot occur because of the complete chromosome interference. **a.** 76%. **b.** 16%. **c.** 0%. **d.** 8%. **e.** PD = 84%, TT = 16%, NPD = 0%.

S5.25. In the case of independently assorting genes, why are parental ditype (PD) and nonparental ditype (NPD) tetrads formed in equal numbers? Why are nonparental ditype tetrads rare for linked genes? ·
ANS S5.25. PD and NPD tetrads are outcomes of equally probable orientations of two bivalents, each carrying one of the heterozygous genes. NPD tetrads are rare for linked genes for three related reasons: recombination is rarer than no recombination in a short genetic interval; double crossing-over (required in forming NPD tetrads for linked genes) is rare even in longer intervals; and, of the double crossover tetrads, only 1/4 of those possible (the four-strand double crossovers) will yield nonparental ditype tetrads.

S5.26. The yeast *Saccharomyces cerevisiae* has unordered tetrads. In a cross made to study the linkage relationships among three genes, the following tetrads were obtained. The cross was between a strain of genotype + *b c* and one of genotype *a* + +.

Tetrad Type	Genotypes of spores in tetrads				Number of tetrads
1	*a* + +	*a* + +	+ *b c*	+ *b c*	135
2	*a b* +	*a b* +	+ + *c*	+ + *c*	124
3	*a* + +	*a* + *c*	+ *b* +	+ *b c*	59
4	*a b* +	*a b c*	+ + +	+ + *c*	70
5	*a* + *c*	*a* + *c*	+ *b* +	+ *b* +	1
6	*a b c*	*a b c*	+ + +	+ + +	1
Total					390

a. From these data, determine which (if any) of the genes are linked.

b. For any linked genes, determine the map distances.

ANS S5.26. a. To determine the linked genes, first consider each possible set of pairs and classify each tetrad type as PD, NPD, and TT with respect to the gene pairs. For *a* and *b*, the tetrad types 1 through 6 are PD, NPD, PD, NPD, PD, and NPD, respectively, totaling 195 PD and 195 NPD; since, PD = NPD, genes *a* and *b* are unlinked. For genes *b* and *c*, the tetrad types 1 through 6 are PD, NPD, TT, TT, NPD, and PD, respectively, totaling 136 PD, 125 NPD, and 129 TT; since NPD is not much smaller than PD, genes *b* and *c* are unlinked. Finally, for genes *a* and *c*, the tetrad types 1 through 6 are PD, PD, TT, TT, NPD, and NPD, respectively, for a total of 259 PD, 2 NPD, and 129 TT. In this case, NPD $\ll$ PD and so genes *a* and *c* are linked. **b.** The map distance between *a* and *c* is calculated as $(1/2) \times ([TT] + 6[NPD])/Total \times 100 = (1/2) \times (129 + 12)/390 \times 100 = 18.1$ percent.

S5.27. Consider a strain of *Neurospora* that exhibits complete chromosomal interference, even across the centromere. Two genes, *A* and *B,* are located in the same chromosome but on different

sides of the centromere. Gene A is 10 map units from the centromere, and gene B is 5 map units from the centromere. Calculate the expected percentage of each of the following types of asci.

 a. Parental ditype
 b. Nonparental ditype
 c. Tetratype
 d. First-division segregation for A, first for B
 e. First-division segregation for A, second for B
 f. Second-division segregation for A, first for B
 g. Second-division segregation for A, second for B

ANS S5.27. Because there is complete interference, the map distance between A and B is 15 map units, and the answer to **b.** is 0 because NPD tetrads result only from double crossovers. In the absence of NPD, the percentage of TT tetrads equals $2 \times$ map distance $= 2 \times 15 = 30$ percent, which is the answer to **c.** The answer to **a.** is obtained by subtraction: PD $= 100 - 30 - 0 = 70$ percent. Relative to the types of segregation, because there is complete interference, it is impossible to observe second-division segregation of both A and B, hence the answer to **g.** is 0. The map distance of A to the centromere is $1/2 \times$ the percentage of second-division segregation of $A = 10$, hence the answer to **f.** is $2 \times 10 = 20$ percent. Similarly, the answer to **e.** is 10 percent. The answer to **d.** is obtained by subtraction: $100 - 20 - 10 = 70$ percent of the tetrads will show first-division segregation of both A and B. In this problem, please note the relations between the answers: **a.** = **d.** and **b.** = **g.** and **c.** = **e.** + **f.** These relate the different types of tetrads (PD, NPD, TT) with first-division and second-division segregation of A and B.

S5.28. In maize, the recessive allele *zn* (zebra necrosis) causes a leaf abnormality and the dominant allele R is necessary for purple aleurone (the outer layer of the kernel). These genes are linked with a recombination frequency of 23%. In a testcross of *Zn R/ zn r*, what are the expected proportions of progeny that have:

 a. Wildtype leaves and colored aleurone?
 b. Necrotic leaves and colored aleurone?
 c. Wildtype leaves and yellow aleurone?
 d. Necrotic leaves and yellow aleurone?

ANS S5.28. a. Gamete *Zn R*, frequency $(1 - 0.23)/2 = 38.5$ percent. **b.** Gamete *zn R*, frequency $0.23/2 = 11.5$ percent. **c.** Gamete *Zn r*, frequency $0.23/2 = 11.5$ percent. **d.** Gamete *zn r*, frequency $(1 - 0.23)/2 = 38.5$ percent.

S5.29. You are a geneticist writing a set of test questions and wish to invent plausible numbers of the possible types of progeny in a three-point testcross to yield a frequency of recombination of 0.2 in "region I," a frequency of recombination of 0.3 in "region II," and an interference value of 2/3. Among 1000 total progeny, how many should be:

 a. Nonrecombinant?
 b. Recombinant in region I only?
 c. Recombinant in region II only?
 d. Recombinant in both regions (double crossovers)?
 e. In each class of progeny above, how should the total number be allocated between the two reciprocal products of recombination?

ANS S5.29. Start with the double recombinants, part **d.** With recombination values of 0.2 and 0.3, the expected number of doubles equals $0.2 \times 0.3 \times 1000 = 60$. The "observed" number of doubles =

expected number × coincidence = 60 × 1/3 = 20 because coincidence = 1 - interference. This is the answer to part **d.** Then solve **b.** and **c.** The number of progeny recombinant in region I = number in region I only + doubles = 0.2 × 1000 = 200. Because the number of doubles = 20, the answer to **b.** is 180. Similarly, the answer to **c.** is 300 - 20 = 280. The number of nonrecombinants is therefore 1000 - 180 - 280 - 20 = 520. As for part **e.**, each of the reciprocal products of recombination should equal about half the total number in each class, adjusted a little to simulate experimental error.

S5.30. What is the answer to Problem **S5.29** in the general case when the frequency of recombination in region I is r_1, that in region II is r_2, and the coincidence equals c?

ANS S5.30. The logic is the same with 0.2 replaced by r_1, 0.3 replaced by r_2, and 1/3 replaced by c. Hence, the answers are: (a) $1000 \times [1 - r_1(1 - r_2c) - r_2(1 - r_1c) - r_1r_2c]$, (b) $1000 \times r_1(1 - r_2c)$, (c) $1000 \times r_2(1 - r_1c)$, and (d) $1000 \times r_1r_2c$. Relative to part (e), in each of these classes, the expected number of each of the reciprocal products of recombination is the number shown divided by 1/2; each double recombinant chromosome has an expected number of $[1000 \times r_1r_2c]/2$.

S5.31. The data shown are 3000 progeny from a testcross of a multiply heterozygous female of *Drosophila melanogaster* carrying the mutant alleles *vg* (*vestigial* wings), *cn* (*cinnabar* eye color), *sm* (*smooth,* with missing bristles), and *c* (*curved* wings). Identify the female genotype, the order of the genes, the map distances in all intervals, and the interference in all pairs of intervals. How many triple crossovers would be expected? How many were observed? Draw genetic map oriented with the smallest outside interval on the left. (Hint: treat the data as sets of three-point crosses to get the gene order.)

vg	*cn*	*sm*	*c*	11		+	*cn*	*sm*	*c*	7
vg	*cn*	*sm*	+	3		+	*cn*	*sm*	+	1031
vg	*cn*	+	*c*	121		+	*cn*	+	*c*	122
vg	+	*sm*	*c*	217		+	*cn*	+	+	229
vg	+	*sm*	+	113		+	+	*sm*	+	129
vg	+	+	*c*	990		+	+	+	*c*	4
vg	+	+	+	6		+	+	+	+	17

ANS S5.31. Gene order *cn vg c sm*; female genotype *cn + + sm/ + vg c +*; define interval 1 = *cn–vg*, interval 2 = interval 1 = *vg–c*, and interval 3 = *c–sm*, then $r_1 = 0.095$, $r_2 = 0.085$, $r_3 = 0.160$; $i_{12} = 0.71$, $i_{23} = 0.68$, $i_{13} = 0.39$; expected number of triples 3.88, observed none.

S5.32. In mice, the alleles *c* for albino color and *p* for pink eyes are recessive to their wildtype counterparts *C* and *P*. The genes are linked with a recombination fraction of 14%. A testcross is carried out, and a single progeny is selected that has an albino color. What is the probability that this progeny also has pink eyes:
 a. If the heterozygous parent is *C P/ c p*?
 b. If the heterozygous parent is *C p/ c P*?
ANS S5.32. The selected gamete carries *c –* , since the progeny is albino. **a.** The probability that a *c – * gamete is actually *c p* equals $(1 - 0.14)/2 = 43$ percent. **b.** The probability that a *c –* gamete is actually *c p* equals $0.14/2 = 7$ percent.

S5.33. In a testcross of a parent heterozygous for each of four linked genes, in which the order of the genes is known, the following numbers of progeny were obtained:

Nonrecombinant	486
Recombinant in region I only	61
Recombinant in region II only	143
Recombinant in region III only	226
Recombinant in regions I and II only	10
Recombinant in regions II and III only	45
Recombinant in regions I and III only	27
Recombinant in regions I and II and III	2

a. What are the map distances in centimorgans of regions I, II, and III? (*Hint*: Solve the problem as in a three-point cross, but remember that recombinants in two or three regions are recombinant for each region separately.)

b. Calculate the values of the interference for regions I + II, II + III, and I + III. Does the ranking of the interference values make intuitive sense?

ANS S5.33. a. Map distance region I = $(61 + 10 + 27 + 2)/1000 \times 100 = 10$ cM; region II = $(143 + 10 + 45 + 2)/1000 \times 100 = 20$ cM; region III = $(226 + 45 + 27 + 2)/1000 \times 100 = 30$ cM. **b.** Expected number of double recombinants for regions I + II, II + III, and I + III are $0.1 \times 0.2 \times 1000 = 20$, $0.2 \times 0.3 \times 1000 = 60$, and $0.1 \times 0.3 \times 1000 = 30$, respectively. Observed numbers are 12, 47, and 29, respectively. (Note that the triple recombinants must be counted as double recombinants in each pair of intervals.) The coincidence values are therefore $12/20 = 0.60$, $47/60 = 0.78$, and $29/30 = 0.97$, respectively. Correspondingly, the interference values across I + II, II + III, and I + III are 0.40, 0.22, and 0.03, respectively. These make intuitive sense because the value of the interference increases as the size of the region decreases.

S5.34. In a fungal organism with ordered tetrads, deduce whether one observes first-division segregation or second-division segregation when the region between a gene and the centromere undergoes

a. A two-strand double crossover

b. Either of the two types of three-strand double crossover

c. A four-strand double crossover

If the four types of double crossover are equally frequent, what proportion of asci formed from double crossing-over will show second-division segregation?

ANS S5.34. a. and **c.**, first-division segregation; **b.** second-division segregation. If the four types of double crossovers are equally frequent, the frequency of second-division segregation will be 1/2.

S5.35. Show that each of the following statements is true in a fungal organism with ordered tetrads,

a. If a configuration of multiple crossovers will result in first-division segregation, then an additional crossover (distal to the existing ones) will convert the ascus to second-division segregation with probability 1.

b. If a configuration of multiple crossovers will result in second-division segregation, then an additional crossover (distal to the existing ones) will convert the ascus to first-division segregation with probability 1/2.

ANS S5.35. a. Consider four chromatids with any configuration of crossing-over yielding first-division segregation, without specifying the exact number or the strands included; in this case, the effect of all the crossing-overs together is equivalent to none at all, hence one additional crossing-over will yield second-division segregation. **b.** Consider four chromatids with any configuration of crossing-over yielding second-division segregation, without specifying the exact number or the

strands included; in this case, the effect of all the crossing-overs together is equivalent to exactly one, hence one additional crossing-over will yield first-division segregation with probability 1/2. The reason is that two-strand doubles and four-strand doubles yield first-division segregation whereas three-strand doubles yield second-division segregation, and the expected ratio of two- : three- : four-strand doubles is 1:2:1.

S5.36. Consider an organism with ordered tetrads in which there are n crossovers between a genetic marker in a chromosome and its centromere. Show that:

 a. If the n crossovers would result in first-division segregation, the probability that one additional crossover will result in second division segregation is 1.

 b. If the n crossovers would result in second-division segregation, the probability that one additional crossover will result still in second division segregation is 1/2.

 c. If X_{n-1} and X_n are the probabilities of second-division segregation after $n-1$ and n crossovers, respectively, then

$$X_n = (1 - X_{n-1}) + \frac{X_{n-1}}{2}$$

 d. If $X_0 = 0$, the above Equation implies that $X_n = (1 - X_{n-1}) + \frac{X_{n-1}}{2}$

$$X_n - \frac{2}{3} = \left(-\frac{2}{3}\right)\left(-\frac{1}{2}\right)^n$$

 e. The graph of X_n for $n = 0, 1, 2, 3$, and so forth, approaches $X_n = 2/3$ in an oscillatory manner.

ANS S5.36. a. One simple way to see the consequence of an additional crossover is to suppose that the new one is the outermost (toward the tip of the chromosome). Any additional crossover then has the consequence of switching the position of one A spore (or adjacent pair of spores if it is an 8-spore ascus) with one a spore (or adjacent pair of spores). The switch converts any first-division segregation ascus into a second-division ascus. **b.** In any second-division segregation ascus, there are four ways to switch an A spore (or adjacent pair of A spores) with an a spore (or adjacent pair of a spores); two of these convert the ascus into a first-division segregation ascus and two do not, so the probability is 1/2. **c.** This equation follows from putting parts **a** and **b** together. **d.** In the Equation in part c, subtract 2/3 from both sides and rearrange to obtain $(X_n - 2/3) = (X_{n-1} - 2/3)(-1/2)$. From this it follows that $(X_n - 2/3) = (X_{n-1} - 2/3)(-1/2) = (X_{n-2} - 2/3)(-1/2)^2 = (X_{n-3} - 2/3)(-1/2)^3 = ... = (X_0 - 2/3)(-1/2)^n$. Hence, when $X_0 = 0$, $(X_n - 2/3) = (-2/3)(-1/2)^n$. **e.** The accompanying graph shows the oscillatory approach to 2/3 for tetrads resulting from 0, 1, 2, 3, ... crossovers between the gene and the centromere.

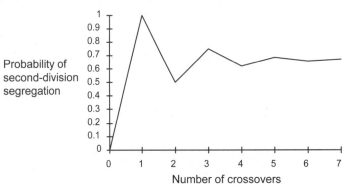

Chapter 6: Molecular Biology of DNA Replication and Recombination
Answers to Chapter-end problems

Fill-ins

1. origin of replication
2. lagging strand
3. DNA ligase
4. dideoxyribose
5. gene conversion
6. rolling-circle replication
7. primer
8. replicon
9. heteroduplex
10. proofreading

Analysis and Applications

ANS 6.1. Because of semiconservative replication equal amounts of $^{14}N^{14}N$ and $^{14}N^{15}N$ would be expected.

ANS 6.2. A replication fork has an asymmetrical structure because of the inability of the DNA polymerase to carry out synthesis in the 3'-to-5' direction, and because of the antiparallel orientation of the strands in the DNA double helix. Both daughter strands are synthesized in the 5'-to-3' direction; therefore, one strand (the leading strand) is synthesized continuously whereas the other strand (the lagging strand) requires the transient existence of the short pieces of DNA known as precursor fragments that serve as replication intermediates. The precursor fragments are joined together by DNA ligase.

ANS 6.3. a. The standard B form of DNA has 3.4 Å per base pair, hence the number of base pairs is $(68 \times 10^4 \text{ Å})(1 \text{ bp}/3.4 \text{ Å}) = 2 \times 10^5$. **b.** There are 10 bp per complete turn, hence 2×10^4 complete turns.

ANS: 6.4. Because new nucleotides are added only to the 3' hydroxyl of the growing strand, and a dideoxynucleotide does not have a 3' hydroxyl group.

ANS: 6.5. Helicase opens double helix, single-stranded DNA binding protein stabilizes single strands, gyrase relieves torsional stress, polymerase III (Pol III) is the major replication enzyme, polymerase I (Pol I) replaces the RNA primers with DNA, DNA ligase seals the nicks in DNA strands, primase creates RNA primer.

ANS 6.6. DNA polymerase joins a 5'-triphosphate with a 3'-OH group, and the outermost two phosphates are released; the resulting phosphodiester bond contains one phosphate. DNA ligase joins a single 5'-P group with a 3'-OH group.

ANS 6.7. The enzyme has polymerizing activity, it is a 3' → 5' exonuclease (the proofreading function), and it is a 5' → 3' exonuclease.

ANS 6.8. Neither RNA polymerases nor primases require a primer to get synthesis started.

ANS 6.9. $(1.3 \times 10^8/50)$ sec × (1 min/60 sec) × (1 hr/60 min) × (1 day/24 hr) = 30 days.

ANS 6.10. The c–d and e–f strands are leading, a–b and g–h strands are lagging; a, d, f, and g are 5' ends, b, c, e, and h are 3' ends.

ANS 6.11. a. In rolling-circle replication, one parental strand remains in the circular part and the other is at the terminus of the branch. Therefore, only half of the parental radioactivity will appear in progeny. **b.** If we assume no recombination between progeny DNA molecules, one progeny phage will be radioactive. If a single recombination occurs, two particles will be radioactive. If recombination is frequent and occurs at random, the radioactivity will be distributed among virtually all the progeny.

ANS 6.12. Samples 1 and 2 are made up of deoxyribonucleotides and therefore are DNA samples. Sample 3 is composed of ribonucleotides and is therefore a sample of RNA. Because of Watson-Crick base pairing, double stranded DNA must have equal proportions of dATP and dTTP as well as of dGTP and dCTP. Only sample 1 has this feature and is therefore likely to be double-stranded DNA. Sample 2 is single-stranded DNA and sample 3 is single-stranded RNA.

ANS 6.13. Rolling-circle replication must be initiated by a single-stranded break; θ replication does not need such a break.

ANS 6.14. (a) Since 18 percent is adenine, 18 percent is also thymine; so [T] = 18 percent. (b) Because [A] + [T] = 36 percent, [G] + [C] equals 64 percent, or [G] = [C] = 32 percent each. Overall, the base composition is [A] = 18 percent, [T] = 18 percent, [G] = 32 percent, and [C] = 32 percent; the [G] + [C] content is 64 percent.

ANS 6.15. a–c follow from the fact that A pairs with T and G pairs with C, and **d** is another statement
of **c.**

ANS 6.16. a. 1/2 "light" : 1/2 "heavy." **b.** 3/4 "light" : 1/4 "heavy." **c.** 7/8 "light" : 1/8 "heavy." The observed results were: **a.** all "intermediate"; **b.** 1/2 "light" : 1/2 "intermediate" : 3/4 "light" : 1/4 "intermediate."

ANS 6.17. a. The distance between nucleotide pairs is 3.4 Å or 0.34 nm. The length of the molecule is 34 μm, or 34×10^3 nm. Therefore, the number of nucleotide pairs equals $(34 \times 10^3)/0.34 = 10^5$. **b.** There are ten nucleotide pairs per turn of the helix, and so the total number of turns equals $10^5/10 = 10^4$.

ANS 6.18. If the Holliday junction is resolved with no recombination of outside markers, one molecule should be "light" and the other "heavy." If the Holliday junction is resolved with recombination of outside markers, one molecule should be "light" on the left-hand side and "heavy" on the right-hand side, and the other the reverse; in this case the density of both molecules would be intermediate.

ANS 6.19. a. First, note that the convention for writing polynucleotide sequences is to put the 5' end at the left. Thus, the complementary sequence to AGTC (which is really 5'-AGTC-3') is 3'-TCAG-5', written in conventional format as GACT (that is, 5'-GACT-3'). Hence, the frequency of CT is the same as that of its complement AG, which is given as 0.15. Similarly, AC = 0.03, TC = 0.08, and AA = 0.10. **b.** If DNA had a parallel structure, the 5' ends of the strands would be together, as would the 3' ends, and so the sequence complementary to 5'-AGTC-3' would be 5'-TCAG-3'. Thus, AG = 0.15 implies that TC = 0.15, and similarly the other observed nearest neighbors would imply that CA = 0.03, CT = 0.08, and AA = 0.10.

ANS 6.20. Remember that the chemical group at the growing end of the leading strand is always a 3'-OH group because DNA polymerases can only add nucleotides to such a group. Because DNA is antiparallel, the opposite end of the leading strand is a 5'-P group. Therefore, **a.** 3'-OH; **b.** 3'-OH; **c.** 5'-P.

ANS 6.21. Rolling-circle replication begins with a single-strand break that produces a 3'-OH group and a 5'-P group. The polymerase extends the 3'-OH terminus and displaces the 5'-P end. Because the DNA strands are antiparallel, the strand complementary to the displaced strand must be terminated by a 3'-OH group.

ANS 6.22. a. The first base in the DNA that is copied is a T, and so the first base in the RNA is an A. RNA grows by addition to the 3'-OH group, and so the 5'-P end remains free. Therefore, the sequence of the eight-nucleotide primer is 5'-AGUCAUGC-3'. **b.** The C at the 3' end has a free –OH; the A at the 5' end has a free *tri*phosphate. **c.** Right to left, because this would require discontinuous replication of the strand shown.

ANS 6.23.

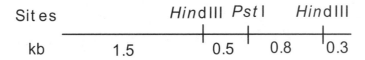

ANS 6.24. In the chromosome on the left, the DNA in each chromatid should have one solid line (labeled strand) and one dashed line (unlabeled strand). In the chromosomes on the right, the darker chromatids should have DNA with both lines solid (both strands labeled), and the lighter chromatid should have one line solid (labeled strand) and one dashed (unlabeled strand).

ANS 6.25. The bands in the gel result from incomplete chains whose synthesis was terminated by incorporation of the dideoxynucleotide indicated at the top. The smaller fragments are at the bottom of the gel, the larger ones at the top. Because DNA strands elongate by addition to their 3' ends, the strand synthesized in the sequencing reactions has the sequence, from bottom to top, of

5'-ACTAGAGACCATGATCCTGTGATGAATAGC-3'. The template strand is both complementary in sequence and antiparallel, and so its sequence is 3'-TGATCTCTGGTACTAGGACACTACTTATCG-5'.

ANS 6.26. For each site, the probability equals the product of the probability of each of the nucleotide pairs in turn, 1/4 for any of the specified pairs and 1/2 for R-Y. The average spacing is the reciprocal of the probability, hence, for *Taq*I, the average distance between sites is 4^4 = 256 base pairs; for *Bam*HI, it is 4^6 = 4096 base pairs; and for *Hae*II, it is $4^4\,2^2$ = 1024 base pairs.

ANS 6.27. It means that recombination must take place after DNA replication, because only two of the four DNA molecules in the tetrad are recombinant.

ANS 6.28. a. C → T mismatch repair in one heteroduplex, G→ A in the other. **b.** T→ C mismatch repair in one heteroduplex, A→ G in the other. **c.** either a T → C mismatch repair in one heteroduplex and a G → A in the other, or a C → T mismatch repair in one heteroduplex and an A → G in the other.

ANS 6.29.
a. 5'-TTAGCCGTATATACCTTTGGAAGGGTATAGGCCCTTATTA-3'
b. 3'-AATCGGCATATATGGAAACCTTCCCATATCCGGGAATAAT-5'

ANS 6.30. The 27th nucleotide from the 5' end is a C in **a** but an A in **b**.

Challenge Problems

ANS 6.31. Such patterns result from breakage and reunion between sister chromatids. For the DNA duplex in the dark regions of the chromosome, both lines should be solid (both strands labeled), and for the DNA in the light regions of the chromosome, one line should be solid (labeled strand) and one dashed (unlabeled strand).

ANS 6.32. a. Segregation is 3 : 1 for both *b* and *c*. **b.** This could be explained by formation of a single heteroduplex spanning the differences in both *b* and *c*, followed by *B* → b and *C* → c mismatch repair in both heteroduplexes. **c.** With respect to *A–D* the tetrad is a tetratype, indicating that the Holliday structure was resolved with recombination of the outside markers. **d.** Yes, except that the Holliday structure is resolved without recombination of outside markers.

ANS 6.33. The 3 : 1 segregation results from mismatch repair of a heteroduplex formed during recombination, with an equal likelihood of recombination between the outside markers. **a.** Recombination at his would have no effect on *co–leu* linkage, so PD >> NPD. **b.** Recombination at *co* would affect *his–leu* linkage, resulting in 50 percent recombinant and 50 percent nonrecombinant gametes (so PD = NPD). **c.** Recombination at *his* would have no effect on *co–leu* linkage, so PD >> NPD.

Supplemental problems with answers

S6.1. Define the following terms:

 a. semiconservative replication

b. Okazaki fragments

c. replicon

d. Gene conversion

e. Mismatch repair

ANS S6.1. a. The mode of replication, in which each strand of a duplex molecule serves as a template for the synthesis of a new complementary strand, and the daughter molecules are composed of one parental and one newly synthesized strand. **b.** Short pieces of DNA produced during discontinuous replication of the lagging strand. **c.** A DNA molecule that has a replication origin. **d.** Gene conversion is the phenomenon in which the products of a meiotic division in a heterozygous genotype are found in a ratio different from the expected 2:2, for example, 5:3; 3:5; 3:1, or 1:3. **e.** Mismatch repair refers to the removal of an improperly paired nucleotide from a DNA and its replacement with one that can pair properly.

S6.2. What is the role of each of the following proteins in DNA replication?

 a. DNA helicase

 b. Single-stranded DNA-binding protein

 c. DNA polymerase

 d. DNA ligase

ANS S6.2. a. DNA helicase can move rapidly along a single strand of DNA; when it encounters a region of double helix, it continues to move along a single strand, thereby prying apart the helix. **b.** Single-stranded DNA-binding protein binds to exposed DNA strands without occluding the bases, which therefore remain available for templating. **c.** DNA polymerase catalyzes the synthesis of DNA from deoxynucleoside 5'-triphosphates using a template strand. The second function of this enzyme is a 3'-to-5' proofreading exonuclease activity. **d.** DNA ligase catalyzes formation of a covalent bond between adjacent 5'-P and 3'-OH termini in a broken polynucleotide strand of double-stranded DNA; in DNA replication, it joins Okazaki fragments together.

S6.3. Which enzyme in DNA replication

 a. alters the helical winding of double-stranded DNA by causing a single-strand break, exchanging the relative position of the strands, and sealing the break?

 b. uses ribonucleoside triphosphates to synthesize short RNA primers?

ANS S6.3. a. Topoisomerase. **b.** Primase.

S6.4. In terms of the mechanism of DNA replication, explain why a linear chromosome without telomeres is expected to become progressively shorter in each generation.

ANS S6.4. Replication of DNA by DNA polymerase can only proceed in the 5' → 3' direction and requires a primer. Therefore, the synthesis of only the leading strand can proceed to the very end of the chromosome. Even though synthesis of the lagging strand can be primed by RNA at the very end (RNA polymerase does not require a primer), the RNA primer is later removed and cannot be replaced by DNA without a special mechanism different from conventional synthesis.

S6.5. What is meant by the statement that the DNA replication fork is asymmetrical?

ANS S6.5. A replication fork has an asymmetrical structure because of the inability of the DNA polymerase to carry out synthesis in the 3'-to-5' direction and because of the antiparallel orientation of the strands in the DNA double helix. Both daughter strands are synthesized in the 5'-to-3' direction; therefore, one strand (the leading strand) is synthesized continuously whereas the other

strand (the lagging strand) requires the transient existence of the short pieces of DNA known as Okazaki fragments that serve as replication intermediates. The Okazaki fragments are joined together by DNA ligase

S6.6. In a DNA duplex undergoing replication, why must one strand (the lagging strand) be synthesized discontinuously?
ANS S6.6. Because new nucleotides can be added only to the 3' end of a growing strand.

S6.7. In the replication of a bacterial chromosome, does replication begin at a random point?
ANS S6.7. No, in most bacteria, as well as in bacteriophage and viruses, replication can be initiated only at a special sequence known as replication origin.

S6.8. Describe why topoisomerase is necessary during replication of the *E. coli* chromosome.
ANS S6.8. Topoisomerase is necessary to relieve the stress caused by the unwinding of DNA during semiconservative replication. This enzyme nicks one strand of the double helix, passes the other strand through the gap, and reanneals the cut.

S6.9. The accompanying drawing is of a replication fork. The ends of each strand are labeled with the letters a through h.
 a. Label the leading and lagging strands and, by the addition of arrowheads, show the direction of movement of the replication fork and the direction of synthesis of each DNA strand or fragment.
 b. Specify which of the letters a through h label 5′ ends and which label 3′ ends.

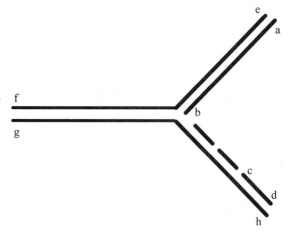

ANS S6.9. See the accompanying diagram.

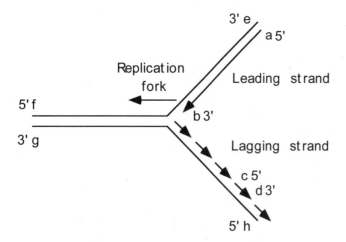

70

S6.10. How many replication forks are found in:

 a. A circular molecule undergoing θ replication?

 b. A circular molecule undergoing rolling-circle replication?

ANS S6.10. a. One or two, depending on whether the replication is unidirectional or bidirectional. **b.** One.

S6.11. The genome of *E. coli* is a circular molecule of 4.6×10^6 nucleotide pairs. Replication starts at a single point and moves in *both directions* around the circle. How long would it take to complete one round of replication, assuming that both replication forks proceed at a typical bacterial rate of replication of 1500 nucleotide pairs per second?

ANS S6.11. $1/2 \times [(4.6 \times 10^6)/ 1.5 \times 10^3)]$ sec $\times$ (1 min/60 sec) = 25.6 min.

S6.12. The haploid genome of the wall cress, *Arabidopsis thaliana,* contains 100,000 kb and has five chromosomes. If a particular chromosome contains 10 percent of the DNA in the haploid genome, what is the approximate time of replication, assuming that there is only one origin of replication (exactly in the middle), that replication is bidirectional, and that the rate of DNA synthesis is

 a. 1500 nucleotide pairs per second (typical of bacterial cells)

 b. 50 nucleotide pairs per second (typical of eukaryotic cells)

ANS S6.12. The molecule is 10^7 base pairs and, since replication is bidirectional, the time required is that needed to replicate 5×10^6 base pairs. **a.** At the rate of 1500 nucleotide pairs per second, the time required is 56 minutes. **b.** At the rate of 50 nucleotide pairs per second, the time required is 28 hours. Replication actually takes less time because there are multiple origins of replication.

S6.13. If the DNA strands in a duplex were parallel rather than antiparallel, but the mechanism of replication were otherwise the same, would the strands in the duplex shown here be replicated continuously (leading) or discontinuously (lagging):

```
5'-NNNNNNNNN-3'
5'-NNNNNNNNN-3'
```

 a. If replication went from left to right?

 b. If replication went from right to left?

ANS S6.13. a. If replication went from left to right, then each strand would be synthesized discontinuously. **b.** If replication went from right to left, then each strand would be synthesized continuously.

S6.14. If replicating could be labeled in such a way that only the first deoxyribonuclotide added to the RNA primer were labeled, would both daughter strands be equally labeled after one complete round of unidirectional replication? Explain your answer.

ANS S6.14. They would be unequally labeled. The leading strand would be lightly labeled (one labeled nucleotide incorporated per origin of replication), and the lagging strand would be more heavily labeled (one labeled nucleotide incorporated per RNA primer).

S6.15. A short region of an mRNA molecule is used as a primer in dideoxy sequencing. After transfer to a filter and autoradiography, the resulting film looks as follows, where the orientation is with the samples loaded at the top and the letters indicate the dideoxynucleotide present during synthesis.

 a. Write the sequence implied by the bands in the gel from the 5′ end to the 3′ end.

 b. Is this the sequence of the elongated RNA strand or the sequence of its complementary DNA strand?

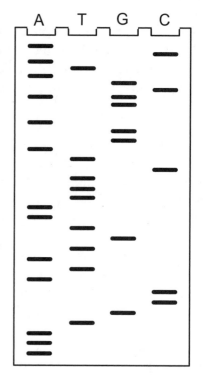

ANS S6.15. a. Read from the bottom of the gel because the shortest fragments are there; as one proceeds up the gel, the fragments get longer and longer. Because DNA elongates at the 3' end, the 5' end of the primer is at the bottom. The sequence is 5'-AAATGCCATACATGTAACTTTCTAGGACGATACA-3'. **b.** Each band results from the terminated product of DNA replication, and so the sequence deduced is that of the elongated RNA used as a primer.

S6.16. In early studies of the properties of the precursor fragments in DNA synthesis, it was shown that these fragments could hybridize to both strands of *E. coli* DNA. This was taken as evidence that they are synthesized on both branches of the replication fork. However, one feature of the replication of *E. coli* DNA that was not known at the time invalidates this conclusion. What is this characteristic?

ANS S616. It is the bidirectionality of replication, which means that Okazaki fragments are formed from opposite parental DNA strands in different regions of the chromosome. At any one replication fork, they come from only one strand.

S6.17. In experiments that confirmed that DNA replication is semiconservative, *E. coli* DNA was labeled by growing cells for a number of generations in a medium containing "heavy" ^{15}N isotope and then observing the densities of the molecules during subsequent generations of growth in a medium containing a great excess of "light" ^{14}N. If DNA replication were conservative, what pattern of molecular densities would have been observed after one generation and after two generations of growth in the ^{14}N-containing medium?

ANS S6.17. After one generation there would be two bands in equal amounts, one with both strands consisting of ^{15}N and the other with both strands consisting of ^{14}N; after two generations, the same two bands would be observed, but in the ratio 1: 3 of ^{15}N^{15}N : ^{14}N^{14}N.

S6.18. A new technique is used for determining the base composition of double-stranded DNA. Rather than giving the relative amounts of each of the four bases, A, T, G, and C, the procedure yields the value of the ratio of A/C. If this ratio is 1/3, what are the relative amounts of each of the four bases?

ANS S6.18. In a double-stranded DNA molecule, A = T and G = C because of complementary base pairing. Therefore, if A/C = 1/3, then C = G = 3 × A. Because A + T + G + C = 1, everything can be

put in terms of A as follows: A + A + 3A + 3A = 1. Hence, A = T = 0.125. This makes C = G = (1 − 0.25)/2 = 0.375. In other words, the DNA is 12.5% A, 12.5% T, 37.5% G, and 37.5% C.

S6.19. How do the DNA sequences shown on the right differ from each other?

ANS S6.19. A run of three G's is present in a at positions 16–18, numbering from the 5' end. The 5' end of a reads 5'-CGTGCCGGTT etc. whereas that in b. reads 5'-CAGGGTCCGGTT etc. Evidently the sequence on the left has had a three-nucleotide insertion or that on the right a three-nucleotide deletion.

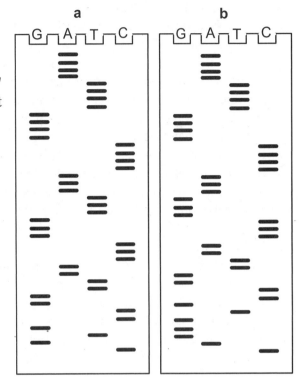

S6.20. The mismatch repair system can detect mismatches that occur in DNA replication and can correct them after replication. In *E. coli*, how does the system use DNA methylation to determine which base in a pair is the incorrect one?

ANS S6.20. To distinguish the template strand from the newly synthesized strand, the system takes advantage of the normal delay in methylation after replication. During an interval of several minutes, the new strand remains undermethylated, which allows the mismatch repair system to identify and correct the mistaken base.

S6.21. What genetic phenomenon observed in certain fungi can be explained by mismatch repair in heteroduplex regions created in the process of recombination?

ANS S6.21. Gene conversion (3 : 1 and other aberrant forms of segregation).

S6.22. Is it correct to say that a Holliday structure and a chiasma are the same?

ANS S6.22. No. A chiasma is a cytological structure observed as an apparent breakage and reunion between nonsister chromatids in a bivalent. Ultimately it results from a physical exchange between both strands of the DNA molecules in these chromatids. A Holliday structure, on the other hand, is the ultramicroscopic cross-shaped configuration resulting from the exchange of a single polynucleotide strand between two DNA duplexes. Both strands of DNA become exchanged only after one possible mode of resolution of the Holliday structure.

S6.23. A DNA molecule containing the alleles *A* and *B* forms a Holliday structure between the genes with another DNA molecule containing *a* and *b*. What does it mean to say that the resolution of the Holliday structure is equally likely to result in recombination of the outside markers as in nonrecombination of the outside markers?

ANS S623. It means that half the time the resulting molecules are *A b* and *a B* (recombinant), and the other half *A b* and *a B* (nonrecombinant).

S6.24. When two mutations are closely linked (for example, two nucleotide substitutions in the same gene), a single gene conversion event may include both sites. This phenomenon is called co-conversion. How would you expect the frequency of co-conversion to depend on the distance between mutant nucleotide sites?

ANS S6.24. Co-conversion can happen only when both sites are included in a heteroduplex region and subject to mismatch repair. The chance that both mutations will be present within a heteroduplex region must decrease dramatically with the distance between the sites. Therefore, the smaller the distance between mutations, the greater the expected frequency of co-conversion.

S6.25. In spite of gene conversion, among gametes chosen at random, one still observes the Mendelian segregation ratio of 1:1 in crosses. Why?

ANS S6.25. Gene conversion does not have a pronounced effect on the segregation ratio because any particular heterozygous gene is very unlikely to be present in the heteroduplex region formed by a genetic exchange. Even in tetrad analysis, usually less than one percent of all asci show gene conversion. (In addition, if conversion is unbiased, on average segregation will still be 1:1.)

Chapter 7: Molecular Organization of Chromosomes
Answers to Chapter-end problems

Fill-ins

1. supercoiled DNA
2. C-value paradox
3. nucleosome core particle
4. 30-nm chromatin fiber
5. interchromatin compartment
6. heterochromatin
7. localized centromere
8. telomere
9. alpha satellite
10. polytene chromosome

Analysis and Applications

ANS 7.1. DNA molecule is a long, thin thread, and its total length in most cells greatly exceeds the diameter of a nucleus, even allowing for a large number of fragments per cell. This forces you to conclude that each DNA molecule must be folded back on itself repeatedly.

ANS 7.2. A nucleosome core particle contains 2 molecules each of histone 2A, 2B, 3, and 4, plus 145 bp of DNA; a nucleosome consists of a core particle plus one molecule of histone H1 and an additional 55 bp of "linker" DNA.

ANS 7.3. Five, assuming one nucleosome per 200 bp.

ANS 7.4. Matching of chromomeres, which are locally folded regions of chromatin. Polytene chromosomes do not divide because the cells in which they exist do not divide.

ANS 7.5. In *Drosophila*, the heterochromatin occupies about 25 percent of each chromosome arm nearest the centromere; these regions are not highly replicated in polytene nuclei but clump together to form the chromocenter. The outer 75% of each is arm is highly replicated and forms the banded regions.

ANS 7.6. a. 120×106 bp/5000 bands = 24 kb/band. **b.** 13,600 genes/5000 bands = 2.7 genes/band.

ANS 7.7. No, because the *E.coli* chromosome is circular. There are no termini.

ANS 7.8. Because DNA replication cannot be initiated at the extreme 3' end of a DNA strand; a short region at each 3' end remains unreplicated.

ANS 7.9. The telomeres would become shorter in each successive generation.

ANS 7.10. The internal sequence gives a sharp band because all the fragments containing the sequence were produced by cleavage of each chromosomal DNA molecule at the nearest restriction site on each side; the fragments are therefore all of the same size. The subtelomeric sequence gives a diffuse band because only the unique restriction site is common to all the fragments; the other end terminates in the telomeric sequence, which can differ in length from one cell to the next.

ANS 7.11. The telomereless chromosome becomes successively shorter with each round of DNA replication. The new w mutations result from the successive shortening when it cuts into w^+ sequences needed for wildtype expression.

ANS 7.12. Because each denatured strand has a complementary sequence at each end, the ends can easily come together to form a hairpin loop, and so these molecules will renature extremely rapidly.

ANS 7.13. a. There are 10 base pairs for every turn of the double helix. With four turns of unwinding, $4 \times 10 = 40$ base pairs are broken. **b.** Each twist compensates for the underwinding of one full turn of the helix; hence, there will be four twists.

ANS 7.14. The supercoiled form is in equilibrium with an underwound form having many unpaired bases. At the instant that a segment is single-stranded, S1 can attack it. Because a nicked circle lacks the strain of supercoiling, there is no tendency to have single-stranded regions, and so a nicked circle is resistant to S1 cleavage.

ANS 7.15. The rate of movement in the gel is determined by overall charge and by the ability of the molecule to penetrate the pores of the gel. Supercoiled and relaxed circles migrate at different rates because they have different conformations.

ANS 7.16. a. Renaturation is concentration-dependent because it requires complementary molecules to collide by chance before the formation of base pairs can form. **b.** Here, the length of the GC tracts are important. Molecule 2 has a long GC segment, which will be the last region to separate. Hence, molecule 1 has the lower temperature for strand separation.

ANS 7.17. The hybrid molecules that can be produced from single-stranded DNA fragments from species A and B are AA, AB, BA, and BB, and these are expected in equal amounts. The molecules with a hybrid ($^{14}N/^{15}N$) density are AB and BA, and these account for 5 percent of the total. Together, AA and BB must make up another 5 percent, and so a total of 10 percent of the base sequences are common to the two species.

ANS 7.18. All such mutations are probably lethal. Because the amino acid sequence of histones is virtually the same in all organisms, this suggests that functional histones are extremely intolerant of amino acid changes.

ANS 7.19. The relatively large number of bands and the diverse locations in the genome among different flies suggests very strongly that the DNA sequence is a transposable element of some kind.

ANS 7.20. To relieve the stress of overwinding the direction of supercoiling is positive, and there are three superhelical turns.

ANS 7.21. One supercoil turn restores 10 base pairs, so the molecule will form a figure 8.

ANS 7.22. No, because there is a dynamic equilibrium between supercoiled molecules with all bases paired and an underwound form with some bases unpaired, and all degrees in between.

ANS 7.23. a. The helix is underwound one complete turn. **b.** Supercoiling does take place. **c.** Negative supercoiling relieves underwinding.

ANS 7.24. With the repeating sequence, any two molecules can form a stable duplex, whereas each random sequence can anneal only with other fragments having the same, or a very similar, sequence.

ANS 7.25. A change of 51 in the percentage of G–C base pairs results in a change of 20.9°C in T_m, hence the relationship is $T_m = 78 + (20.9/51)(g - 22)$ °C, or $T_m = 69.0 + 0.41 \times g$ °C.

ANS 7.26. a. $g = 30$, $T_m = 81.3$°C. **b.** $g = 50$, $T_m = 89.5$°C. **c.** $g = 70$, $T_m = 97.7$°C.

ANS 7.27. $g = (T_m - 69.0)/0.41$. **a.** $g = 38.4$ percent G + C. **b.** $g = 43.9$ percent G + C.

Challenge Problems

ANS 7.28. In the first experiment, the nucleosomes form at random positions in different molecules. In the second experiment, the protein binds to a unique sequence in all the molecules, and the nucleosomes form by sequential addition of histone octamers on both sites of the protein-binding site. Because nuclease attacks only in the linker regions, the cuts are made in small regions that are highly localized.

ANS 7.29. a. 10 percent with Cot 10^{-3} (highly repetitive), 60 percent with Cot 10^{-1} (moderately repetitive), and 30 percent with Cot 10^3 (unique). **b.** Ratio of Cot reciprocals equals $10^3 : 10^1 : 10^{-3}$, hence 1 copy of each unique sequence implies 10^4 copies of the moderately repetitive sequence and 10^6 copies of the highly repetitive sequences.

Supplemental problems with answers

S7.1. What are the principal molecular constituents of the nucleosome?
ANS S7.1. Each nucleosome consists of one molecule of histone H1, two molecules each of H2A, H2B, H3 and H4, and a segment of duplex DNA containing about 200 nucleotide pairs.

S7.2. Is it possible for a gene of average size to be present in a single nucleosome?
ANS S7.2. No. The average polypeptide chain contains more than 100 amino acids, which would require a minimum of 300 base pairs in the DNA. Most genes in eukaryotes are very much longer, consisting of thousands or tens of thousands of base pairs. The DNA fragment associated with a single nucleosome is about 200 base pairs, and so it is not possible for an average gene to be present in a single nucleosome.

S7.3. A geneticist wishes to isolate mutations that affect the amino acid sequence of any of the histone genes H2, H3A, H3B, and H4. What is the likely phenotype of such a mutation?
ANS S7.3. The amino acid sequences of these histones are strongly conserved in evolution. This observation suggests that organisms are very intolerant of changes in these proteins, so mutant organisms are likely to be lethal.

S7.4. In spermatogenesis in many male animals, the normal somatic-cell histones are removed from the DNA and replaced with a still more highly basic (arginine-rich and lysine-rich) set of sperm-specific histones. Suggest one possible explanation.
ANS S7.4. The more highly basic histones enable greater compaction of DNA and the formation of the dense chromatin mass in the sperm head.

S7.5. What are principal structural levels of chromosome organization?
ANS S7.5. Assembly of DNA with histones is considered as the first level; it results in a seven-fold reduction in length of the DNA duplex and formation of a beaded flexible fiber 11 nm in diameter. The second level is the formation of a so called 30-nm fiber, which is a left-handed superhelix or solenoid with six nucleosomes per turn. Finally, the 30-nm fiber condenses into a chromatid of the compact metaphase chromosome with the help of a "scaffold" of nonhistone chromosomal proteins.

S7.6. Why are centromeres and telomeres required for chromosomes to be genetically stable?
Ans S7.6. The centromere is necessary for chromosome movement in both mitosis and meiosis; without a centromere, a chromosome will quickly be lost. The telomere is essential for chromosome stability because it enables correct replication of the chromosome tip and prevents fusion with other chromosome ends.

S7.7. The nematode *C. elegans* has holocentric chromosomes. If the chromosomes in a cell are fragmented into many pieces by treatment with x rays, how would you expect each fragment to behave in cell division?
ANS S7.7. Each fragment would be expected to behave as if it were an independent holocentric chromosome.

S7.8. Name three features that distinguish euchromatin from heterochromatin.
ANS S7.8. Heterochromatin may be distinguished from euchromatin by the fact that it stains densely during interphase when the euchromatin does now, by its low rate of recombination between genetic markers, and by its large quantity of highly repetitive satelite DNA sequences.

S7.9. Explain why topoisomerase is necessary during replication of the *E.coli* chromosome.
ANS S7.9. Topoisomerase is necessary to relieve the stress caused by the unwinding of DNA during semiconservative replication. This enzyme nicks one strand of the double helix, passes the other strand through it, and reanneals the cut.

S7.10. What is one possible reason why there is usually a single gene in the genome coding for a particular protein, whereas genes for rRNA and tRNA are repeated many times?
ANS S7.10. Because ribosomes and tRNAs are used in the synthesis of every protein in the cell, the amount of rRNA and tRNA must be present in abundance. This need is satisfied by having multiple copies of each of the genes.

S7.11. The X-linked recessive mutation *singed* (*sn*) causes gnarled bristles in *Drosophila*. In a stock of wildtype flies, you find a single male that has the singed phenotype.

 a. Diagram a crossing scheme that you will use to generate a true-breeding line of *sn* flies. Note that, other than the single singed male, you have only wildtype flies available.

 b. In wildtype flies, the *sn* gene is contained within an 8-kb *Bam*HI restriction fragment. When you digest genomic DNA from the mutant line with *Bam*HI and probe with the 8-kb restriction fragment on a Southern blot, the size of the labeled fragment on the filter is 13 kb. What possible explanations could account for this finding?

ANS S7.11. a. First cross the singed male to wildtype females. This cross will yield wildtype males and heterozygous females. If these progeny are allow to inter-breed, the result will be heterozygous and homozygous wildtype females, all of which have the wildtype phenotype, and hemizygous mutant and wildtype males, which can be distinguish from each other. Mate the F_2 singed males individually with the F_2 females. About half of the crosses will yield both singed females and singed males, which can be selected and crossed to create the true-breeding strain. **b.** The difference in sizes of the restriction fragment could be due either to the insertion of DNA between the two restriction sites or to the elimination of one of the two flanking *Bam*HI restriction sites.

S7.12. A genetically engineered strain of *Drosophila virilis* (strain 1) is homozygous for the recessive mutation *y* (yellow), an X-linked mutation that causes yellow body color. This strain also carries, at a site in the X chromosome, a genetically engineered transposable element called *Hermes* into which a copy of the y^+ gene was inserted; the engineered *Hermes* element is unable to produce the transposase protein needed for transposition of the element. Another genetically engineered strain, strain 2, is also homozygous *y* but contains a copy of *Hermes* that can produce the transposase in each homolog of chromosome 3. A female of strain 1 is crossed with a male of strain 2. The phenotypically wildtype F_1 males are crossed with yellow females. About 5 percent of the F_2 progeny males have wildtype body color. Give two possible explanations of how these males might arise.

ANS S7.12. A male that is wildtype could inherit the y^+ gene contained within the X-linked *Hermes* element provided there was nondisjunction in the mother; the nondisjunctional males would therefore be XO and sterile. Given the relatively high frequency of such males, nondisjunction is very unlikely to be the correct explanation. The more likely possibility is that the *Hermes* transposase mobilized the y^+-containing *Hermes* element and transposed it to an autosome, from which it was transmitted to a male. The autosomal y^+-*Hermes* would be dominant to the X-linked *y* mutation, and the males would have wildtype body color.

S7.13. The term "satellite DNA" was originally coined for highly repetitive simple sequences that, in equilibrium density-gradient centrifugation in CsCl, formed a distinct band (a "satellite" band) different from the bulk of the genomic DNA, because of a difference in density of the DNA fractions. You analyze the genome organization of a new species by the kinetics of DNA renaturation and find that 10 percent of DNA is represented by a highly repetitive simple sequence. Does this mean that, after equilibrium density-gradient centrifugation in CsCl, you will find a satellite band?

ANS S7.13. Not necessarily. A highly repetitive simple sequence may or may not have a different density than the bulk of the genomic DNA. A satellite band will be observed in equilibrium density-gradient centrifugation in CsCl only if there is a difference in density.

S7.14. DNA from species A that is labeled with ^{14}N and randomly fragmented is renatured with an equal concentration of DNA from species B that is labeled with ^{15}N and also randomly fragmented. The resulting mixture of molecules is centrifuged to equilibrium in CsCl. Ten percent of the total renatured DNA has a hybrid density. What fraction of the base sequences in the two species will be similar enough to renature?

ANS S7.14. 20 percent. For every sequence capable of cross-hybridizing to yield a $^{14}N^{15}N$ hybrid there are $^{14}N^{14}N$ and $^{15}N^{15}N$ hybrids that are not detected. The $^{14}N^{14}N$, $^{14}N^{15}N$, and $^{15}N^{15}N$ hybrids are expected in a ratio of 1 : 2 : 1, and so the 10 percent $^{14}N^{15}N$ indicates a total of 20 percent DNA sequences capable of hybridizing.

S7.15. You are studying the denaturation of two unusual DNA molecules, both consisting of 99 percent AT base pairs. Both molecules have the same melting temperature. However, observations in the electron microscope indicate that the strands of one of the molecules do not separate completely until raised to a temperature 12°C higher than that required for complete separation of the strands of the other molecule. Suggest an explanation.

ANS S7.15. The few G–C base pairs in the more stable molecule are probably clustered. The clustered G–C pairs hold the strands together more strongly than dispersed G–C pairs, and so the temperature must be higher to obtain complete strand separation.

S7.16. Which of the DNA molecules shown here would require a higher temperature for denaturation?

 a.
```
5'-ACTGTCATCGAT-3'
3'-TGACAGTAGCTA-5'
```

 b.
```
5'-TAGCTACTGTCA-3'
3'-ATCGATGACAGT-5'
```

ANS S7.16. The molecules are identical except that their strand polarity is reversed. Since denaturation does not depend upon the strand polarity, they should have identical denaturation temperatures.

S7.17. A molecule of 5000 nucleotide pairs consists of the repeating sequence 5'-ACGTAG-3'. How would the melting temperature of this molecule compare to that of another molecule of the same length and base composition (50 percent G + C) but with a random sequence?

ANS S7.17. The repetitive sequence will affect the rate of renaturation but not the melting temperature, and so the melting temperatures of the molecules are expected to be the same.

S7.18. A Cot analysis is carried out with DNA obtained from a particular plant species. The chloroplast DNA is readily detected as a rapidly reannealing fraction because of its abundance in the DNA sample. Plants of the same species are maintained in the dark for several weeks until they lose

all their chlorophyll and the leaves become white. DNA from these plants has the same Cot curve as observed in plants maintained in the light. What does this result tell you about the loss of chlorophyll?

ANS S7.18. The result implies that the loss of chlorophyll is not accompanied by loss of chloroplasts.

S7.19. For the Cot curve shown in the figure:
 a. What fraction of the DNA is contained in components that are unique? In components that are repetitive?
 b. If the unique sequences are present once per haploid genome, how many copies per haploid genome are there of the other two classes?
 c. Using the scale at the top, estimate the total haploid genome size of this organism.

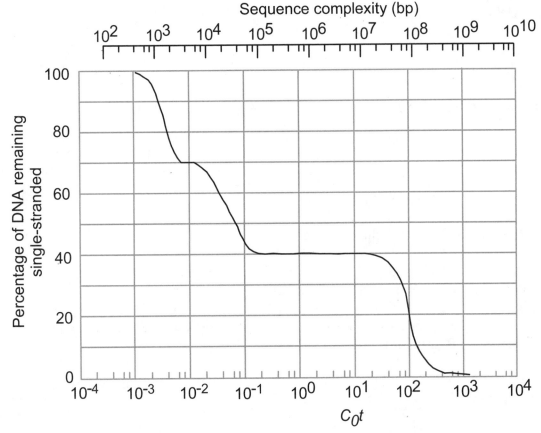

ANS S7.19. a. 30 percent consists of repetitive DNA with a Cot of 3×10^{-3}, 30 percent consists of repetitive DNA with a Cot of 3×10^{-2}, and 40 percent consists of unique-sequence DNA with a Cot of 10^2. **b.** The sequence classes have relative abundances of $1/(3 \times 10^{-3}) = 333$, $1/(3 \times 10^{-2}) = 33$, and $1/10^2 = 10^{-2}$, respectively. If each unique sequence is present once per haploid genome, the repetitive classes have 33,300 and 3300 copies, respectively. **c.** The corrected Cot values are $0.30 \times 3 \times 10^{-3} = 9 \times 10^{-4}$, $0.30 \times 3 \times 10^{-2} = 9 \times 10^{-3}$, and $0.40 \times 10^2 = 40$, respectively. These correspond to sequence complexities of 400 bp, 4000 bp, and 1.4×10^7 bp, respectively. Then the total genome size is estimated as $33,300 \times 400 + 3300 \times 4000 + 1 \times 1.4 \times 10^7 = 4.05 \times 10^7$ bp, or 40.5 Mb.

Chapter 8: Human Karyotypes and Chromosome Behavior.
Answers to Chapter-end problems

Fill-ins

1. haplotype
2. X inactivation
3. unequal crossing-over
4. paracentric inversion
5. alternate segregation
6. Robertsonian translocation
7. semisterility
8. monoploid
9. sexual polyploidization
10. allopolyploid

Analysis and Applications

ANS 8.1. 47, +21 (trisomy 21); 47, XYY; 47, XXY; and 27, XXX.

ANS 8.2. 45, X

ANS 8.3. No; one would expect a high proportion of progeny with an extra sex chromosome, because of the sex-chromosome trisomy in the parent.

ANS 8.4. 2; they represent inactivated X chromosomes.

ANS 8.5. a. The Klinefelter karyotype is 47,XXY, hence one Barr body; **b.** The Turner karyotype is 45,X, hence no Barr bodies; **c.** The Down syndrome karyotype is 47,+21; people with this condition have one Barr body if the kayotype is 47,XX,+21 (female) or no Barr bodies if the karyotype is 47,XY,+21 (male); **d.** Males with the karyotype 47,XYY have no Barr bodies; **e.** Females with the karyotype 47,XXX have two Barr bodies.

ANS 8.6. The chromosomes underwent replication with no cell division (endoreduplication), resulting in an autotetraploid.

ANS 8.7. The only 45-chromosome karyotype found at appreciable frequencies in spontaneous abortions in 45,X, and so 45,X is the probable karyotype. Had the fetus survived, it would have been a 45,X female with Turner syndrome.

ANS 8.8. The recessive allele is X-linked, and the pattern of presence or absence of sweat glands in mosaic females result from random inactivation of either of the X chromosomes in females that are heterozygous.

ANS 8.9. Because the X chromosome in the 45,X daughter contains the color-blindness allele, the 45,X daughter must have received the X chromosome from her father through a normal X-bearing

sperm. The nondisjunction must therefore have occurred in the mother, resulting in an egg cell lacking an X chromosome.

ANS 8.10. The mother has a Robertsonian translocation that includes chromosome 21. The child with Down syndrome has 46 chromosomes, including two copies of the normal chromosome 21 plus an additional copy attached to another chromosome (the Robertsonian translocation). This differs from the usual situation in which Down syndrome children have trisomy 21 (karyotype 47,+21).

ANS 8.11. The inversion has the sequence *A B E D C F G*, the deletion *A B F G*. The possible translocated chromosomes are (a) *A B C D E T U V* and *M N O P Q R S F G* or (b) *A B C D E S R Q P O N M* and *V U T F G*. One of these possibilities includes two monocentric chromosomes and the other includes a dicentric and an acentric. Only the translocation with two monocentrics is genetically stable.

ANS 8.12. The order is (*a e*) *d f c b*, where the parentheses mean that the order of (*a e*) cannot be determined from these data; the answer *b c f d* (*a e*) is also correct.

ANS 8.13. Genes *b, a, c, e, d,* and *f* are located in bands 1, 2, 3, 4, 5, and 6, respectively. The reasoning is as follows. Because deletion 1 uncovers any gene in band 1 but the other deletions do not, the pattern $- + + + +$ observed for gene *b* puts *b* in band 1. Deletions 1–3 uncover band 2 but deletions 4–5 do not, and so the pattern $- - - + +$ observed for gene *a* localizes gene *a* to band 2. Genes in band 3 are uncovered by deletion 1–4 but not 5, and so the pattern $- - - - +$ implies that gene *c* is in band 3. Band 4 is uncovered by deletions 3–5 but not 1–2, which means that gene *e*, with pattern $+ + - - -$, is in band 4. Genes in band 5 are uncovered by deletions 4–5 but not 1–3, and so the pattern $+ + + - -$ observed for gene *d* places it in band 5. Genes in band 6 are uncovered by deletion 5 but not 1–4, and so the pattern $+ + + + -$ puts gene *f* in band 6.

ANS 8.14. The result is one normal chromosome and one inverted chromosome (these derive from chromatids not involved in either crossover), a normal chromosome carrying the alleles *A B c D E*, and an inverted chromosome carrying the alleles *a b C d e*. Note that the two-strand double crossover has transferred an allele between the normal and the inverted chromosomes.

ANS 8.15. The most likely explanation is an inversion. In the original strain the inversion is homozygous, and so no problems arise in meiosis. The F_1 is heterozygous, and crossing-over within the inversion produces the dicentrics and acentrics. Because the crossover products are not recovered, the frequency of recombination is greatly reduced in the chromosome pair in which the inversion is heterozygous, and so the inversion is probably in chromosome 6.

ANS 8.16. Starting with chromosome (**c**) compare the chromosomes pairwise to find those that differ by a single inversion. In this manner, you can deduce that inversion of the i–d–c region in (**c**) gave rise to (**d**) inversion of the h–g–c–d region in (**d**) gave rise to (**a**) and inversion of the c–d–e–f region in (**a**) gave rise to (**b**) Because you were told that (**c**) is the ancestral sequence, the evolutionary ancestry is (**c**) → (**d**) → (**a**) → (**b**)

ANS 8.17. The group of 4 synapsed chromosomes implies that a reciprocal translocation has taken place. The group of 4 includes both parts of the reciprocal translocation and their nontranslocated homologues.

ANS 8.18. Translocation heterozygotes are semisterile because adjacent segregation from the four synapsed chromosomes in meiosis produces aneuploid gametes, which have large parts of chromosomes missing or present in excess. The aneuploid gametes fail to function in plants, and in animals they result in zygote lethality. The translocation homozygote is fully fertile because the translocated chromosomes undergo synapsis in pairs, and segregation is completely regular. In the cross translocation homozygote × normal homozygote, all progeny are expected to be semisterile.

ANS 8.19. Three, according to which genome entered last: (AA × BB) × CC, (AA × CC) × BB, or (BB × CC) × AA.

ANS 8.20. 15 altogether: 12 are permutations of the general form [(AA × BB) × (CC)] × DD)], where first an allotetraploid is created, then an allohexaploid, and then the allooctoploid; and 3 are permutations of the general form [(AA × BB) × (CC × DD)], where two allotetraploids undergo hybdridization and endoreduplication.

ANS 8.21. 9 altogether: [(AA × BB) × (BB)] × CC)], [(AA × BB) × (CC)] × BB)], [(BB × CC) × (BB)] × AA)], [(BB × CC × (AA)] × BB)], [(BB × BB) × (AA)] × CC)], [(BB × BB) × (CC)] × AA)], [(AA × C) × (BB)] × BB)], [(AA × BB× (BB × CC)], [(AA × CC) × (BB × BB)].

ANS 8.22. An autopolyploid series is formed by the combination of identical sets of chromosomes. Therefore the chromosome numbers must be even multiples of the monoploid number, or 10 (diploid), 20 (tetraploid), 30, 40, and 50.

ANS 8.23. Species S is an allotetraploid of A and B formed by hybridization of A and B, after which the chromosomes in the hybrid became duplicated. The univalent chromosomes in the S × A cross are the 12 chromosomes from B, and the univalent chromosomes in the S × B cross are the 14 chromosomes from A.

ANS 8.24. In this male, there was a reciprocal translocation between the *Curly*-bearing chromosome and the Y chromosome. Because there is no crossing-over in the male, all Y-bearing sperm that give rise to viable progeny contain *Cy* and all X-bearing sperm that give rise to viable progeny contain *Cy*$^+$.

ANS 8.25. In this male, the tip of the X chromosome containing y^+ became attached to the Y chromosome, giving the genotype y X / y^+ Y. The gametes are y X and y^+ Y, and so all of the offspring are either yellow females or wildtype males.

ANS 8.26. Viable progeny are expected to result only from adjacent segregation, in which the Y chromosome segregates with the normal chromosome 2 and the two parts of the X–2 translocation segregate together. The expected result is 50 percent ruby, dumpy males and 50 percent nonruby, nondumpy females.

ANS 8.27. The *A B c D E* chromosome results from two-strand double crossing-over in the *B–C* and *C–D* regions. The double recombinant chromosome still has the inversion.

ANS 8.28. Because semisterility is associated with the presence of the translocation, determining the recombination frequency between each of the mutations and the translocation breakpoint follows the same logic as mapping any other kind of genetic marker. For the parental classes, the mutations and the translocation are on different chromosomes. Members of the recombinant classes are those plants that show both the mutation in question and semisterility or neither semisterility nor the mutation in question. The recombination frequency between *brachytic* and the translocation breakpoint is therefore $(17 + 25 + 19 + 8)/682 = 0.102$; the recombination frequency between *fine-stripe* and the translocation breakpoint is $(19 + 6 + 1 + 25)/682 = 0.075$.

ANS 8.29. a. $r = (39 + 31)/(39 + 231 + 287 + 31) = 11.9$ map units. **b.** $1 : 1 : 1 : 1$.

ANS 8.30. The wildtype yeast strain is disomic for chromosome 2, and the result of the cross is a trisomic. Segregation of markers on this chromosome, like *his*7, is aberrant, but segregation of markers on the other chromosomes is completely normal.

Challenge Problems

ANS 8.31. a. *A B C D E*; *A B c D E*; *a d C b e*; *a d c b e*. **b.** *A B C D E*; *A B c d a*; *e b c D E*; *e b C d a*. **c.** *A B C d a*; *e b C D E*; *A B c D E*; *a d c b e*. **d.** *A B C d a*; *e b C D E*; *A B c d a*; *e b c D E*.

ANS 8.32. This is solved like a three-point linkage problem where, in this case, the middle marker is either T (for presence of the translocation breakpoint) or N (for normal chromosome structure). The cross is rb^+ T dp^+ /rb N dp ∞ rb N dp / rb N dp. The double recombinants have expected frequency $0.10 \times 0.30 = 0.03$, the rb^+–T recombinants have frequency $0.10 – 0.03 = 0.07$, and the T – dp^+ recombinants have frequency $0.30 – 0.03 = 0.27$, the others being nonrecombinant. Among 1000 progeny the expected numbers are therefore: rb^+ T dp^+ 315, rb N dp 315 (nonrecombinants), rb^+ N dp 35, rb T dp^+ 35 (recombination in the interval rb^+–T); rb^+ T dp 135, rb N dp^+ 135 (recombination in the interval T – dp^+); rb^+ N dp^+ 15, rb Tdp 15 (recombination in both intervals).

ANS 8.33. a. The bivalent is composed of *AA* 1/3 of the time and of *Aa* 2/3 of the time. The first situation yields 4 : 0 tetrads of the form *Aa* : *Aa* : *A* : *A*; the second situation, because there is complete centromere linkage, yields 4 : 0 tetrads of the form *A* : *A* : *Aa* : *Aa* half the time and 2 : 2 tetrads of the form *AA* : *AA* : *a* : *a* the other half. Overall the ratio of 4 : 0 to 3 : 1 tetrads is $(1/3) \times 1 + (2/3) \times (1/2) : (2/3) \times (1/2) = 2 : 1$. No 3 : 1 tetrads are expected. **b.** The bivalent are as described above. With an*AA* bivalent all tetrads are 4 : 0 tetrads as explained above; with an *Aa* bivalent, because there is no centromere linkage, there is first-division segregation 1/3 of the time and second-division segregation 2/3 of the time. The first-division segregation results in 1/2 tetrads that are 4 : 0 and 1/2 that are 2 : 1, as explained earlier; and second-division segregation results in 3 : 1 tetrads that are *AA* : *Aa* : *A* : *a*. Altogether, the 4 : 0, 2 : 2, and 3 : 1 tetrads are expected in the proportions $(1/3) \times 1 + (2/3) \times (1/3) \times (1/2) : (2/3) \times (1/3) \times (1/2) : (2/3) \times (2/3) \times (1) = 4 : 1 : 4$.

Supplemental problems with answers

S8.1. *Drosophila* and human beings have very different mechanisms of sex determination. Which of the following statements correctly describes the phenotype of an XXY organism in both species?
> **a.** Fertile male in *Drosophila,* sterile female in humans.
> **b.** Sterile female in *Drosophila,* fertile male in humans.
> **c.** Fertile female in *Drosophila,* fertile male in humans.
> **d.** Fertile female in *Drosophila,* sterile male in humans.
> **e.** Fertile female in *Drosophila,* fertile female in humans.

ASN S8.1. **d.** in human beings, the 47, XXY condition is the Klinefelter syndrome.

S8.2. What are the consequences of X-chromosome inactivation in mammals?
> **a.** The formation of Barr bodies
> **b.** A mutation
> **c.** A mosaic expression of heterozygous X-linked genes in different female cells
> **d.** A mosaic expression of heterozygous autosomal genes in females
> **e.** Turner syndrome

ANS S8.2 **a.** and **c**

S8.3. Nondisjunction of chromosomes in meiosis may take place at the first or the second meiotic division. If nondisjunction of the XY pair of chromosomes took place at the first division in the formation of sperm, which of the following chromosomal types of sperm could be formed?
> **a.** XY
> **b.** YY
> **c.** XX
> **d.** X
> **e.** Y

ANS S8.3. **a.**

S8.4. Which of the following human disorders can result from nondisjunction during the formation of the egg?
> **a.** Down syndrome
> **b.** Klinefelter syndrome
> **c.** XYY male

ANS S8.4. **a.**

S8.5. Why are abnormalities in the number of sex chromosomes in mammals usually less severe in their phenotypic effects than abnormalities in the number of autosomes?

ANS S8.5. The effects of extra Y chromosomes are relatively mild because the mammalian Y chromosome is largely heterochromatic and contains very few genes. Extra X chromosomes have milder effect compared to autosomes because, in mammals, all X chromosomes except one are genetically inactivated very early in embryonic development.

S8.6. What kind of abnormality in chromosome structure can:
> **a.** Change a metacentric chromosome into a submetacentric chromosome.
> **b.** Fuse two acrocentric chromosomes into one metacentric chromosome.

ANS S8.6. a. A pericentric inversion. **b.** A Robertsonian translocation.

S8.7. What are the consequences of a single crossover within the inverted region of a pair of homologous chromosomes with the gene order is *A B C D* in one and *a c b d* in the other, in each of the following cases?

 a. The centromere is not included within the inversion.

 b. The centromere is included within the inversion.

ANS S8.7. These kinds of problems are almost impossible to solve without drawing a diagram. The accompanying illustration shows how pairing within a heterozygous inversion results in a looped configuration. Crossing-over occurs at the four-strand stage of meiosis, but for simplicity only the chromatids participating in the crossover are diagrammed. Part A illustrates the situation when the centromere is not included within the inversion. The crossover chromatids consist of a dicentric (two centromeres) and an acentric (no centromere), and the products are duplicated for the terminal region containing *A* and deficient for the terminal region containing *D*, or the other way around. The noncrossover chromatids are the parental *A B C D* and *a c b d* monocentric chromosomes. Part B illustrates the situation when the centromere is included in the inversion. The duplications and deficiencies are the same as in part A, but in this case both products are monocentrics. As before, the noncrossover chromatids are the parental *A B C D* and *a c b d* configurations.

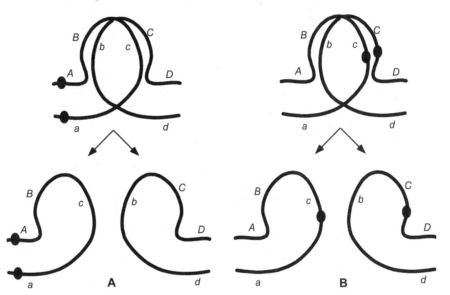

S8.8. What role might inversions play in evolution?

ANS S8.8. An inverted chromosome has some of its genes in reverse order and, if the inversion is a pericentric inversion, the centromere is in a different position. The progeny of two organisms heterozygous for an inversion contain only the parental types of chromosomes because gametes resulting from crossing-over within the inverted region are not recovered. Therefore, an inversion can act as a "crossover suppressor" that links groups of potentially favorable genes.

S8.9. In human beings, trisomy 21 is the cause of Down syndrome. Ordinarily, only one child with Down syndrome is seen in a sibship. Occasionally, a sibship with multiple affected children is observed. In one such family, a pair of normal parents had seven children. Four were normal, and three had an atypical form of Down syndrome. In this atypical form, the slowed growth, mental handicap, transverse crease on the palm of the hand, and short broad hands were present, but the ear and heart defects often observed with Down syndrome were not present. One of the normal children

gave rise to five offspring, two of whom had the same atypical form of Down syndrome. Provide a genetic explanation for this atypical form of Down syndrome and for its inheritance pattern.

ANS S8.9. All forms of Down syndrome are caused by trisomy 21. The form that recurs in this family is most likely due to a Robertsonian translocation involving chromosome 21. The multiple affected children result from one of the normal parents being a carrier of the translocation. The atypical form of Down syndrome in this kindred may result from one or more genes present in (or missing from) the translocated chromosome 21.

S8.10. *Drosophila* males of genotype ry^+/ry^+ are irradiated and crossed with ry/ry females (ry = rosy colored eyes). About 1/3000 progeny are phenotypically rosy. Most of these are due to newly induced ry mutations in the male, and most of the new alleles never undergo reverse mutation to ry^+.

 a. What types of mutations are these nonreverting ry alleles likely to be?

 b. How would one use a Southern blot to confirm this hypothesis?

ANS S8.10. a. small deletions. **b.** Identify one or more restriction enzymes that cleave DNA fragments of known size from the ry^+ allele, then carry out Southern blots using ry^+ probe DNA to examine the flies bearing the new mutant alleles; deletion mutations will have at least one of the expected fragments missing or altered in size.

S8.11. Colchicine is used to cause a doubling of chromosome number in many plant species. Starting with a diploid strain of watermelon (*Citrullus lanatus*), outline a series of crosses you would use to create a pentaploid strain of this species.

ANS S8.11. One approach would be to treat the diploid with colchicine to yield a tetraploid, which undergoes meiosis producing diploid gametes ($2n$). Cross the tetraploid with the diploid to obtain the triploid ($3n$) and again treat with colchicine to yield the hexaploid ($6n$), which produces triploid gametes ($3n$). Now cross the hexaploid with the tetraploid to obtain the pentaploid ($3n + 2n$).

S8.12. Explain why, in *Drosophila,* triploid flies are much more likely to survive than trisomics.

ANS S8.12. Gene dosage: the proper ratio of all genes is maintained in diploids and triploids, and so the gene balance is not disturbed. However, trisomics have an improper ratio of genes in the trisomic chromosome relative to genes in the other chromosomes, and this unbalance is usually fatal.

S8.13. In two closely related species of Drosophila, one has the gene sequence *A B C D E F G* along a chromosome, whereas the other has the gene sequence *A B F E D C G* along the homologous chromosome. How could this finding be explained? Can the ancestral sequence be inferred from these data?

ANS S8.13. One of the species has an inversion relative to the other, but from these data one cannot specify the ancestral sequence. In the species with the inversion, the inversion must have began as a single chromosome in the population that ultimately became fixed (homozygous).

S8.14. Recessive alleles *a, b, c, d, e, f,* and *g* are closely linked, but their order is unknown. A set of 7 deletions are recovered after x-ray treatment. The mutations they uncover are as follows: (1) *a* and *b*; (2) *a, b,* and *e*; (3) *b* and *c*; (4) *c*; (5) *d* and *f*; (6) *d, f,* and *g*; and (7) *e* and *g*. What is the order of the genes? Which deletions, if any, are uninformative as to the gene order?

ANS S8.14. (*d f*) *g e a b c*; inversions (4) and (5) are uninformative as to gene order.

S8.15. In a certain fertile tetraploid plant, a locus with alleles A and a is situated very near the centromere of its chromosome. If a tetraploid plant of genotype $AAaa$ is crossed with a diploid plant of genotype aa, what genotypic ratios are expected? What phenotypic ratios are expected if A is dominant to a? (Assume that homologous chromosomes in the tetraploid form pairs at random and that all gametes produced by the tetraploid are diploid. Assume also that the dominant phenotype is expressed whenever at least one A allele is present.)

ANS S8.15. Recombination between the gene and its centromere can be ignored because the gene is very near the centromere. If the chromosomes in the tetraploid pair at random, 1/3 of the time the pairs will be AA versus aa and 2/3 of the time Aa versus Aa. In the former case, all the gametes will be Aa, because an A is received from one chromosome pair and an a from the other. In the latter case, the gametes are AA, Aa, and aa in the ratio 1 : 2 : 1. The overall frequencies of AA : Aa : aa gametes are therefore $2/3 \times 1/4 : 1/3 \times 1 + 2/3 \times 1/2 : 2/3 \times 1/4 = 2/12 : 8/12 : 2/12 = 1 : 4 : 1$. Because the diploid parent produces only a-bearing gametes, the progeny genotypes are AAa, Aaa, and aaa in the ratio 1 : 4 : 1. The ratio of phenotypes is 5 dominant : 1 recessive.

S8.16. Explain the apparent paradox that familial retinoblastoma is regarded as an example of a recessive oncogene (tumor suppressor gene) even though it is inherited in pedigrees as an autosomal dominant. Familial retinoblastomas are generally bilateral (that is, there are multiple independent tumors in both eyes of affected individuals), whereas sporadic retinoblastoma is generally limited to one eye and to fewer independent tumors. Account for these observations.

ANS S8.16. The paradox is resolved by noting that a mutant allele associated retinoblastoma is recessive in any cell, but the probability of a wildtype allele mutating over a lifetime is fairly high. Hence, if a person inherits a recessive mutant allele, the chance that the homologous wildtype allele will mutate in at least one retinal cell over a lifetime is so great that the inherited gene appears to be dominant (although the actual tumor cells are homozygous recessive). Most inherited tumors are bilateral because there are so many retinal cells that more than one mutation is likely. In the presence of an already mutated gene, each new mutation results in another tumor. However, in the absence of a mutant gene, tumors can only result from two mutations in the same cell, which is unlikely enough that most such tumors are limited to one eye.

S8.17. Two strains of a plant called shepherd's purse (*Capsella bursa-pastoris*), a widespread lawn and roadside weed of the mustard family, are compared. In strain 1, the recombination frequency between genes A and B is 6 percent, whereas in strain 2, it is 50 percent. The F_1 progeny from a cross between these strains produce gametes with the following properties: About half are viable and contain only nonrecombinant chromosomes, and about half are nonviable. How can these results be explained?

ANS S8.17. The genes are genetically linked in one strain and unlinked in the other, and the F_1 progeny are semisterile. The most probable explanation is that one of the parental strains is homozygous for a reciprocal translocation.

S8.18. True-breeding tetrasomic organisms are much easier to create than true-breeding trisomic organisms. Suggest a reason for this observation.

ANS S8.18. In a tetrasomic organism, the four chromosomes frequently synapse in pairs or as a group of four, and each gamete usually receives one chromatid from each of the four homologous chromosomes. The result is that the tetrasomic condition can be perpetuated by self-fertilization. In the trisomic, either two chromosomes pair and the third remains a univalent, or the three

chromosomes form a trivalent, and in either case the result is that one gamete receives two copies of the trisomic chromosome and the other one copy. The trisomic condition cannot be perpetuated by self-fertilization.

S8.19. In plants, a cross between a diploid organism and a tetraploid organism of the same species is usually more fertile than that between a diploid organism and a triploid organism of the same species. Suggest a possible explanation.

ANS S8.19. The tetraploid organism usually produces diploid gametes and the diploid organism usually produces haploid gametes; the result of the cross is that all progeny are triploid. In contrast, a triploid produces many types of unbalanced gametes that are monosomic for some chromosomes and disomic for others. The chromosomally unbalanced gametes may fail to function or, in crosses with the diploid, produce inviable progeny. The result is a relatively infertile cross.

S8.20. In *Drosophila melanogaster,* the genes for *brown eyes* (*bw*) and *humpy thorax* (*hy*) are about 12 map units distant on the same arm of chromosome 2. A paracentric inversion spans about one-third of the region but does not include these genes. What recombinant frequency between *bw* and *hy* would you expect in each of the following?
> **a.** Females that are homozygous for the inversion
> **b.** Females that are heterozygous for the inversion

ANS S8.20 a. In the homozygote, there is no impediment to crossing-over. Therefore, for a map distance of 12 map units, one should expect to observe 12 percent recombination because, over this length of genetic interval, multiple crossing-over can be neglected. **b.** In heterozygotes, the products of crossing-over that take place within the inversion loop would not be recovered. Because the inversion covers about 1/3 of the interval between the genes, the recombination frequency is expected to be about 2/3 of normal, or (2/3)(12) = 8 percent.

S8.21. The sequence of genes in a normal human chromosome is *123 ∗ 456789,* where the raised dot (∗) represents the centromere. Aberrant chromosomes with the following arrangements of genes were observed.
> I. *123 ∗ 476589*
> II. *123 ∗ 46789*
> III. *1654 ∗ 32789*
> IV. *123 ∗ 4566789*
> **a.** Identify each chromosome as a paracentric inversion, pericentric inversion, deletion, or duplication, and diagram how each rearrangement would pair with the normal homolog in meiosis.
> **b.** Draw the meiotic products of a crossover between genes *5* and *6* when chromosome I pairs with a wildtype chromosome.
> **c.** Draw the products of a crossover between genes *5* and *6* when chromosome III pairs with a wildtype chromosome.

ANS S8.21. a. Chromosome type I is a paracentric inversion with breakpoints between *4* and *5* and also between *7* and *8*. The pairing configuration is as follows. Note that, at the time of pairing, each chromosome consists of two chromatids.

Chromosome type II is a deletion for the region containing gene *5*; the breakpoints are between *4* and *5* and between *5* and *6*. The pairing configuration is:

Chromosome type III is a pericentric inversion with breakpoints between *1* and *2* and between *6* and *7*, which pair as follows:

Chromosome type IV is a duplication for the region containing *6*. The pairing configuration again forms a loop:

b. The four products of crossing-over are:

1 2 3 ● 4 5 6 7 8 9

1 2 3 ● 4 5 6 7 4 ● 3 2 1

1 2 3 ● 4 7 6 5 8 9

9 8 7 6 5 8 9

91

c. The four products of crossing-over are:

```
1 2 3  ● 4 5 6 7 8 9

1 2 3  ● 4 5 6 1

9 8 7 6 5 4  ● 3 2 7 8 9

1 6 5 4  ● 3 2 7 8 9
```

S8.22. Semisterile tomato plants heterozygous for a reciprocal translocation between chromosomes 5 and 11 were crossed with chromosomally normal plants homozygous for the recessive mutant broad leaf on chromosome 11. When semisterile F_1 plants were crossed with the plants of broad-leaf parental type, the following phenotypes were found in the backcross progeny:

semisterile broad leaf 38
fertile broad leaf 242
semisterile normal leaf 282
fertile normal leaf 33

 a. What is the recombination frequency between the broad-leaf gene and the translocation breakpoint in chromosome 11?

 b. What ratio of phenotypes in the backcross progeny would have been expected if the broad-leaf gene had not been on the chromosome involved in the translocation?

ANS S8.22. (a) The translocation breakpoint is mapped just like any other gene; the phenotype is dominant semisterility. In this case, the recombination fraction between the broad-leaf gene and the translocation breakpoint is (38 + 33)/595 = 11.9 percent; (b) In the gene is unlinked to the translocation breakpoint, it shows independent assortment, and so the expectation is 25 percent for each of the four classes of progeny.

S8.23. Semisterile tomato plants heterozygous for the same translocation referred to in the previous problem were crossed with chromosomally normal plants homozygous for the recessive mutants *wilty* and *leafy* in chromosome 5. When semisterile F_1 plants were crossed with plants of *wilty, leafy* parental genotype, the following phenotypes were found in the backcross progeny.

	Semisterile	Fertile	Total
wildtype	333	19	352
wilty	17	6	23
leafy	1	8	9
wilty and leafy	25	273	298

What is the map distance between the two genes and the map distance between each of the genes and the translocation breakpoint in chromosome 5?

ANS S8.23. As in the previous problem, the translocation breakpoint is mapped just like any other gene with a dominant phenotype of semisterility. The data can be analyzed as a set of three two-point crosses. The recombination frequencies are wilty–leafy, (17 + 1 + 6 + 8)/682 = 4.7 percent; wilty–breakpoint, (19 + 8 + 17 + 25)/682 = 10.1 percent; leafy–breakpoint, (19 + 6 + 1 + 25)/682 = 7.5 percent.

S8.24. The accompanying diagrams depict wildtype chromosomes 2 and 3 from a certain plant. The filled circles represent the respective centromeres.

 a. Show how these chromosomes would pair in meiosis in an individual heterozygous for an inversion that includes genes *E, F,* and *G* as well as heterozygous for a reciprocal translocation between chromosomes 2 and 3 with breakpoints between *B* and *C* in 2 and between *K* and *L* in 3.

 b. Suppose that the breakpoints of the above inversion are sufficiently close to genes *D* and *H* that recombination between the genes is completely eliminated when the inversion is heterozygous. A plant heterozygous for the inversion and the translocation and of genotype *Dd Hh* is crossed with a plant with normal chromosomes and of genotype *dd hh*. The most frequent classes of offspring are *dd Hh* semisterile and *Dd hh* ertile. The rarest types are *Dd hh* semisterile and *dd Hh* fertile, which together have a combined frequency of 0.15. What is the recombination frequency between *D* and the translocation breakpoint?

ANS S8.24. a. The pairing configuration is that of an inversion combined with a translocation. There are two possible answers to this question: the one shown below, in which the inversion is in the structurally normal chromosome, and another similar configuration in which the translocated chromosome contains the inversion. In either case, it is important to remember that, at the time of pairing, each homologous chromosome consists of two chromatids attached to a common centromere

b. The most frequent offspring reveal the allelic configurations in the heterozygous parent, in this case *d, H,* semisterile and *D, h,* fertile. This result implies that *d* and *H* are located in the translocated chromosome and *D* and *h* in the normal homologous chromosomes. Since the inversion prevents recovery of the recombinants between the *D* and *H* genes, all gametes must carry either *d H* or *D h*. The *dd Hh* fertile and *Dd hh* semisterile progeny must therefore arise from recombination between *D* and the translocation breakpoint, and so the *D*– breakpoint distance is 15 map units.

S8.25. Six mutations of bacteriophage T4 (*a* through *f*) are isolated and crossed in all pairwise combinations to three deletion mutations (numbered 1–3) with the results shown below. In the table, R means that wildtype recombinants were observed and 0 means that there were no wildtype recombinants.

Point mutations	*a*	*b*	*c*	*d*	*e*	*f*
Deletions 1	0	0	R	R	R	R
Deletions 2	0	R	0	0	0	0
Deletions 3	0	0	R	0	0	0

In parallel with the above experiments, the mutations were tested in all possible pairwise combinations for complementation. The results are tabulated below, where + indicates complementation and – indicates no complementation.

	a	b	c	d	e	f
a	−	+	+	−	+	+
b	+	−	+	+	+	+
c	+	+	−	+	−	+
d	−	+	+	−	+	+
e	+	+	−	+	−	+
f	+	+	+	+	+	−

Assuming that complementation indicates that two mutations are in different genes, combine the deletion mapping and the complementation data to determine the most likely relative order of the mutations. Group the mutations into allelic classes, and determine the position and extent of the three deletions.

ANS S8.25. There are four complementation groups and these determine the allelic classes:

 Group 1: mutations *a* and *d*

 Group 2: mutation *b*

 Group 3: mutations *c* and *e*

 Group 4: mutation *f*

The deletion mapping can be used to order the mutant sites in the genetic map. Deletion 1 is deficient for all sites except that in *c*, since *c* is the only mutation with which wildtype recombinants can be generated. Similarly, deletion 2 is deficient for all sites except that in *b* and deletion 3 is deficient only for sites *a* and *b*. Because *a* and *d* are in the same complementation group, they must be closely linked, and similarly for *c* and *e*. Hence, as a start, we need only map *a, b, c,* and *f,* which, according to the deletion data, must have the following order (the bars represent the extent of each deletion):

This map, which can also be drawn in the reverse orientation, is the only map consistent with the deletion data. As noted, the mutation *d* must be close to *a* but, because deletion 1 eliminates site *a* but not *d*, then *d* must be to the left of *a*. Similarly, *e* must be close to *c* but, because deletion 3 eliminates site *e* but not *c*, then *e* must be to the right of *c*. The final map is:

The distances shown between the genes are arbitrary, but these could be determined by recombination mapping.

Chapter 9: Genetics of Bacteria and Their Viruses
Answers to Chapter-end problems

Fill-ins

1. conjugation
2. lysogen
3. counterselected marker
4. generalized transduction
5. F' plasmid
6. interrupted-mating technique
7. integrase
8. auxotroph
9. plasmid
10. cointegrate

Analysis and Applications

ANS 9.1. a. The overall dilution factor is 10^9, of which 0.1 ml yields 36 plaques. Hence there are 360 viable phage per ml in the final dilution, or 360×10^9 in the original suspension; the original phage titer was therefore 3.6×10^{11} viable phage per ml. **b.** 0.1 ml of a 10^6-fold dilution yields 42 colonies, which implies $42 \times 10^7 = 4.2 \times 10^8$ viable bacteria per ml in the original suspension.

ANS 9.2. The final dilution should contain 500 viable cells per ml, which is a 10^5-fold dilution of the original suspension. You could do any combination of 100-fold and 10-fold dilutions that multiply to 10^5; for example, two 100-fold dilutions and one 10-fold dilution, five 10-fold dilutions, or one 100-fold dilution and three 10-fold dilutions.

ANS 9.3. The T2*h* plaques will be clear because both strains are sensitive; the T2 plaques will be turbid because of the resistance of the B/2 cells.

ANS 9.4. Minimal medium containing galactose and biotin; the galactose would require presence of gal^+ and the biotin would allow both bio^+ and bio^- to grow.

ANS 9.5. The *E. coli* genome contains approximately 4,700 kilobase pairs, which implies approximately 47 kb per minute. Because the λ genome is 50 kb, the genetic length of the prophage is approximately one minute (more precisely, 47/50 = 0.94 minutes).

ANS 9.6. Infect an *E. coli* λ lysogen with P1. The λ lysogen contains λ prophage, and so some of the resulting P1 phage will include the part of the chromosome containing the prophage.

ANS 9.7. After circularization and integration at the bacterial *att* site, the map is
. . .*att D E F A B C att*

ANS 9.8. The specialized-transducing particles originate from aberrant prophage excision.

ANS 9.9. a. The identical bands were present in the original strain. **b.** The new bands are the result of transposition of IS5 to new locations in the genome. **c.** There are 3 transpositions per 12 lineages per 50 years, $3/(12 \times 50) = 0.005$ transpositions per lineage per year. **d.** Each colony has 5 elements that were present in the original strain, so the transposition rate per element is $0.005/5 = 0.001$ transpositions per element per year in each lineage.

ANS 9.10. Plate on minimal medium without leucine (selects for Leu$^+$) but containing streptomycin (selects for Str-r). The leu^+ allele is the selected marker and str-r the counterselected marker.

ANS 9.11. Strain B produces a restriction enzyme that cleaves the restriction site and also a modification enzyme that methylates a cytosine in the site to render it resistant to cleavage. In this way strain B protects its own DNA from destruction. Unmodified DNA infecting B is usually cleaved, but a few molecules are modified prior to cleavage and escape. Phage resulting from these molecules can then infect B efficiently. However, if they infect strain A, which lacks both the restriction enzyme and the modification enzyme, then the resulting DNA is unmodified and the phage containing it can infect strain B with only low efficiency.

ANS 9.13. The mean number of phage per cell equals 1. If you know the Poisson distribution, then it is apparent that the proportion of uninfected cells is $e^{-1} = 0.37$. If you do not know the Poisson distribution, then the answer can be calculated as follows. The probability that a bacterial cell escapes infection by a particular phage is $1 - 10^{-6} = 0.999999$ and the probability that it escapes infection by all one million phages is $P_0 = (0.999999)^{1000000}$. Therefore, $\ln P_0 = 1000000 \times \ln (0.999999) = -1$, and so $P_0 = e^{-1} = 0.37$.

ANS 9.13. a. Medium containing lactose, tryotophan, histidine, and streptomycin. **b.** Medium containing galactose, tryptophan, histidine, and streptomycin. **c.** Medium containing glucose (or any sugar other than lactose or galactose), histidine, and streptomycin. **d.** Medium containing glucose (or any sugar other than lactose or galactose), tryptophan, and streptomycin.

ANS 9.14. a. Medium containing galactose, tryptophan, histidine, and streptomycin. **b.** Medium containing glucose (or any sugar other than galactose), histidine, and streptomycin. **c.** Medium including glucose (or any sugar other than galactose), tryptophan, and streptomycin. **d.** Medium consisting of glucose (or any sugar other than galactose) and streptomycin.

ANS 9.15. Apparently, h and tet are closely linked, and so recombinants containing the h^+ allele of the Hfr tend to also to contain the tet-s allele of the Hfr, and these recombinants are eliminated by the counterselection for tet-r.

ANS 9.16. All receive the a^+ allele, but whether or not a particular b^+ str-r recombinant contains a^+ depends on the positions of the genetic exchanges.

ANS 9.17. Depending on the size of the F', it could be F' g, F' g h, F' g h i, and so forth, or F' f, F' f e, F' f e d, and so forth.

ANS 9.18. The first selection is for Met$^+$ and so *lac*$^+$ must have been transferred. The probability that a marker that is transferred is incorporated into the recombinants is about 50 percent, and so about 50 percent of the recombinants would be expected to be *lac*$^+$. The second selection is for Lac$^+$, and *met*$^+$ is a late marker. The great majority of mating pairs will spontaneously break apart before transfer of *met*$^+$, and so the frequency of *met*$^+$ recombinants in this experiment will be close to zero.

ANS 9.19. The order 500 *his*$^+$, 250 *leu*$^+$, 50 *trp*$^+$ implies that the genes are transferred in the order *his leu trp*. The *met* mutation is the counterselected marker that prevents growth of the Hfr parent. The medium containing histidine selects for *leu*$^+$ *trp*$^+$, and the number is small because both genes must be incorporated by recombination.

ANS 9.20. a. The map order and distances from the *E. coli* cross is *pro*–14–*met*–2–*arg*–6–*ile*, that from the *S. enterica* cross is *ile*–14–*arg*–4–*met*–25–*pro*. These are the same except for being written in the reverse order. **b.** The *E. coli* Hfr transfers *pro* first, the *S. enterica* Hfr transfers *ile* first, and the directions of transfer are opposite. **c.** The total region is 22 minutes in *E. coli* but 43 minutes in *S. enterica*, hence the *S. enterica* Hfr transfers the chromosome only half as fast as the *E. coli* Hfr.

ANS 9.21. a, c, e, f, and **g** are true.

ANS 9.22. The three possible orders are (1) *pur–pro–his,* (2) *pur–his–pro,* and (3) *pro–pur–his*. The predictions of the three orders are: (1) Virtually all *pur*$^+$ *his*$^-$ transductants should be *pro*$^-$, but this is not true. (2) Virtually all *pur*$^+$ *pro*$^-$ transductants should be *his*$^-$, but this is not true. (3) Some *pur*$^+$ *pro*$^-$ transductants will be *his*$^-$, and some *pur*$^+$ *his*$^-$ transductants will be *pro*$^-$ (depending on where the exchanges occur). Order (3) is the only one that is not contradicted by the data.

ANS 9.23. a. Use $m = 2 - 2d^{1/3}$, in which *m* is map distance in minutes and *d* cotransduction frequency. With the values of *d* given, the map distances are 0.74, 0.41, and 0.18 minutes, respectively. **b.** Use $d = [1 - (m/2)]^3$. With the values of *m* given, cotransduction frequencies are 0.42, 0.12, and 0, respectively. For markers greater than two minutes apart, the frequency of cotransduction equals zero. **c.** Map distance *a–b* equals 0.66 minutes, *b–c* equals 1.07 minutes, and these are additive, giving 1.73 minutes for the distance *a–c*. Predicted cotransduction frequency for this map distance is 0.002.

ANS 9.24. It is probable that the *amp-r* gene in the natural isolate was present in a transposable element. Transposition into λ occurs in a small proportion of cases and, when these infect the laboratory strain, the transposable element can transpose into the chromosome before the infecting λ is lost.

ANS 9.25. The *tet-r* gene in the phage was included in a transposable element. Transposition occurred in the lysogen to another location in the *E. coli* chromosome, and when the prophage was lost the antibiotic resistance remained.

ANS 9.26. Both the order of times of entry and the level of the plateaus imply that the order of gene transfer is *a b c d*. The times of entry are obtained by plotting the number of recombinants of each type versus time and extrapolating back to the time axis. The values are *a,* 10 minutes; *b,* 15 minutes; *c,* 20 minutes; *d,* 30 minutes. The low plateau value for the *d* gene probably results from close linkage with *str-s* because, in this case, the *d* allele in the F' strain would tend to be inherited along with the *str-r* allele.

ANS 9.27. The deletion map is shown in the accompanying illustration. A completely equivalent map can be obtained by flipping this one horizontally.

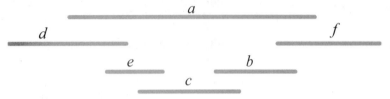

ANS 9.28. The genetic map shows the genetic intervals defined by the deletion endpoints and the locations of the mutations with respect to these intervals.

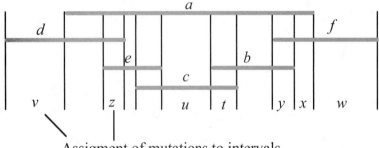

Assigment of mutations to intervals based on recombination data.

ANS 9.29. The mutations *v* and *z* are in the rIIB cistron whereas the mutations *t,u,w,x,* and *y* are in the rIIA cistron. As indicated in the genetic map, the boundary between the cistrons lies between the left end of the *c* deletion and the right end of the *e* deletion.

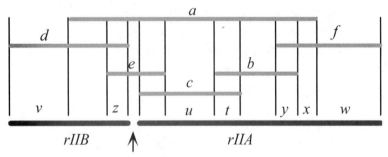

Interval in which boundary between *rIIA* and *rIIB* resides.

The matrix for complementation among the deletions must be as follows:

	a	b	c	d	e	f
a	−	−	−	−	−	−
b		−	−	+	−	−
c			−	+	−	−
d				−	−	+
e					−	−
f						−

ANS 9.30. The mean number of P2 phage per cell is 3, and the probability of a cell remaining uninfected by P2 is $e^{-3} = 0.050$; the mean number of P4 phage per cell is 2, and the probability of a cell remaining uninfected by P4 is $e^{-2} = 0.135$. **a.** $0.050 \times 0.135 \times 10^8 = 6.75 \times 10^5$. **b.** $6.75 \times 10^5 + 0.050 \times (1 - 0.135) \times 10^8 = 5.00 \times 10^6$. **c.** $(1 - 0.050) \times 0.135 \times 10^8 = 1.28 \times 10^7$. **d.** $(1 - 0.050) \times (1 - 0.135) \times 10^8 = 8.22 \times 10^7$.

Challenge Problems

ANS 9.31. The λ prophage itself is being transduced as part of the chromosome. It maps next to *gal*. Hence, when phage 363 is grown on strain D, 6% of the Gal⁺ transductants are lysogenic, whereas none of the Thr⁺ or Lac⁺ transductants are lysogenic. The reciprocal cross gives the same basic result, only here λ is being removed from the chromosome and being replaced by phage-free DNA. Hence, about 8% of the Gal⁺ transductants are nonlysogenic. As expected from the close linkage of the phage λ attachment site and *gal*, no linkage is seen for the other two markers.

ANS 9.32. The genetic map is in the shape of a figure 8, with the duplicate genes assigned to the same position exactly at the crosspoint in the middle. Since the duplicate genes are treated as a single gene, the genetic map must have a shape that would allow transfer of this genetic marker twice. The genetic map is as follows:

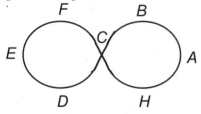

ANS 9.33. a. To amplify the known sequence the 3' ends of the primers should point toward the middle, hence the should be 5'-GGTAAA-3' and 3'-AAATGG-5'. **b.** Note that these are the same, hence only one primer is needed because of the inverted repeats. **c.** For inverse PCR the 3' ends of the primers should point outward, hence they should be 3'-CCATTT-5' and 5'-TTTACC-3'. These again are the same. (Note that PCR with these primers will not amplify anything unless the fragment containing the known sequence has been circularized.) **d.** Cleavage of the PCR product would result in two fragments, one consisting of the originally left-hand-flanking sequence and the other the

originally right-hand-flanking sequence. **e.** The flanking sequences are separated by a unique *Eco*RI site.

Supplemental problems with answers

S9.1. Define the following terms:
a. Transformation
b. Conjugation
c. Transduction
d. Transposition
e. Temperate phage
Ans S9.1. a. Transformation is the process of genetic alteration of a cell or an organism by uptake of DNA. **b.** Conjugation is the process by which DNA is transferred from a donor bacterial cell to a recipient cell by cell-to-cell contact. **c.** Transduction is the process by which bacterial DNA is transferred from one bacterial cell to another using a phage particle as a vehicle. **d.** Transposition is the process in which a DNA sequence is transferred from one position to another within a genome. **e.** A temperate phage is a phage capable of both a lysogenic and a lytic cycle.

S9.2. How many plaques can be formed by a single bacteriophage particle? A bacteriophage is adsorbed by a bacterium in a liquid growth medium. Before lysis, the infected cell is added to a suspension of cells that are plated on solid medium to form a lawn. How many plaques will result?
ANS S9.2. One plaque per phage. One plaque, because the plating was done before lysis, and so the progeny phage are confined to one tiny area.

S9.3. Describe the differences between phage λ and F- plasmid integration into bacterial chromosome.
ANS S9.3. Integration of phage λ requires a special attachment site in the bacterial chromosome and is integrated via a phage encoded integrase enzyme, whereas the F plasmid is able to integrate into virtually any site on the bacterial chromosome.

S9.4. How do the sizes of bacteriophage genomes compare with the sizes of plasmids?
ANS S9.4. Most bacteriophage genomes are of the same order of magnitude as large plasmids, but small plasmids can be much smaller than a bacteriophage genome.

S9.5. Is it possible for a plasmid without any genes to exist?
ANS S9.5. Yes, as long as it has a replication origin.

S9.6. What process is responsible for the conversion of an F^+ bacterial cell into an Hfr cell?
ANS S9.6. A single recombination event that joins the circular F plasmid with the circular bacterial chromosome.

S9.7. What is the major difference between the lytic cycle and the lysogenic cycle?
ANS S9.7. In the lytic cycle, progeny phage are produced and the host bacterial cell is lysed. In the lysogenic cycle, the DNA of an infecting phage becomes part of the genetic material of the cell, no progeny particles are produced, and the infected bacterial cell survives.

S9.8. Why are specialized transducing particles of phage λ generated only when a lysogen is induced to produce phage rather than in the process of lytic infection?

ANS S9.8. Transducing particles of λ are formed only by aberrant excision of prophage DNA from the bacterial chromosome.

S9.9. Why is generalized transduction not the preferred method for mapping two unknown mutants relative to one another on the bacterial chromosome?

ANS S9.9. Mapping genes by cotransduction requires that the genes be very closely linked in order to be transduced together. Two mutations discovered at random are very unlikely to be so closely linked as to allow cotransduction.

S9.10. A temperate phage has the gene order *a b c d e f g h,* whereas the prophage of the same phage has the gene order *g h a b c d e f.* What information does this circular permutation give you about the location of the phage attachment site?

ANS S9.10. The attachment site, *att*, must be between genes *f* and *g*.

S9.11. Recombination in phage λ crosses reveals the order of certain genes to be

where *cos* represents the cohesive ends and *att* is the phage attachment site. What order of the genes would be found if the λ prophage were mapped by generalized P1 transduction of an *E. coli* strain lysogenic for phage λ?

ANS S9.11. In answering this question, remember that after joining of the cohesive ends, the prophage is formed by recombination at the attachment site, as shown in part A of the accompanying diagram. (The bacterial chromosome is not drawn to scale.) The order of the phage genes in the prophage is as shown in parts B and C.

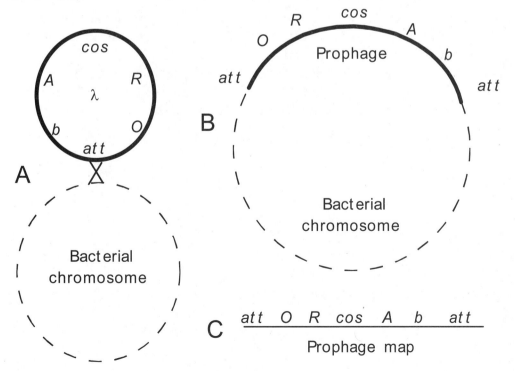

S9.12. You are studying a biochemical pathway in *Neurospora* that leads to the production of substance A. You isolate a set of mutations, each of which is unable to grow on minimal medium unless it is supplemented with A. By performing appropriate matings, you group all the mutants into four complementation groups (genes) designated *a1, a2, a3,* and *a4.* You know beforehand that the biochemical pathway for the production of A includes four intermediates: B, C, D, and E. You test the nutritional requirements of your mutants by growing them on minimal medium supplemented with each of these intermediates in turn. The results are summarized in the accompanying table, where the plus signs indicate growth and the minus signs indicate failure to grow.

	A	B	C	D	E
a1	+	+	+	−	+
a2	+	−	+	−	+
a3	+	−	−	−	+
a4	+	−	−	−	−

Determine in what order the substances A, B, C, D, and E are most likely to participate in the biochemical pathway, and indicate the enzymatic steps by arrows. Label each arrow with the name of the gene that codes for the corresponding enzyme.

ANS S9.12. The principle to be applied is that, under ideal circumstances, a mutation in a gene coding for any enzyme in a metabolic pathway will be able to grow on medium supplemented with an intermediate that comes after the step catalyzed by the enzyme but unable to grow on medium supplemented with an intermediate that comes prior to the step. Hence, the data in the table indicate the following pathway:

$$D \xrightarrow{a1} B \xrightarrow{a2} C \xrightarrow{a3} E \xrightarrow{a4} A$$

S9.13. A experiment was carried out in *E. coli* to map five genes around the chromosome using each of three different Hfr strains. The genetic markers were *bio, met, phe, his,* and *trp.* The Hfr strains were found to transfer the genetic markers at the times indicated in the accompanying table. Construct a genetic map of the *E. coli* chromosome that includes all five genetic markers, the genetic distances in minutes between adjacent gene pairs, and the origin and direction of transfer of each Hfr. Complete the missing entries in the table, indicated by the question marks.

Hfr1 markers	*bio*	*met*	*phe*	*his*
Time of entry	26	44	66	?
Hfr2 markers	*phe*	*met*	*bio*	*trp*
Time of entry	?	26	44	75
Hfr3 markers	*phe*	*his*	?	*bio*
Time of entry	6	27	35	?

ANS S9.13. The map implied by the time-of-entry data is as follows:

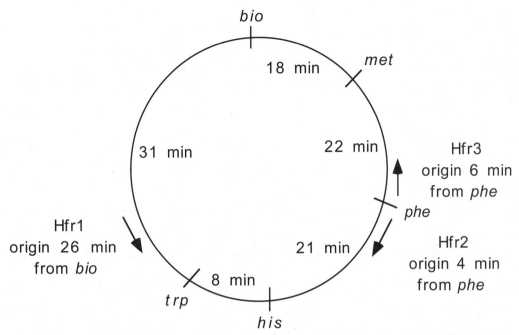

The entries corresponding to the question marks should be, for *his* in Hfr1, 87 min; for *phe* in Hfr2, 4 min; at 35 min in Hfr3, *trp*; and for *bio* in Hfr3, 66 min.

S9.14. In an uninterrupted Hfr × F⁻ mating, there is a plateau (maximum frequency of recombination) for each marker that decreases the farther the marker is from the origin of transfer. However, markers that enter very early (within approximately one minute after transfer commences) have a low plateau value, indicating that are unlikely to be incorporated into the recipient by recombination. How can this be explained?

ANS S9.14. A minimum of two exchanges are necessary to incorporate any marker into the chromosome, one exchange on each side. When the distance between the origin of transfer and the marker is very short, there is little opportunity for recombination on the origin side of the marker.

S9.15. A first-year graduate student carried out transformation of an *E. coli* strain of genotype *trp⁻ azi⁻ phe⁻ gal⁻ pur⁻ his⁻ ser⁻* using a plasmid with the selectable markers *amp-r kan-r trp⁺ azi⁺ bio⁺ phe⁺ pur⁺ tet-r*. After transformation, he plated the cells on minimal medium containing galactose as a carbon source along with histidine and serine and added ampicillin and kanamycin to select for the transformants. After incubating the plates overnight, the student returned to the lab to discover that no colonies had formed! Then he realized that he had made a mistake. What was it?

ANS S9.15. He tried to grow the cells on galactose but the plasmid does not contain *gal⁺*. Otherwise, the strategy is fine. The plasmid contains the *amp^R* and *kan^R* genes, which confer resistance to the ampicillin and kanamycin present in the medium. The plasmid also rescues *trp⁻ azi⁻ bio⁻ phe⁻* and *pur⁻*. That leaves *gal⁻*, *his⁻*, and *ser⁻* uncomplemented. The supplement of histidine and serine takes care of *his⁻* and *ser⁻*, but trying to grow the cells on galactose was an error.

S9.16. The genes *A, B, G, H, I,* and *T* were tested in all possible pairs for cotransduction with bacteriophage P1. Only the following pairs were found able to be cotransduced: *G* and *H, G* and *I, T* and *A, I* and *B, A* and *H*. What is the order of the genes along the chromosome? Explain your logic.

ANS S9.16. Any phage transduces one, small contiguous piece of DNA. Cotransduction therefore indicates very close linkage. Hence, *G* and *H* are close, and *G* and *I* are close, but *H* and *I* are not close (because they do not cotransduce), and so the order of these three genes must be *I G H* (or the reverse). The location of the other three genes can be deduced similarly: *A* is close to *H*, *B* is close to *I*, and *T* must be close to *A* but not close to *H*. Hence, the order is *B I G H A T* or, equivalently, *T A H G I B*.

S9.17. When an Hfr strain that is also a phage λ lysogen is crossed with an F⁻ nonlysogenic strain, most of the F⁻ cells undergo lysis shortly after transfer of the prophage, but this does not happen if the F⁻ strain is also a λ lysogen. Suggest an explanation.

ANS S9.17. The phage repressor is not present in the F⁻ nonlysogenic strain, so when the prophage is transferred, phage induction and the lytic cycle takes place, bursting the bacterium. In an F⁻ lysogenic strain, however, the phage repressor is present, so the prophage remains repressed.

S9.18. On continued growth of a culture of a λ lysogen, rare cells become nonlysogenic by spontaneous loss of the prophage. Such a loss is the result of prophage excision without subsequent development of the phage lytic cycle. The lysogen is said to have been *cured*. A lysogen is created using a λ phage carrying the transposon Tn*5*, which carries resistance factors for kanamycin and neomycin. Cells that have been cured of the phage are selected by virtue of their resistance to infection by *rII* mutants of phage T4. Among 1000 cured colonies, 197 are still resistant to kanamycin and neomycin. How can this be explained?

ANS S9.18. In the lineage of the cured cell, the Tn*5* transposed into another site (or sites) in the bacterial genome.

S9.19. Among the 197 kanamycin-resistant, neomycin-resistant colonies that originated as described in Problem **S9.18**, 16 are *prototrophs,* which means unable to grow on minimal medium unless supplemented with an amino acid or some other nutrient.
a. What hypothesis can explain the relatively high frequency of prototrophs?
b. What transduction experiment using phage P1 could be carried out to test this hypothesis?
ANS S9.19. a. One hypothesis is that, in each lineage of a prototroph, the Tn*5* transposed into a gene encoding an enzyme in the biochemical pathway for synthesis of the required nutrient; the Tn*5* insertion interrupts the gene, rendering it nonfunctional. **b.** Prepare P1 phage from each strain that requires a nutrient, and transduce a wildtype (auxotrophic) strain, selecting for resistance to kanamycin and neomycin. If the resulting strains require the same nutrient as the P1 donor did, then the knockout mutation cotransduces with the Tn*5*, which supports the hypothesis.

S9.20. Bacteriophage P1 was grown on a wildtype strain of *E. coli,* and the resulting progeny phage were used to infect a strain with three mutations, *arg⁻, pro⁻,* and *his⁻,* each of which results in a requirement for an amino acid: arginine, proline, and histidine, respectively. Equal volumes of the infected culture were spread on plates containing minimal medium supplemented with various combinations of the amino acids, and the colonies appearing on each plate were counted. The results are shown here. In each row, the + signs indicate the amino acids present in the medium.

Plate number	Supplement Arginine	Proline	Histidine	Number of colonies
1	+	+	0	1000
2	+	0	+	1000
3	0	+	+	1000
4	+	0	0	200
5	0	+	0	100
6	0	0	+	0

a. For each of the six types of medium, list the donor markers that must be present to allow the transduced cell to form colonies.

b. Using these results, construct a genetic map of the *arg, pro, his* region showing the relative order of the genes and the cotransduction frequencies between the markers.

ANS S9.20. a. If an amino acid is not present in the medium, then the transduced cell must have received the wildtype allele of the gene in order to grow. Hence, the selections in the various media are as follows:

Plate number	Supplements	Donor marker(s) needed for growth
1	arginine, proline	his^+
2	arginine, histidine	pro^+
3	proline, histidine	arg^+
4	arginine	pro^+, his^+
5	proline	arg^+, his^+
6	histidine	arg^+, pro^+

b. The frequency of cotransduction between two genetic markers is the frequency with which colonies that contain one marker also contain the other. The cotransduction frequencies are therefore 0.2 for *pro–his*, 0.1 for *arg–his*, and 0 for *arg–pro*. The resulting genetic map is as shown below. Note that the markers with the greatest frequency of cotransduction are the closest.

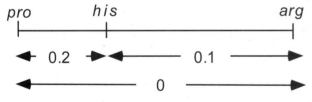

S9.21. On EMB-lactose agar, Lac⁺ colonies are purple and Lac⁻ colonies are white. If several thousand F' lac^+/lac^- cells are plated, a few sectored colonies appear. The sectored colonies have a purple half and a white half, or a wedge of white in an otherwise purple background, but sectored colonies that are predominantly white are not found. Explain the cause of the sectoring.

ANS S9.21 The white sectors derive from a cell lineage in the colony that, at one point, lost the F' lac^+ plasmid, hence all the descendant cells are white. (This example also indicates that parent cells and their descendants remain in physical proximity in the colony.) Predominantly white colonies are not found because, if the founding cell of a colony has lost the F' lac^+, there is not way the F' lac^+ plasmid can be regained.

S9.22. The order of genes in the λ phage virion is *A B C D E att int xis N cI O P Q S R*
a. Given that the bacterial attachment site, *att,* is between *gal* and *bio* in the bacterial chromosome, what is the prophage gene order?
b. A new phage is discovered whose gene order is identical in the virion and in the prophage. What does this say about the location of the *att* site with respect to the termini of the phage chromosome?
c. A wildtype λ lysogen is infected with another λ phage carrying a genetic marker, *Z,* located between *E* and *att.* The superinfection gives rise to a rare, doubly lysogenic *E. coli* strain that carries both λ and λ-Z prophage. Assuming that the second phage also entered the chromosome at an *att* site, diagram two possible arrangements of the prophages in the bacterial chromosome, and indicate the locations of the bacterial genes *gal* and *bio.*
ANS S9.22. a. The *cos* sites that allow circularization of the phage are at the ends, and recombination takes place at the *att* site. Hence the prophage gene order is *gal–att int xis N cI O P Q S R A B C D E att–bio.* **b.** In this phage, the attachment site must be located on one end of the phage chromosome, just inside the *cos* site. **c.** The superinfecting phage can enter into either the left or the right *att* site, yielding either *gal–att int xis . . . D E Z–att int xis . . . D E att–bio* or *gal–att int xis . . . D E–att int xis. . . D E Z att–bio.*

S9.23. Four Hfr strains of *E. coli* transfer their genetic material in the following order. Construct a genetic map of the *E. coli* chromosome that includes all the markers listed here and the distances in minutes between adjacent gene pairs.

Hfr1 markers	*mal*	*met*	*thi*	*thr*	*trp*	
Time of entry	10	17	22	33	57	
Hfr2 markers	*his*	*phe*	*arg*	*mal*		
Time of entry	18	23	35	45		
Hfr3 markers	*phe*	*his*	*bio*	*azi*	*thr*	*thi*
Time of entry	6	11	33	48	49	60
Hfr4 markers	*arg*	*thy*	*met*	*thr*		
Time of entry	15	21	32	48		

ANS S9.23. The genetic map is deduced from the markers whose transfer was examined in two or more Hfr strains, in this case *mal, met, thi, thr, his, phe, and arg*. Then the markers examined in only one strain are filled in, in this case *trp, bio, azi, and thy*. The genetic map, with the distances in minutes, is:

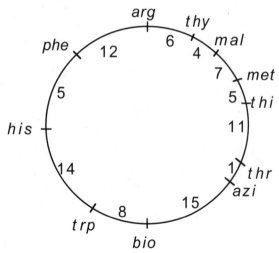

S9.24. An F′ factor consisting of the *E. coli* sex factor, F, and a segment of the bacterial chromosome that includes the wildtype tryptophan synthetase A gene ($trpA^+$) was isolated. The F′ *trpA* factor was introduced by conjugation into an F⁻ strain with a single nucleotide mutation in the *trpA* gene, and the resulting exconjugants were F′ $trpA^+$/$trpA^-$ partial diploids. These cells were streaked to obtain single colonies, and each colony was inoculated into liquid nutrient medium. When mixed with female cells, most of the resulting cultures transferred only the original F′ *trpA* factor. However, a very small percentage of the cultures transferred a variable length of the bacterial chromosome, starting with the *trpA* gene. These cultures fell into two classes. Class 1 transferred $trpA^+$ early, whereas class 2 transferred $trpA^-$ early.

a. Draw a diagram of the interaction between the F′ factor and the bacterial chromosome, showing how the cells of class 1 are likely to have arisen.

b. Draw a similar diagram showing the probable origin of cells of class 2.

ANS S9.24. The Hfr is created by recombination between the *trpA* gene in the F′*trpA* and the *trpA⁻* gene in the bacterial chromosome. Whether $trpA^+$ or $trpA^-$ is transferred first depends on the position of the recombination relative to the site of the $trpA^-$ mutation. In the diagrams below, the asterisk indicates the site of the $trpA^-$ mutation. The bacterial chromosome is not drawn to scale.

S9.25. For nonreverting mutations *A–D* in the *rIIA* cistron are regarded as deletions. Phage containing the individual deletions were crosses in all pairwise combinations. Three crosses—and only three crosses—yielded $rIIA^+$ recombinants: *A* x *D*, *B* x *C*, and *C* x *D*. The deletions were then used to map 7 revertable "point mutations" (nucleotide substitutions), each of which undergoes recombination with all the others. The table shows the result of crosses of phage carrying each deletion with phage carrying each of the point mutations: + means $rIIA^+$ progeny were recovered, – means no $rIIA^+$ progeny were recovered. The experiments were large enough to recover $rIIA^+$ recombinants if they occurred.

	1	2	3	4	5	6	7
A	−	−	+	+	+	+	−
B	+	−	+	+	−	−	+
C	−	+	+	−	+	+	+
D	+	+	−	+	+	−	+

a. Draw a map of the *rIIA* cistron showing the relative positions of the deletions *A–D*.

b. Show where in the map each of the point mutations is located.

ANS S9.25. a. In the accompanying map, the deletion and overlap sizes are arbitrary because the deletion data pertain only to overlaps, not to the size of each deletion or the magnitude of the overlaps. **b.** The deletions and their overlaps delineate the 7 regions separated by the dotted lines. One point mutation is within each region, ordered as shown.

Chapter 10: Molecular Biology of Gene Expression
Answers to Chapter-end problems

Fill-ins

1. aminoacyl-tRNA synthetase
2. polycistronic mRNA
3. chaperone
4. spliceosome
5. promoter
6. colinearity
7. nonsense-mediated decay
8. open reading frame (ORF)
9. release
10. anticodon

Analysis and Applications

ANS 10.1. a. Phe, Ser, Leu, and Pro. **b.** Lys, Arg, Glu, and Gly.

ANS 10.2. a. 27. **b.** 27. **c.** 18.

ANS 10.3. a. Lys, Asn, Thr, Gln, His, and Pro. **b.** Pro, Arg, Gly, Ala.

ANS 10.4. UAR and UGA.

ANS 10.5. 126, or about 69 percent.

ANS 10.6. Only Met (AUG) and Trp (W).

ANS 10.7. The start codon is AUG, which codes for methionine; the stop codons are UAA, UAG, and UGA. The probability of a start codon is 1/32 (1/64 x 2), and the probability of a stop codon is 3/32. The average distance between stop codons is 64/3 = 21.3 codons.

ANS 10.8. The mRNA sequence is 5'-AAAAUGCCCUUAAUCUCAGCGUCCUAC-3', and translation begins with the first AUG, coding for methionine. The amino acid sequence coded by this region is Met–Pro–Leu–Ile–Ser–Ala–Ser–Tyr.

ANS 10.9. a. The original DNA must have the sequence 5'-ATG-3'/3'-TAC-5', where the bottom strand (written to the right of the slash) is the one transcribed; the inversion contains the codon 5'-CAT-3'/3'-GTA-5', where again the bottom strand is transcribed. The mRNA therefore contains 5'-CAU-3' (the "reverse complement" of the oriuginal codon), which specifies His. **b.** No. (This answer can be obtained by checking the reverse complements of each of the codons in turn.) **c.** The nonsense codons are 5'-UAA-3', 5'-UAG-3', and 5'-UGA-3', which have reverse complements 5'-UUA-3', 5'-CUA-3', and 5'-UCA-3', respectively, which encode Leu, Leu, and Ser, respectively. **d.** Same answer as part **c.**

ANS 10.10: 5'-GUCAUCGAAGCCGUA-3'. The stem and loop is as shown here

ANS 10.11. With a G at the 5' end, the first codon is GUU, which codes for valine; and with a G at the 3' end, the last codon is UUG, which codes for leucine.

ANS 10.12. Codons are read from the 5' end of the mRNA, and the first amino acid in a polypeptide chain is at the amino terminus. If the G were at the 5' end, the first codon would be GAA, coding for glutamic acid at the amino terminus of the polypeptide. If the G were at the 3' end, the last codon would be AAG, coding for arginine at the carboxyl terminus. Thus, the G was added at the 5' end.

ANS 10.13. GUG codes for valine and UGU codes for cysteine. Therefore, an alternating polypeptide containing only valine and cysteine would be made.

ANS 10.14. The artificial mRNA can be read in any one of three reading frames, depending on wher translation starts. The reading frames are GUC GUC GUC . . ., UCG UCG UCG . . ., and CGU CGU CGU The first codes for polyvaline, the second polyserine, and the third polyarginine.

ANS 10.15. The possible codons, their frequencies, and the amino acids coded are as follows:

DISPLAY: AAA $(3/4)^3 = 0.422$ Lys

AAC $(3/4)^2(1/4) = 0.141$ Asn

ACA $(3/4)^2(1/4) = 0.141$ Thr

CAA $(3/4)^2(1/4) = 0.141$ Gln

CCA $(3/4)(1/4)^2 = 0.047$ Pro

$$CAC \ (3/4)(1/4)^2 = 0.047 \ His$$
$$ACC \ (3/4)(1/4)^2 = 0.047 \ Thr$$
$$CCC \ (1/4)^3 = 0.015 \ Pro$$

Therefore, amino acids in the random polymer and their frequencies are lysine (42.1 percent), asparagine (14.1 percent), threonine (18.8 percent), glutamine (14.1 percent), histidine (4.7 percent), and proline (6.2 percent).

ANS 10.16. Methionine has 1 codon, histidine 2, and threonine 4, and so the total number is $1 \times 2 \times 4 = 8$. The sequence AUGCAYACN encompasses them all. Because arginine has six codons, the possible number of sequences coding for Met–Arg–Thr is $1 \times 6 \times 4 = 24$. The sequences are AUGCGNACN (16 possibilities) and AUGAGRACN (8 possibilities).

ANS 10.17. a. AAAN would be translated as AAA–AAN, yielding Lys–Lys, and AAGN as AAG–AGN, yielding either Lys–Ser or Lys–Arg, hence Lys could be followed only by Lys, Ser, or Arg. **b.** Ile, Met, or Thr. **c.** Cys or Trp (unless Met is the final amino acid in the chain). **d.** Only Gly.

ANS 10.18. The final four nucleotides in the open reading frame must be NUAA, NUAG, or NUGA. The last amino acid must therefore correspond to NUA (Leu, Ile, or Val, depending on the identity of N), NUA (also Leu, Ile, or Val), or NUG (Leu, Met, or Val). Hence, every polypeptide would have to terminate with either Leu, Ile, Val, or Met.

ANS 10.19. a. UGGNN would be translated as UGG–GNN, so any amino acid with a codon beginning with G could follow Trp, namely, Val, Ala, Asp, Glu, or Gly. **b.** Same answer as in part **a.**

ANS 10.20. The terminal nucleotides would have to be NNUAA, NNUAG, or NNUGA, with the last amino acid encoded by NNU. This formula rules out Trp, Gln, Met, Lys, or Glu as the carboxyl amino acid.

ANS 10.21. a. AUGN would be translated as AUG–UGN, so the second amino acid could be Cys or Trp. **b.** Translation is AUG–GNN, so the second amino acid could be Val, Ala, Asp, Glu, or Gly.

ANS 10.22. Because the pairing of codon and anticodon are antiparallel, it is convenient to write the anticodon as 3'-UAI-5'. The first two codon positions are therefore 5'-AU-3', and the third is either A, U or C (because each can pair with I). The possible codons are 5'-AUA-3', 5'-AUU-3', and 5'-AUC-3', all of which code for isoleucine.

ANS 10.23. In theory, the codon 5'-UGG-3' (tryptophan) could pair with either 3'-ACC-5' or 3'-ACU-5'. However, 3'-ACU-5' can also pair with 5'-UGA-3', which is a chain-termination codon. If this anticodon were used for tryptophan, an amino acid would be inserted instead of terminating the chain. Therefore, the other anticodon (3'-ACC-5') is the one used.

ANS 10.24. a. The deletion must have fused the amino-coding terminus of the *B* gene with the carboxyl-coding terminus of the *A* gene. The nontranscribed strand must therefore be oriented 5'-*B*–*A*-3'. **b.** The number of bases deleted must be a multiple of three, otherwise the carboxyl terminus would not have the correct reading frame.

ANS 10.25. a.The nontranscribed strand is given, and so the wildtype reading frame of the mRNA is AU<u>G</u> CAU CCG GGC UC<u>A</u> UUA GUC U . . ., which codes for Met–His–Pro–Gly–Ser–Leu–Val– **b.** The mutant X mRNA reading frame is AU<u>G</u> GCA UCC GGG CUC <u>A</u>UU AGU CU . . ., which codes for Met–Ala–Ser–Gly–Leu–Ile–Ser–Leu– **c.** The mutant Y mRNA reading frame is AU<u>G</u> CAU CCG GGC UCU UAG UCU . . ., which codes for Met–His–Pro–Gly–Ser (the UAG is a termination codon). **d.**The double-mutant mRNA reading frame is AU<u>G</u> GCA UCC GGG CUC UUA GUC U . . ., which codes for Met–Ala–Ser–Gly–Leu–Leu–Val– Note that the double mutant differs from wildtype only in the region between the insertion and deletion mutations, in which the reading frame is shifted.

ANS 10.26. The probability of a correct amino acid at a particular site is 0.999, and so the probability of all 300 amino acids being correctly translated is $(0.999)^{300} = 0.74$, or approximately 3/4.

ANS 10.27. Each loop represents an intron, and so the total number is seven introns.

ANS 10.28. If transcribed from left to right, the transcribed strand is the bottom one, and the mRNA sequence is AGA **CUU CAG GCU CAA CGU** GGU, which codes for Arg–Leu–Gln–Ala–Gln–Arg–Gly. To invert the molecule, the strands must be interchanged in order to preserve the correct polarity, and so the sequence of the inverted molecule is

$\qquad$ 5'-AGA**ACGTTGAGCCTGAAG**GGT-3'
$\qquad$ 3'-TCT**TGCAACTCGGACTTC**CCA-5'

This codes for an mRNA with sequence AGA **ACG UUG AGC CUG AAG** GGU, which codes for Arg–Thr–Leu–Ser–Leu–Lys–Gly.

ANS 10.29. The DNA nontemplate strand is

$\qquad$ 5'-TAACGTATGCTTGACCTCCAAGCAATCGATGCCAGCTCAAGG-3'

and so the mRNA for this region is

$\qquad$ 5'-UAACGUAUGCUUGACCUCCAAGCAAUCGAUGCCAGCUCAAGG-3'

Translation in all three possible reading frames yields (in the singe-letter amino acid codes)

$\qquad$ 5'-UAACGUAUGCUUGACCUCCAAGCAAUCGAUGCCAGCUCAAGG-3'
$\qquad\qquad$ * R M L D L Q A I D A S S R
$\qquad\qquad$ N V C L T S K Q S M P A Q
$\qquad\qquad$ T Y A * P P S N R C Q L K

Since the sequence is from the middle of an exon, you do not know the reading frame. However, two of the possible reading frames contain stop codons (*). Therefore, the only sequence without stop codons must be correct since you know that the sequence comes from the middle of exonof an active gene. So the correct amino acid sequence of the polypeptide is —N V C L T S K Q S M P A Q—

ANS 10.30: a. 5'-UACCAUGUCAAACAGCGUAUGGUAGCAGUG-3'.
b. Met–Ser–Asn–Ser–Val–Trp.

Challenge Problems

ANS 10.31. Mutant 1 indicates the sequence AUGAARUAG, where R means any purine. Mutant 2 indicates the sequence AUGAU[U or C or A]GUNUAA, where N means any nucleotide. Since mutation 2 is a deletion in the second codon, the second codon in the wildtype gene must be either ?AU, A?U, or AU?, where the question mark indicates the deleted nucleotide; also, the third codon in the wildtype gene must be [U or C or A]GU, the fourth codon must be NUA, and the fifth must be A??. Similarly, since mutation 1 is an insertion in the second codon, the second codon in the wildtype gene must consist of three of the four bases AARU; also, the third codon in the wildtype gene must be AG?. The only consistent possibility for codon 2 is AAU, which codes for Asn. The third codon must be AGU, which codes for Ser. That leaves, for codon 4, the possibilities Val and Lys, only Val of which is coded by NUA, where N = G. Finally, the fifth codon must be AAR (Lys).

Hence, the sequence of the nontranscribed strand of the wildtype gene, as nearly as can be determined from the data given, and separated into codons, is 5'-ATG-AAT-AGT-GTA-AAR-3'. Mutation 1 has a single nucleotide addition in codon 2 that yields a codon for Lys, so it must be an addition of a purine (R) at position 6 or of an A at either position 4 or 5. Mutation 2 has a single nucleotide deletion that yields a codon for Ile, which means that the A at either position 3 or position 4 was deleted.

ANS 10.32. a. 5'-GAUCAAUAUGCAU GCU CUCGGGGGCCCCCGAGAGCAU GCAUAUUGAUCAUAAUAUAU-3'
b. Met–His–Ala–Leu–Gly–Gly–Pro–Arg–Glu–His–Ala–Tyr

ANS 10.33. a. Met–Phe–Tyr. **b.** Met–Phe–Tyr–Leu–Met–Phe–Tyr–Leu–Met–Phe–Tyr–Leu–etc. for an indefinite length, because the mRNA contains no stop codon. **c.** Met–Ser–Leu–Leu–Asn–Val–Phe–Thr–Glu–Cys–Leu–Tyr. **d.** The mRNA in part **b** is translated in the same reading frame in every pass, and no stop codon is ever encountered; that in part **c** undergoes a frameshift in every pass, and after three rounds shifts back into the normal reading frame and hits the stop codon. **e.** Met–Ser–Leu–Leu–Asn–Val–Phe–Thr. (In this case a new stop codon is encountered in the second pass.)

Supplemental problems with answers

S10.1. Describe the main features of the genetic code.
ANS S10.1. The genetic code consists of "words," or codons, three bases in length, each of which specifies a single amino acid to be inserted into the growing polypeptide chain (except for three special codons that code for termination of synthesis). The codons are nonoverlapping and, in the messenger RNA, are read without interruption from a fixed starting point to the termination codon. The code is degenerate, or redundant, which means that the same amino acid can be specified by more than one codon. The code is also (almost) universal, which means that, apart from a few organisms and organelles that are exceptions, it is the same in all organisms.

S10.2. If the triplet codons in the genetic code were read in an overlapping fashion, would there be any constraints on the amino acid sequences found in proteins?
ANS S10.2. Yes, certain amino acids would be found to be neighbors more often than expected by chance, because each codon would be involved in the specification of two, and possibly up to three, neighboring amino acids.

S10.3. If DNA consisted of only two nucleotides (say, A and T) in any sequence, what is the minimal number of adjacent nucleotides that would be needed to specify uniquely each of the 20 amino acids?

ANS S10.3. The requirement is that $2^n \geq 20$, or $n = 5$. If the codons were 4 nucleotides, then only 16 amino acids could be specified because $2^4 = 16$. A codon of 5 nucleotides does the job because $2^5 = 32$; in fact, it leaves a little room for stop codons and degeneracy.

S10.4. If DNA consisted of three possible base pairs (say, A—T, G—C, and X—Y), what is the minimal number of adjacent nucleotides that would be needed to specify uniquely each of the 20 amino acids?

ANS S10.4. In this case the requirement is $6^n \geq 20$, or $n = 2$.

S10.5. A DNA strand consists of any sequence of four kinds of nucleotides. Suppose there were only 16 different amino acids instead of 20. Which of the following statements would be correct descriptions of the minimal number of nucleotides necessary to create a genetic code?
 a. 1
 b. 2, provided that chain termination does not require a special codon
 c. 3, provided that chain termination does require a special codon
 d. 2, no matter how chain termination is accomplished
 e. statements **b.** and **c.**

ANS S10.5. With 16 codons for amino acids and one for a stop codon, the minimal number is $4^n \geq 17$, so $n = 3$; without the need for a stop codon, the minimal number is $4^n \geq 16$, so $n = 2$. Hence, statement (e) is correct.

S10.6. In the standard genetic code, synonymous codons often have the feature that the third nucleotide in the codon is either of the pyrimidines (T or C) or either of the purines (A or G) because of "wobble" in the base pairing at the third position of the codon. If this rule were followed consistently for all codons, would it be possible to have a triplet code that specifies 20 amino acids and one stop codon? Would there be any room for degeneracy?

ANS S10.6. If the rule were followed consistently, the first two nucleotides of each codon could be any of the four possible (A, T, G, or C) but the third could be only "pyrimidine" (T or C) or only "purine" (A or G). Hence, the number of possible codons would be $4 \times 4 \times 2 = 32$, which allows coding for 20 amino acids, one stop codon, and leaves 11 additional codons for redundancy.

S10.7. Which of the following statements is true of polypeptide chains and nucleotide chains?
 a. Both have a sugar-phosphate backbone.
 b. Both are chains consisting of 20 types of repeating units.
 c. Both types of molecules contain unambiguous and interconvertible triplet codes.
 d. Both types of polymers are linear and unbranched.
 e. None of the above.

ANS S10.7. Only statement **d.** is true.

S10.8. The notion that a strand of DNA serves as a template for transcription of an RNA that is translated into a polypeptide is known as the "central dogma" of gene expression. All three types of molecules have a polarity. In the DNA template and the RNA transcript, the polarity is determined

by the free 3′ and 5′ groups at opposite ends of the polynucleotide chains; in a polypeptide, the polarity is determined by the free amino group (N terminal) and carboxyl group (C terminal) at opposite ends. Each statement below describes one possible polarity of the DNA template, the RNA transcript, and the polypeptide chain, respectively, in temporal order of use as a template or in synthesis. Which is correct?

 a. 5′ to 3′ DNA; 3′ to 5′ RNA; N terminal to C terminal.
 b. 3′ to 5′ DNA; 3′ to 5′ RNA; N terminal to C terminal.
 c. 3′ to 5′ DNA; 3′ to 5′ RNA; C terminal to N terminal.
 d. 3′ to 5′ DNA; 5′ to 3′ RNA; N terminal to C terminal.
 e. 5′ to 3′ DNA; 5′ to 3′ RNA; C terminal to N terminal.

ANS S10.8. The 5' end of the RNA transcript is formed first, so **a.** through **c.** are all wrong. The 5' end of the RNA transcript is transcribed from the 3' end of the DNA template, so **e.** is wrong. The additional statement in **e.** that the amino end of the polypeptide is synthesized first serves as a confirmation of the correctness of statement **d.**

S10.9. Which of the following features of a protein structure is most directly determined by the genetic code?

 a. Its shape
 b. Its secondary structure
 c. Its catalytic or structural role
 d. Its amino acid sequence
 e. Its subunit composition (quaternary structure)

ANS S10.9. Only (d); the other features are formed secondarily.

S10.10. The structure below is that of a dipeptide composed of alanine and glycine.

```
  H   H  O   H   H   O
  |   |  ||  |   |   ||
H–N – C – C – N – C – C – OH
      |           |
      H          H–C–H
                  |
                  H
```

 a. Which end, left or right, is the amino terminal end?
 b. Which amino acid is at the amino terminal end?
 c. Which end, left or right, is the carboxyl terminal end?
 d. Which amino acid is at the carboxyl terminal end?
 e. Which bond is the peptide bond?

ANS S10.10. a. The amino terminal end is at the left. **b.** The amino terminal amino acid is glycine. **c.** The carboxyl end is at the right. **d.** The carboxyl amino acid is alanine. **e.** The peptide bond is the 4th horizontal bond (C–N) from the left.

S10.11. Summarize the studies in phage T4 that provided the first genetic evidence for a triplet code.
ANS S10.11. A triplet code was demonstrated genetically by the discovery that, in the *rII* gene of phage T4, certain three-base insertions or deletions were compatible with gene function.

S10.12. An alternating polymer AGAG is used as a messenger RNA in an *in vitro* protein-synthesizing system that does not need a start codon. What types of polypeptide chain are expected?
ANS S10.12. One expects a polypeptide containing the amino acids arginine (codon AGA) and glycine (codon GAG) in alternating order.

S11.13. In a segment of DNA that contains overlapping genes, would you expect the two proteins to terminate at the same site or have the same number of amino acids? Explain.
ANS S10.13. They would not be expected to terminate at the same site because no sequence of four bases contains two overlapping stop codons. Although they would not be expected to have the same number of amino acids, they might, according to where each protein starts and stops.

S10.14. What unique feature of the 5′ end of a eukaryotic mRNA distinguishes it from a prokaryotic mRNA?
ANS S10.14. The 5' end of an eukaryotic mRNA is modified by the addition of a "cap" that includes an unusual chemical linkage.

S10.15. Consider the two codons AGA and AGG, which code for the amino acid arginine. A, C, U, G, or I is allowed in the 5′ position of the anticodon.

 a. What is the minimum number of tRNAArg types needed to translate these codons?

 b. For each of the tRNAArg types in part (a), what is the anticodon?
ANS S10.15. a. Only one is needed; **b.** 5'-UCU-3'.

S10.16. A wildtype protein has glutamic acid (Glu) at amino acid position 56. A mutation is found in which glutamic acid is replaced with a different amino acid. Among the reverse mutations that restore protein function, some have threonine (Thr) at the position, some have isoleucine (Ile), and some have glutamic acid. Assuming that the original mutation and all the revertants result from single nucleotide substitutions, determine the wildtype codon for position 56, that of the original mutation, and those of the revertants.
ANS S10.16. The codons for Glu are GAR, where R means any purine. The codons for Thr are ACN, where N means any nucleotide, and those for Ile are AUU, AUC, and AUA. Hence, Glu → Thr or Glu → Ile requires at least two steps, including both of the first two codon positions. If the original mutation were in the second codon position, it would not be possible for a single additional mutation to yield either Ile or Thr. The original mutation must therefore be in the first position of the Glu codon, yielding AAR. Another mutation AAR → ACR yields Thr. However, to have a single additional mutation yield Ile, the third position must be A, for then AAA → AUA yields Ile. Hence, the original codon is GAA (Glu), the original mutation is AAA (Lys), which undergoes additional mutation to either ACA (Thr), AUA (Ile), or GAA (Glu).

S10.17. What amino acid sequence would correspond to the following mRNA sequence?
5′-GCAUCAGAAUGUAGGGAGACA-3′
(If you use the conventional single-letter abbreviations for the amino acids, shown below, you will find a secret.)

Ala—>A	Arg—>R	Asn—>N	Asp—>D	Cys—>C	Gln—>Q	Glu—>E
Gly —>G	His—>H	Ile—>I	Leu—>L	Lys—>K	Met—>M	Phe—>F
Pro—>P	Ser —>S	Thr—>T	Trp—>W	Tyr—>Y	Val—>V	

ANS S10.17. Ala-Ser-Glu-Cys-Arg-Glu-Thr, which, in the single-letter abbreviations, is: ASECRET.

S10.18. If the following double-stranded DNA molecule is transcribed from the bottom strand, does transcription start at the left or right end? What is the mRNA sequence? If translation starts at the first AUG, what is the polypeptide sequence?

5'-CGCTAGCATGGAGAACGACGAATTGAGCCCAGAAGCGTCATGAGG-3'

3'-GCCATCGTACCTCTTGCTGCTTAACTCGGGTCTTCGCAGTACTCC-5'

ANS S10.18. Transcription proceeds 3' to 5' along the template strand, so transcription begins at the left. The mRNA sequence is that same as that of the nontranscribed DNA strand except that U replaces T, namely, the mRNA is

5'-CGCUAGC AUG GAG AAC GAC GAA UUG AGC CCA GAA GCG UCA UGA GG-3'

When translated from the AUG (Met) codon at the left, the polypeptide sequence is: Met-Glu-Asn-Asp-Glu-Leu-Ser-Pro-Ala-Ser or, in the single-letter codes:

<p style="text-align:center">MENDELSPEAS</p>

S10.19. The Sanger DNA Sequencing Centre in Hinxton, Cambridgeshire, is named after Fred Sanger, who in 1980 shared a Nobel Prize in Chemistry for his contributions to the determination of base sequences in nucleic acids. (It was his second; the first was awarded in 1958 for his work on the determination of amino acid sequences in proteins.) In the entrance to the Sanger Centre is a stained glass window containing the following code:

<p style="text-align:center">TGATAATAGTTCAGGGAAGATTGATCCGCAAACGGTGAGCGTTAATGATAG</p>

 a. A tribute is revealed when this sequence is translated according to the standard genetic code using the single-letter abbreviations for the amino acids. What is it?

 b. The DNA sequence has not been found among the approximately 10 billion nucleotides thus far sequenced in a wide variaty of organisms. Suggest a reason why this might be the case.

ANS S10.19. a. Using a dot to denote a "stop" codon, the sequence decodes to

<p style="text-align:center">•••F R E D•S A N G E R•••</p>

b. It would be very unlikely in a short protein-coding sequence to find three *different* stop codons at each end and one in the middle. And the probability that a random sequence would match the one shown is $1/4^{17} = 5.8 \times 10^{-11}$. (Differences in G + C content will alter this calculation, but not enough to affect the conclusion that we would need to sequence about ten times as much DNA to have a reasonable chance of finding the Hinxton sequence in the DNA of a living organism.)

S10.20. The following table shows matching regions of the DNA, mRNA, tRNA, and amino acids encoded in a particular gene. The mRNA is shown with its 5' end at the left, and the tRNA anticodon is shown with its 3' end at the left. The vertical lines define the reading frame.

```
DNA double helix    - C - - - A T - C - - - - - - - - - A T - - G T
                    T - - - - - T - - - - - - - - - C A - - - - - -
mRNA                - - A A C - - - - - - - - - - - G C - - - G C - -
tRNA anticodon      - - - - - - - - - - G C A - - - - - - - - - - - -
Amino acids         |     |       |       |     | Trp |     |       |
|
```

a. Complete the nucleic acid sequences, assuming Watson-Crick pairing between each codon and anticodon.

b. Is the DNA strand transcribed the top or the bottom strand?

c. Translate the mRNA in all three reading frames.

d. Specify the nucleic acid strand(s) whose sequence could be used as a probe:

i. In a Southern blot hybridization, in which the hybridization is carried out against genomic DNA.

ii. In a Northern blot hybridization, in which the hybridization is carried out against mRNA.

ANS S10.20.

a. DNA double helix A C T T G A T A C G C A A C C C G T A T C G G T

 T G A A C T A T G C G T T G G G C A T A G C C A

mRNA U G A A C U A U G C G U U G G G C A U A G C C A

tRNA anticodon A C U U G A U A C G C A A C C C G U A U C G G U

b. The top strand is transcribed.

c. Reading frames UGA ACU AUG CGU UGG GCA UAG CCA

 * Thr Met Arg Trp Ala * Pro

 U GAA CUA UGC GUU GGG CAU AGC CA

 Glu Leu Cys Val Gly His Ser

 UG AAC UAU GCG UUG GGC AUA GCC A

 Asn Tyr Ala Leu Gly Ile Ala

d. In a Southern blot hybridization, double-stranded DNA is denatured and transferred to a filter, so the probe can be complementary to either strand. Thus, either strand of the DNA molecule may be used. (The mRNA could also be used, although this is not usually done in practice because RNA is easily degraded.) A Northern blot hybridization detects mRNA immobilized on a membrane. Thus, the probe should be a strand complementary to the mRNA and should therefore be the top strand of the DNA as written here.

S10.21. Part of a DNA molecule containing a single short intron has the sequence

5′-ATAGCTCGACGGAAGGTCGACCAAATTTCGCAGGAGCTCGCT-3′

3′-TATCGAGCTGCCTTCCAGCTGGTTTAAAGCGTCCTCGAGCGA-5′

and the corresponding polypeptide has the sequence

Ile—Ala—Arg—Arg—Lys—Leu—Ala

Find the intron.

ANS S10.21. The codons for the amino acid sequence are AU[Uor C or A]GCN[CGN or AGR][CGN or AGR]AAR[CUN or AAR]GCN, where the square brackets indicate one of the included possibilities. Considering the first two codons, the nontranscribed strand of DNA must include the sequence 5'-AT•GC•-3', where the dots are (almost) any nucleotide. This pattern is found only once, at the extreme left of the top strand, and so this must be the nontranscribed strand. The codons that match the amino acid sequence are AUA-GCT-CGA-CGG-AAG, but the match is only though these first five codons. The intron thus begins at nucleotide 16. Additional searching reveals that the amino acids Leu-Ala have the codons CTCGCT found at the 3' end of the nontranscribed strand. The intron sequence is therefore

5'-GTCGACCAAATTTCGCAGGAG-3'

3'-CAGCTGGTTTAAAGCGTCCTC-5'

S10.22. A double mutation produced by recombination contains two single nucleotide frameshifts separated by about 20 base pairs. The first is an insertion and the second a deletion. The amino acid sequence of the wildtype and that of the mutant polypeptide in this part of the protein are

Wildtype: Lys—Lys—Tyr—His—Gln—Trp—Thr—Cys—Asn

Mutant: Lys—Gln—Ile—Pro—Pro—Val—Asp—Met—Asn

What are the original and the double-mutant mRNA sequences? Which nucleotide in the wildtype sequence is the frameshift addition? Which nucleotide in the double-mutant sequence is the frameshift deletion? (In working this problem, it will be convenient to use the conventional symbols Y for unknown pyrimidine, R for unknown purine, N for unknown nucleotide, and H for A, C, T.)

ANS S10.22. Using Y for unknown pyrimidine, R for unknown purine, N for unknown nucleotide, and H for either A or C or T, the wildtype and double-mutant mRNA codons are:

```
Wildtype: 5'-AAR AAR UAY CAY CAR UGG ACN UGY AAY-3'
Mutant:   5'-AAR CAR AUH CCN CCN GUN GAY AUG AAY-3'
```

Comparing these sequence, it can be deduced that the first frameshift addition is the C at position 4 in the double-mutant gene. Realigning the sequences taking this into account, we obtain:

```
Wildtype: 5'-AAR  AAR UAY CAY CAR UGG ACN UGY AAY-3'
Mutant:   5'-AARC ARA UHC CNC CNG UNG AYA UGA AY-3'
```

Now it is also clear that the single nucleotide deletion in the wildtype gene must be the Y in the 4th nucleotide position from the 3' end. Realigning again to take this into account, we have

```
Wildtype: 5'-AAR  AAR UAY CAY CAR UGG ACN UGY AAY-3'
Mutant:   5'-AARC ARA UHC CNC CNG UNG AYA UG  AAY-3'
```

Hence, the complete sequences, as completely as they can be resolved from the data, are:

```
Wildtype: 5'-AAR AAA UAC CAC CAG UGG ACA UGY AAY-3'
Mutant:   5'-AAR CAA AUA CCA CCA GUG GAC AUG AAY-3'
```

S10.23. The following RNA sequence is a fragment derived from a polycistronic messenger RNA including two genes.

5'-CUUAUGGAAGUAAACCCGAGC-3'

This fragment is known to include the initiation codon of one protein and the termination codon of the other.

 a. Determine the first four amino acids of the protein whose initiation codon is in the fragment.

 b. Determine the last two amino acids of the protein whose translation terminates in the fragment.

 c. What is unusual about these genes?

 d. What would be the consequence of a frameshift mutation that deleted the G from the initiation codon?

ANS S10.23. a. The initiation codon is AUG and so the first four amino acids of the protein that is initiated in the fragment are Met-Glu-Val-Asn. **b.** The only possible termination codon is UAA which is preceded by codons for Trp-Ly. **c.** The coding sequences overlap and are in different reading frames. **d.** The initiation codon would be recreated by the adjacent G and so translation would begin; however, the deletion shifts the reading frame to that of the other gene, and so termination occurs at the UAA codon.

S10.24. A strain of *E. coli* carries a mutation that completely inactivates the enzyme encoded in the gene. Several revertants with partly or fully restored activity were selected and the amino acid

sequence of the enzyme determined. The only differences found were at position 10 in the polypeptide chain.

Revertant 1 had Thr.

Revertant 2 had Glu.

Revertant 3 had Met.

Revertant 4 had Arg.

Assume that the initial mutation itself, as well as each revertant, resulted from a single nucleotide substitution.

 a. What amino acid is present at position 10 in the mutant protein?

 b. What codon in the messenger RNA would encode this amino acid?

ANS S10.24. The only position in the genetic code that can, in one step, mutate to either Thr, Glu, Met, or Arg is the lysine codon AAG. Hence (a) Lys and (b) AAG.

S10.25. Make a sketch of a mature eukaryotic messenger RNA molecule hybridized to the transcribed strand of DNA of a gene that contains two introns, oriented with the promoter region of the DNA at the left. Clearly label the DNA and the mRNA. Use the following letters to label the location and/or boundaries of each segment. Some letters may be used several times, as appropriate; some, which are not applicable, may not be used at all.

 a. 5′ end

 b. 3′ end

 c. Promoter region

 d. Attenuator

 e. Intron

 f. Exon

 g. Polyadenylation signal

 h. Leader region

 i. Shine-Dalgarno sequence

 j. Translation start codon

 k. Translation stop codon

 l. 5′ cap

 m. Poly-A tail

ANS S10.25.

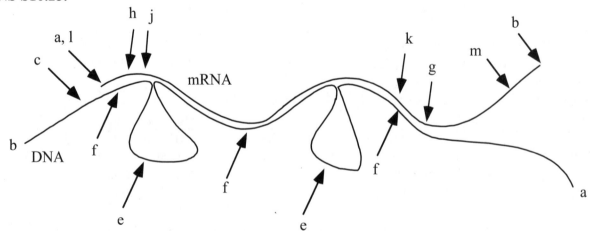

S10.26. Alternative splicing can introduce serious ambiguities into the classical complementation test for allelism. To see this for yourself, consider the primary transcript and its alternately spliced mRNAs, A and B, in the accompanying illustration, where both A and B are required for the normal phenotype.

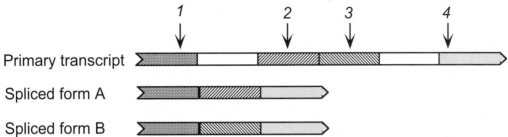

The numbers 1–4 indicate the positions of "knockout" missense mutations in the protein-coding regions of each of the exons.

 a. What complementation matrix would be expected from combinations of these mutations?

 b. What pattern is observed when the alleles are configured in a circle and noncomplementing pairs joined by a line?

 c. In what sense do all of the mutations fall into the same complementation group?

 d. In what sense do all of the mutations not fall into the same complementation group?

 e. Do you think that the complementation test has utility in this case? Explain why or why not.

ANS S10.26.

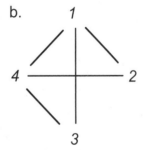

c. The mutations all fall into the same complementation group in the sense that there are some mutations (1 and 4) that fail to complement all others.

d. The mutations do not fall into the same complementation group because *2* and *3* do show complementation.

e. One could argue that the complementation test still has utility because it tells us that the mutations are all connected in some fashion; in particular, mutations in exons that are in common between A and B fail to complement. One could also argue that the complementation test fails in this case because the results are not completely unambigous.

Chapter 11: Molecular Mechanisms of Gene Regulation
Answers to Chapter-end problems

Fill-ins

1. positive regulation
2. operon
3. β-galactosidase
4. constitutive
5. aporepressor
6. enhancer
7. antisense RNA
8. kissing complex
9. RNA interference (RNAi)
10. epigenetic

Analysis and Applications

ANS 11.1. The enzymes are expressed constitutively because glucose is metabolized in virtually all cells. However, the levels of enzyme are regulated to prevent runaway synthesis or inadequate synthesis.

ANS 11.2. The hemoglobin mRNA has a very long lifetime before being degraded.

ANS 11.3. a. Transcription. **b.** RNA processing. **c.** Translation.

ANS 11.4. The repressor gene need not be near because the repressor is diffusible. The *trp* repressor is one example in which the repressor gene is located quite far from the structural genes.

ANS 11.5. There are two possibilities. The first is that there are two repressor-binding sites (one contained in the *Eco*RI–*Bam*HI fragment and the other in the *Hin*dIII–*Sac*I fragment), which act synergistically. Each alone allows about a 10-fold repression, but together the repression is 100 fold. This hypothesis could be tested by sequencing the restriction fragments; if each contains a repressor-binding site, a region of similar sequence should be found in each fragment. Another hypothesis is that the repressor-binding site is very large, extending across the entire *Eco*RI–*Sac*I region. In this case the *Bam*HI–*Hin*dIII fragment should also be part of the repressor-binding site, so deletion of this fragment should have a major effect, whereas, with two separate binding sites, the deletion would have at most a minor effect.

ANS 11.6. The mutant gene should bind more of the activator protein or bind it more efficiently. Therefore, the mutant gene should be induced with lower levels of the activator protein or expressed at higher levels than the wildtype gene, or both.

ANS 11.7. An inversion not only inverts the sequence but, because the DNA strands in a duplex are antiparallel, exchanges the strands. The inversion of a promoter sequence would have a profound effect because the mutant promoter is in the wrong strand pointing in the wrong direction. One

would expect little or no effect of the inversion of an enhancer element, because enhancers are targets for DNA binding proteins irrespective of orientation in the DNA.

ANS 11.8. a. β-galactosidase (*lacZ* product), lactose permease (*lacY* product), and the transacetylase (*lacA* product). **b.** The promoter region becomes inaccessible to RNA polymerase. **c.** Repressor synthesis is constitutive.

ANS 11.9. At 37 °C, both *lacZ⁻* and *lacY⁻* are phenotyipcally Lac⁻; at 30 °C, the *lacY⁻* strain is Lac⁺ and the *lacZ⁻* strains is Lac⁻.

ANS 11.10. Inducers combine with repressors and prevent them from binding with the operator regions of the respective operons.

ANS 11.11. The cAMP concentration is low in the presence of glucose. Both types of mutation are phenotypically Lac⁻. The cAMP-CRP binding does not interfere with repressor binding because the DNA binding sites are distinct.

ANS 11.12. No; there is often a polar effect in which the relative amount of each protein synthesized decreases toward the 3' end of the mRNA.

ANS 11.13. With a repressor, the inducer is usually an early (often the first) substrate in the pathway, and the repressor is inactivated by combining with the inducer. With an aporepressor, the effector molecule is usually the product of the pathway, and the aporepressor is activated by the binding.

ANS 11.14. a. A missense mutation in A could be a missense mutation in B, a synonymous mutation in B (not changing the amino acid sequence) or a nonsense mutation. **b.** A deletion in one reading frame is also a deletion in the other. **c.** A frameshift mutation in one reading frame is also a frameshift mutation in the other.

ANS 11.15. The attenuator is not a binding site for any protein, and RNA synthesis does not begin at an attenuator. An attenuator is strictly a potential termination site for transcription.

ANS 11.16. a. When proline is at a sufficiently low level that the aporepressor is no longer bound and transcription is derepressed. **b.** When the level of charged proline tRNA is high enough that translation proceeds through the leader sequence. **c.** When the level of charged proline tRNA is low enough the translation stalls at the proline codons in the leader sequence.

ANS 11.17. a. When the level of histidine is low enough that the *his* aporepressor is no longer bound, derepressing transcription. **b.** When the level of charged tryptophan tRNA is high enough that translation of the leader polypeptide can take place. **c.** When the level of charged tryptophan tRNA is so low that translation stalls at the *trp* codons in the leader sequence.

ANS 11.18. It would eliminate attenuation. The tryptophan operon would be fully transcribed when tryptophan is not present in the growth medium, with no fine tuning of the level of transcription regulated through the availability of charged tryptophan tRNA.

ANS 11.19. Amino acids that normally have among the lowest levels of charged tRNA in the cell should have few codons in the leader mRNA, otherwise stalling would take place even at the normal low levels; whereas amino acids that have among the highest levels of charged tRNA in the cell should include multiple codons in the leader mRNA, otherwise stalling might not take place often enough.

ANS 11.20. The α cell would be unable to switch to the **a** mating type.

ANS 11.21. The **a**1 protein functions only in combination with the α2 protein in diploids; hence, the *MAT*a' haploid cell would appear normal. However, the diploid *MAT*a'/*MAT*α has the phenotype of an α haploid. The reason is that the genotype lacks an active **a**1–α2 complex to repress the haploid-specific genes as well as repressing α1, and the α1 gene product activates the α-specific genes.

ANS 11.22. The mutant diploid *MAT*a/*MAT*α has the phenotype of an α haploid. As in Problem 11-15, the genotype lacks an active **a**1–α2 complex to repress the haploid-specific genes as well as α1, and the α1 gene product activates the α-specific genes.

ANS 11.23. In the absence of lactose or glucose, two proteins are bound––the *lac* repressor and CRP-cAMP. In the presence of glucose, only the repressor is bound.

ANS 11.24. a. The strain is constitutive and has either the genotype *lacI*$^-$ or *lacO*c. **b.** The second mutant must be *lacZ*$^-$ because no β-galactosidase is made and, because permease synthesis is induced by lactose, the mutant must have a normal repressor-operator system. Therefore, the genotype is *lacI*$^+$ *lacO*$^+$ *lacZ*$^-$ *lacY*$^+$. **c.** Because the partial diploid is regulated, the operator in the operon with a functional *lacZ* gene must be wildtype. Hence, the mutant in part (a) must be *lacI*$^-$.

ANS 11.25. The *lac* genes are transferred by the Hfr cell and enter the recipient. No repressor is present in the recipient initially, and so *lac* mRNA is made. However, the *lacI* gene is also transferred to the recipient, and soon afterward the repressor is made and *lac* transcription stops.

ANS 11.26. Amino acids with codons one step away from the nonsense codon, because their tRNA genes are the most likely to mutate to nonsense suppressors. For UGA, these are UGC (Cys), UGU (Cys), UGG (Trp), UUA (Leu), UCA (Ser), AGA (Arg), CGA (Arg), and GGA (Gly).

ANS 11.27. The mutant clearly lacks a general system that regulates sugar metabolism, and the most likely possibility is the cAMP-dependent regulatory system. Several mutations can prevent activity of this system. For example, the mutant could make either a defective CRP protein (which either fails to bind to the promoter or is unresponsive to cAMP) or have an inactive adenyl cyclase gene and be unable to synthesize cAMP.

ANS 11.28. a. Species A, all sites methylated in egg DNA, sites 1 and 3 methylated in sperm DNA; species B, sites 2 and 3 methylated in both egg DNA and sperm DNA; species C, no sites methylated in egg DNA, sites 1 and 2 methylated in sperm DNA. **b.** Species A and C show differential methylation in the gamates. **c.** Species A shows greater methylation in egg DNA.

ANS 11.29. Wildtype *lac* mRNA, or that containing either of the point mutations, should yield a band at 5 kb; mRNA containing *lacZ** will be shorter by 2 kb, and that containing *lacY** shorter by 0.5 kb. The expected pattern of bands is shown in the accompanying diagram.

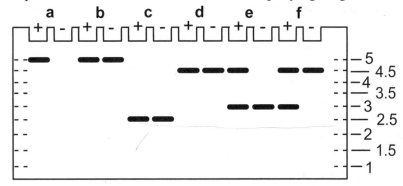

ANS 11.30. The *lacZ⁻* and *lacY⁻* mutant alleles still produce normal-length polypeptide chains, whereas the deletions are said to produce no polypeptide product. Hence the expected pattern of bands in the Western blot are as shown here.

Challenge Problems

ANS 11.31. a. No enzyme synthesis; the mutation is *cis*-dominant because lack of RNA polymerase binding to the promoter prevents transcription of the adjacent genes. **b.** Enzymes synthesized; this one is *cis*-dominant because failure to bind the repressor cannot prevent constitutive transcription of the adjacent genes. **c.** Enzymes synthesized; this mutation is recessive because the defective repressor can be complemented by a wildtype repressor in the same cell. **d.** Enzymes synthesized; the mutation is recessive because the mutant repressor can be complemented by a wildtype repressor in the same cell. **e.** No enzyme synthesis; this mutation is dominant because the repressor is always activated and all *his* transcription is prevented.

ANS 11.32. The wildtype mRNA reads AA**A** CAC CAC CAU CAU CAC CAU CAU CCU GAC, which codes for Lys–His–His–His–His–His–His–His–Pro–Asp. The mutant mRNA reads AA**A** ACA CCA CCA UCA UCA CCA UCA UCC UGA C, which codes for Lys–Thr–Pro–Pro–Ser–Ser–Pro–Ser–Ser (the UGA is a normal stop codon). The expected phenotype of the mutant is His⁻ because of lack of attenuation by low levels of histidine. That is, translation of the attenuator occurs

(preventing efficient transcription of the operon) even when the level of histidine within the cell is very low. However, low levels of proline or serine will prevent translation of the attenuator and allow transcription of the histidine operon.

ANS 11.33. One hypothesis is that the *Eco*RI fragment contains a tissue-specific enhancer that promotes transcription in photoreceptor cells. The hypothesis could be tested by inserting the *Eco*RI fragment near other genes to test for enhanced expression in photoreceptor cells.

Supplemental problems with answers

S11.1. Define the following terms:
 a. Enhancer
 b. Attenuator
 c. *Cis*-dominant mutation
 d. Autoregulation
 e. Combinatorial control
 f. Polycistronic mRNA
 g. Transcriptional activation by recruitment

ANS S11.1. a. An enhancer is a DNA sequence in eukaryotes and their viruses that increases the rate of transcription of nearby genes; the main features of enhancers are that they do not need to be immediately adjacent to the affected gene and that their activity is independent of orientation with respect to the gene. **b.** An attenuator, found only in prokaryotes, is a regulatory base sequence near the beginning of an mRNA molecule at which transcription can be terminated by translation of the nascent message; when present, the attenuator precedes the main coding sequence. **c.** A *cis*-dominant mutation affects the expression of only those genes that are located on the same DNA molecule as the mutation does itself. **d.** Autoregulation of gene expression means regulation of a gene by its own gene product. **e.** Combinatorial control is a strategy of gene regulation in which a relatively small number of regulatory elements are used in various combinations to control the expression of a much larger number of genes. **f.** A polycistronic mRNA molecule is one from which more than one polypeptides is translated. **g.** A model of transcriptional activation in which a transcriptional activator, upon binding to its DNA target sequence, physical interacts with one or more components of the RNA polymerase holoenzyme and recruits (attracts) the transcription complex to the promoter region of the gene.

S11.2. How do gene and genome organizations differ in eukaryotes and prokaryotes?
ANS S11.2. Important differences include: Genes in eukaryotes are split into exons and introns and the primary transcript must be processed before translation. Prokaryotic genomes have few repeated DNA sequences, whereas a large portion of eukaryotic genome consists of repeats with different levels of reiteration. DNA in eukaryotes is bound to histones and to various kinds of nonhistone chromosomal proteins that are not found in prokaryotes. In contrast to prokaryotes, a large fraction of the eukaryotic genome is not transcribed, and a substantial part of each transcript containing introns is not translated. Transcription and translation in prokaryotes are coupled; in eukaryotes, the primary transcript is produced in the nucleus and the processed mRNA transported into cytoplasm where translation takes place. Polycistronic mRNA is common in prokaryotes but not in eukaryotes.

S11.3. At what different levels can gene expression be regulated?

ANS S11.3. Gene expression can be regulated at the levels of DNA structure, transcription, RNA processing, translation, and mRNA stability. There are also various mechanisms of post-translational regulation (protein processing, stability, and so forth).

S11.4. Give some examples of gene regulation by alterations in the DNA.
ANS S11.4. Examples of this kind of regulation include: gene amplification (for example, of rRNA in the oocyte of *Xenopus*), gene rearrangement (for example, in mating-type interconversion in *S. cerevisae*), DNA splicing (for example, in the immunoglobulin genes in mammals), and DNA methylation (most notably in the coding regions upstream of many eukaryotic genes).

S11.5. What phenotype would be expected in mutant of *Bacillus subtilis* with the deletion of a gene, which encodes Trap protein?
ANS S11.5. The expected phenotype would be Trp^+ because in the absence of TRAP multimers the complete *trp* operon is transcribed independently of the levels of tryptophan.

S11.6. Why is the *lac* operon of *E. coli* not inducible in the presence of glucose?
ANS S11.6. In the presence of glucose, bacterial cells have very low levels of cAMP. Without cAMP, the binding of the CRP protein cannot take place, transcription cannot be activated, and no *lac* proteins are made. Lack of induction is true even if lactose is present. The system assures that primary carbon sources are exhausted before the cell expends energy for the synthesis of new enzymes to utilize secondary carbon sources.

S11.7. In eukaryotic organisms, the amounts of some proteins found in the cell are known to vary substantially with environmental conditions, whereas the amount of mRNA for these same proteins remains relatively constant. What mechanisms of regulation might be responsible for this phenomenon?
ANS S11.7. The rate of translation, as well as stability of polypeptide chains, might control the abundance of a protein without changing the amount of its mRNA.

S11.8. Two genotypes of *E. coli* are grown and assayed for levels of the enzymes of the *lac* operon. Using the information provided here for these two genotypes, predict the enzyme levels for the other genotypes listed in **a.** through **d.** (The levels of activity are expressed in arbitrary units relative to those observed under the induced conditions.)

Genotype	Uninduced level		Induced level	
	Z	Y	Z	Y
$I^- O Z^- Y^-$	0.1	0.1	100	100
$I^- O^c Z^- Y^-$	25	25	100	100

a. $I^- O Z^- Y^-$

b. F' $I^- O Z^- Y^- / I^- O Z^- Y^-$

c. F' $I^- O Z^- Y^- / I^- O^c Z^- Y^-$

d. F' $I^- O Z^- Y^- / I^- O^c Z^- Y^-$

127

ANS S11.8. The predicted levels are shown in the table.

	Uninduced level		Induced level	
	Z	Y	Z	Y
Genotype				
a.	100	100	100	100
b.	0.1	0.1	100	100
c.	25	25	100	100
d.	25	25	100	100

S11.9. Imagine a bacterial species in which the methionine operon is regulated only by an attenuator and there is no repressor. In its mode of operation, the methionine attenuator is exactly analogous to the *trp* attenuator of *E. coli*. The relevant portion of the attenuator sequence is

5′ -AAA<u>A</u>TGATGATGATGATGATGATGGACGAT-3′

The translation start site is located upstream from this sequence, and the AUG codons in the region

shown cannot be used for translation initiation. What phenotype (constitutive, wildtype, or *met⁻*) would you expect of each of the following types of mutations? Explain your reasoning.

 a. The boldface A is deleted.

 b. Both the boldface and the underlined A are deleted.

 c. The first three As in the sequence are deleted.

ANS S11.9. a. Constitutive. Deletion of **A** causes a frameshift that switches the reading frame from ATG ATG, and so forth, to TGA TGA, and so forth. TGA is a stop codon, therefore the attenuator

will not be translated through and transcription will go unabated. **b.** *met⁻*. Deletion of the two A's changes the reading frame from ATG ATG, and so forth, to GAT GAT, and so forth. GAT is an Asp codon. Therefore, translation will proceed through even when the concentration of methionine is very low, and transcription will terminate prematurely. **c.** Wildtype. A deletion of all three A's does not change the reading frame.

S11.10. How many proteins are bound to the *trp* operon when

 a. Tryptophan and glucose are present?

 b. Tryptophan and glucose are absent?

 c. Tryptophan is present and glucose is absent?

ANS S11.10. Glucose is irrelevant because it does not participate in regulation of the *trp* operon. **a.** 1;

b. 0; **c.** 1.

S11.11. Why are mutations of the *lac* operator often called *cis*-dominant? Why are some constitutive mutations of the *lac* repressor (*lacI*) called *trans*-recessive? Can you think of a way in which a noninducible mutation in the *lacI* gene might be *trans*-dominant?

ANS S11.11. Mutations of operators are called *cis*-dominant because, to display their effect, they must be present in the same DNA molecule as the gene they control (that is, the regulatory sequence and the gene must be in a *cis* configuration). Because the phenotypic effects are observed in merodiploids carrying a normal operator on the other genetic element (for example, in an F′*lac* plasmid) the mutations are said to be *cis*-dominant. Constitutive mutations in *lacI* are called trans-

recessive because their effect is overridden by a copy of *lacI⁺* anywhere in the genome (that is, in *trans* configuration relative to the mutant allele). Finally, one can imagine mutations of *lacI* that bind to the operator in preference to the inducer. Such a mutant protein would repress all *lac* operons even

if normal repressor molecules were present. Such mutations would therefore be dominant to the normal repressor. Mutants of this type are known; they are called "superrepressor" mutants, designated *lacI*[S].

S11.12. An *E. coli* mutant strain synthesizes β-galactosidase whether or not the inducer is present. What genetic defect(s) might be responsible for this phenotype?

ANS S11.12. A constitutive phenotype can be the result of either a *lacI*[-] or a *lacO*[C] mutations.

S11.13. Temperature-sensitive mutations in the *lacI* gene of *E. coli* render the repressor nonfunctional (unable to bind the operator) at 42°C but leave it fully functional at 30°C. Under which of the following conditions would β-galactosidase be produced?
 a. In the presence of lactose at 30°C
 b. In the presence of lactose at 42°C
 c. In the absence of lactose at 30°C
 d. In the absence of lactose at 42°C

ANS S11.13. a. Yes; the repressor is functional, and the presence of lactose activates transcription of the *lac* genes. **b.** and **d.** Yes; at 42 °C, the repressor cannot bind the operator, which means that the *lac* operon is transcribed whether or not the inducer is present. **c.** No; at this temperature, the repressor functions normally and, since lactose is absent, the *lac* operon is repressed.

S11.14. Many metabolic pathways are regulated by so-called feedback inhibition, in which the first enzyme in the pathway becomes inhibited by interacting with the final product of the entire pathway if the final product is present in a sufficient amount. Explain why a metabolic pathway should evolve in such a way that the first enzyme in the pathway is inhibited rather than the last enzyme in the pathway.

ANS S11.14. Inhibition of the last enzyme would still permit accumulation of useless (and maybe even harmful) intermediates. Inhibition of the first enzyme would eliminate the production of these intermediates.

S11.15. Among cells of a *lacI*[+] *lacO*[+] *lacZ*[+] *lacY*[+] strain of *E. coli*, a mutation was found in which the *lacY* gene underwent a precise inversion without any change in the coding region. However, the strain was found to be defective in the production of the permease. Why?

ANS S11.15. The polycistronic mRNA contains a transcript of a *lacY* gene from the wrong DNA strand of the operon.

S11.16. A λ phage mutant is isolated that is unable to produce cro repressor. What would be the outcome if *cro*[-] phage infects *E. coli,*?

ANS S11.16. In the absence of cro protein, cI determines the outcome of the infection. The result is the formation of a λ lysogen.

S11.17. What would be the outcome, if λ lysogen, mentioned in the previous problem, acquired a plasmid carrying multiple copies of a wildtype gene for cro protein?

ANS S11.17. cro protein will be overproduced due to the multiple copies of a gene resulting in lysis and production of phage particles.

S11.18. Cristina, a young immunologist, told her friend Jorge, who studied molecular biology, that there are 10^8 different antibodies produced by human B cells. To her astonishment, Jorge strongly disagreed, saying that there are not enough genes in the human genome to code for such a great variety of immunoglobulins. Who is right? Is there any way to reconcile their views?

ANS S11.18. There is no need for them to argue; both statements are true. Numerous sequences exist in the mammalian genome (including the human genome) that can serve as alternatives for various regions in the final coding sequence for a particular antibody. A random combination of the alternatives is created by DNA cutting and rejoining, producing a great variety of possible genes that enables the immune system to recognize and attack most bacteria and viruses. For instance, in mice, the light chains are formed by combinations of 250 V and 4 J regions, yielding $250 \times 4 = 1000$ possible chains. For the heavy chains, there are approximately 250 V, 10 D, and 4 J regions, producing $250 \times 10 \times 4 = 10,000$ possible combinations. Because any light chain can combine with any heavy chain, there are at least $1000 \times 10,000 = 10^7$ possible types of antibodies. There are two additional sources of antibody variability: the V regions are susceptible to a high rate of somatic mutation in B cells, and there are different ways to splice DNA at the V-J (or V-D-J) junctions. Thus, a relatively small number of sequences (about 500) can produce all the variation in immunoglobulins.

S11.19. You are engaged in the study of a gene, the transcription of which is activated in a particular tissue by a steroid hormone. From cultured cells isolated from this tissue, you are able to isolate mutant cells that no longer respond to the hormone. What are some possible explanations?

ANS S11.19. Three likely possibilities are: (1) a mutation in the receptor gene, so that the receptor is absent or can no longer bind to the hormone; (2) a mutation in, or deletion of, a DNA sequence that specifically binds to the receptor-hormone complex; (3) a mutation that makes it more difficult for the hormone to penetrate the cell.

S11.20. A laboratory strain of *E. coli* produces β-galactosidase constitutively and permease inducibly, despite the fact that these two proteins are co-regulated in the *lac* operon in wildtype strains. What is the genotype of the *lac* operon in this strain?

ANS S11.20. More then likely the strain carries an F' *lac* of some type. The genotype *lacI*$^+$ *lacO*c *lacZ*$^+$ *lacY*$^-$ / *lacI*$^+$ *lacO*$^+$ *lacZ*$^-$ *lacY*$^+$ would have the phenotype described.

Chapter 12: Genomics, Proteomics, and Transgenics
Answers to Chapter-end problems

Fill-ins

1. plasmid
2. sticky ends
3. reverse transcriptase PCR (RT-PCR)
4. positional cloning
5. contig
6. DNA microarray
7. two-hybrid analysis
8. gene targeting
9. transgenic organism
10. T DNA

Analysis and Applications

ANS 12.1. 16 possible sites, of which 4 are palindromes.

ANS 12.2. 64 possible sites; the chance that two different sites have compatible ends is 1/4, because the 5' overhang of one must be a Watson-Crick pairing partner with the 5' overhang of the other.

ANS 12.3. The probability that GGCCN is an *Eac*I site is $(1/2)(1/4) = 1/8$ and the probability that NGGCC is an *Eac*I site is $(1/4)(1/2) = 1/8$. The probability of exactly one *Eac*I site is therefore $(1/8)(7/8) + (7/8)(1/8) = 7/32$, and the probability of two *Eac*I sites is $(1/8)^2 = 1/64$.

ANS 12.4. The "R" of one site must be complementary to the "Y" of the other site, so the probability is 1/2.

ANS 12.5. No. Each of the fragments can be either in the original or the reverse orientation, yielding 8 possibilities, of which only 2 reconstitute the original plasmid (those with all three fragments in the original orientation or all three in the reverse orientation).

ANS 12.6.

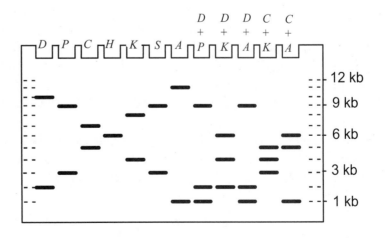

ANS 12.7. **a.** E >> C. **b.** E << C. **c.** E = C. **d.** E > G. **e.** E < C.

ANS 12.8. Genes encoding proteins that are used in the synthesis of amino acids, nucleosides and nucleotides, vitamins, and other small molecules not present in minimal medium that are present in complete medium.

ANS 12.9. The DNA content per average band equals about $1.2 \times 10^8/5000 = 24$ kb, per average lettered subdivision equals approximately $1.2 \times 10^8/600 = 200$ kb, and per average numbered section equals about $1.2 \times 10^8/100 = 1.2$ Mb. A YAC with a 200-kb insert contains the DNA equivalent to about 8 salivary bands, 1 lettered subdivisions, and 0.17 numbered sections. An 80-kb P1 clone contains the DNA equivalent of about 3 salivary bands, 0.4 lettered subdivisions, and 0.07 numbered sections.

ANS 12.10. The ends may be blunt or they may be cohesive (sticky) with either a 3' overhang or a 5' overhang.

ANS 12.11. All restriction fragments have the same ends because the restriction sites are all the same and they are cleaved in the same places. Opposite ends of the same fragment must also be identical because restriction sites are palindromes.

ANS 12.12. No. The complement of 5'-GGCC-3' is 3'-CCGG-5'.

ANS 12.13. The insertion disrupts the gene, and sensitivity to the antibiotic shows that the vector has an inserted DNA sequence. The second antibiotic-resistance gene is needed to select transformants.

ANS 12.14. a. Probability of a *Taq*I site is $1/6 \times 1/3 \times 1/3 \times 1/6 = 1/324$, and so *Taq*I cleavage is expected every 324 base pairs; probability of a *Mae*III site is $1/3 \times 1/6 \times 1 \times 1/6 \times 1/3 = 1/324$, and so *Mae*III cleavage is expected every 324 base pairs. **b.** Answers are the same as in part (a) because, for both *Taq*I and *Mae*III sites, the number of A + T = the number of G + C.

ANS 12.15. Comparison of the genomic and cDNA sequences tells you where the introns are in the genomic sequence. The genomic sequence contains the introns and the cDNA does not.

ANS 12.16. Bacterial cells do not normally recognize eukaryotic promoters, and if transcription does occur, the transcript will usually contain introns that the bacterial cell cannot remove. If these problems are overcome, the protein may still not be produced because the mRNA lacks a bacterial ribosome-binding site, or because the protein might require posttranslational processing, or because the protein might be unstable in bacterial cells and subject to degradation.

ANS 12.17. You must use cDNA under suitable promoter that functions in prokaryotic system. Eukaryotic genomic DNA includes regulatory elements that will not work in bacteria and introns that cannot be spliced out of RNA in prokaryotic cells.

ANS 12.18. The finding is that the 3.6-kb and 5.3-kb fragments in the free phage are joined to form an 8.9 kb fragment in the intracellular form. This suggests that the 3.6-kb and 5.3-kb fragments are terminal fragments of a linear molecule and that the intracellular form is circular.

ANS 12.19. The ends are clearly inverted repeats, suggesting that the inserted sequence is a transposable element.

ANS 12.20. A base substitution may destroy a restriction site and prevent two potential fragments from being separated or a deletion may eliminate a restriction site.

ANS 12.21. The gene probably contains an *Eco*RI site that disrupts the gene in the process of cloning; the gene does not contain a *Hin*dIII site.

ANS 12.22. a. The *tet-r* gene is not cleaved with *Bgl*I, and so addition of tetracycline to the medium requires that the colonies be tetracycline resistant (Tet-r) and hence contain the plasmid. **b.** Cells with the phenotypes Tet-r Kan-r or Tet-r Kan-s will form colonies. **c.** Colonies with the phenotype Tet-r Kan-s contain inserts within the cleaved *kan* gene.

ANS 12.23. The multiple bands of the same size in many of the lanes implies that the restriction sites are very symmetrically disposed, as illustrated here.

ANS 12.24. Each segment in the restriction map shown here is 1 kb.

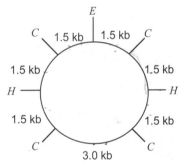

ANS 12.25. An insertion of two bases is generated within the codon, resulting in a frameshift. Therefore, all colonies should be Lac⁻.

ANS 12.26. The *Pst*I fragment can be inserted in two possible orientations, only one of which will place the promoter in the correct orientation to allow transcription of the coding sequence. The two orientations are expected in equal proportions, so if only one clone is studied, it has a 50 percent chance of having the fragment inserted in the wrong orientation.

ANS 12.27. Yes, it does. Note that the *Pst*I fragment containing the coding sequence is inverted with respect to the promoter that flanks the MCS.

ANS 12.28. The restriction map is shown here. This type of clone would be expected to transcribe the gene of interest, because the *Pst*I fragment containing the coding sequence is in the correct orientation with respect to the promoter flanking the MCS.

ANS 12.29. Use *Dde*I and *Sac*I. The resulting restriction map is as shown here. (Note that the small *Dde*I–*Sac*I restriction fragment is deleted from the MCS by the double digestion.)

ANS 12.30. The restriction map is shown in the adjoining figure.

Rest of plasmid between
*Pst*I and *Sal*I = 2.45 kb.

Challenge Problems

ANS 12.31.

Red (Cy5)	Wildtype *α* cells	Wildtype *α* cells	Wildtype *a* cells	*ΔMAT a1* cells	*ΔMAT α1* cells	*ΔMAT(α2α1)* *ΔMAT a1*
Green (Cy3)	Wildtype *a* cells	Wildtype *a/α* cells	Wildtype *a/α* cells	Wildtype *a* cells	Wildtype *α* cells	Wildtype *a* cells
MAT α1	Red	Red	None	None	Green	None
MAT α2	Red	Yellow	Green	None	Yellow	None
MAT a1	Green	Green	Yellow	Green	None	Green
αsg	Red	Red	None	None	Green	None
asg	Green	None	Red	Yellow	None	Yellow
hsg	Yellow	Red	Red	Yellow	Yellow	Yellow

ANS 12.32. a. For plasmid A use *Sac*I–*Xho*II. **b.** For plasmid B use *Sac*I–*Dde*I. **c.** The resulting restriction maps are

From plasmid A

From plasmid B

ANS 12.33. The plasmids could be distinguished in a number of ways. For example, recombinant plasmids of type A contain only one *Hin*dIII site whereas those of type B contain two; also, the A types would yield a small *Dde*I–*Xho*II fragment whereas the B types would yield a larger *Dde*I–*Xho*II fragment, and so forth.

Supplemental problems with answers

S12.1. Define the following terms:
 a. Vector
 b. Restriction site
 c. Palindrome
 d. Cohesive end
 e. Blunt end
 f. Complementary DNA
 g. Insertional inactivation
 h. Colony hybridization assay
 i. Transgenic organism

ANS S12.1. a. A vector is a DNA molecule, capable of replication, into which a DNA segment can be inserted by recombinant DNA techniques. **b.** A restriction site is the base sequence at which a particular restriction endonuclease cleaves a double-stranded DNA molecule. **c.** A palindrome is a segment of double-stranded DNA in which the sequence of bases is identical in both strands, taking the polarity into account. **d.** A cohesive end (or sticky end) is a single-stranded region at the ends of a double-stranded DNA molecule that can adhere to a complementary single-stranded sequence at the other end or in another molecule. **e.** A blunt end of a double-stranded DNA molecule is one in which all terminal bases are paired. **f.** Complementary DNA is a double-stranded DNA molecule made by copying RNA with reverse transcriptase. **g.** Insertional inactivation is the inactivation of a gene by interruption of its coding sequence; this method is used in genetic engineering to detect an insertion of a foreign DNA into a vector. **h.** The colony hybridization assay is a technique for identifying colonies containing a particular cloned gene; many colonies are transferred to a filter, lysed, and exposed to a labeled DNA or RNA complementary to the DNA sequence of interest. **i.** A transgenic organism is one in which a novel DNA sequence has been incorporated into the germline.

S12.2. What are some of the principal practical applications of genetic engineering?

ANS S12.2. At the present time, the main uses of recombinant DNA technology are: (1) the creation of cells capable of synthesizing economically important molecules (insulin, blood-clotting factors, and so forth); (2) the manipulation of the genotype of different organisms of commercial value (creation of plants resistant to an herbicide or an insect pest); (3) prenatal detection of disease (cystic fibrosis, sickle cell anemia, and many others); (4) research in molecular biology (for instance, in the study of eukaryotic gene regulation); (5) gene therapy (though not yet realized in practice).

S12.3. Reverse transcriptase, like most enzymes that make DNA, requires a primer. Explain why, when cDNA is to be made for the purpose of cloning a eukaryotic gene, a convenient primer is a short sequence of poly(dT)? Why does this method not work with a prokaryotic messenger RNA?

ANS S12.3. A processed eukaryotic mRNA generally includes a poly-A tail at the 3' end. Poly(dT) will anneal to this tail and prime DNA synthesis. The method does not work with a prokaryotic mRNA because there is no poly-A tail.

S12.4. A DNA molecule has 23 occurrences of the sequence 5'-AATT-3' along one strand. How many times does the same sequence occur along the other strand?

ANS S12.4. It also occurs 23 times in the other strand, because the sequence is a palindrome.

S12.5. After doing a restriction digest with the enzyme *Sse*I, which has the recognition site 5'-CCTGCA/GG-3' (the slash indicates the position of the cleavage), you wish to separate the fragments in an agarose gel. In order to choose the proper concentration of agarose, you need to know the expected size of the fragments. Assuming equivalent amounts of each of the four nucleotides in the target DNA, what average-size fragment would you expect?

ANS S12.5. Assuming a random distribution of bases and an equal content of each of the four nucleotide bases, a specific DNA sequence of n nucleotides is expected to occur, on average, every 4^n nucleotides. Hence, a recognition site for an 8-cutter, such as *Sse*I, would be expected every $4^8 = 65536$ bases, yielding fragments averaging approximately 65.5 kb in length. To separate such long fragments efficiently you would need to employ either conventional gel electrophoresis using an extremely low agarose concentration ($\leq 0.3\%$, which is very inconvenient to work with) or to separate the fragments with pulse field gel electrophoresis.

S12.6. How many clones are needed to establish a library of DNA from a species of monkey with a diploid genome size of 6×10^9 base pairs if (1) fragments whose sizes average 2×10^4 base pairs are used, and (2) one wishes 99 percent of the genomic sequences to be in the library? (*Hint*: If the genome is cloned at random with x-fold coverage, the probability that a particular sequence will be missing is e^{-x}.)

ANS S12.6. The hint says that, if the genome were represented x times in the library, the probability that a particular sequence would be missing is e^{-x}, which we want to equal 0.01. Hence $x = 4.6$. Because one haploid representation of the genome equals $(6 \times 10^9)/2 = 3 \times 10^9$ base pairs, and the average insert size is 2×10^4 base pairs, one requires $[(3 \times 10^9)/(2 \times 10^4)] \times 4.6 = 6.9 \times 10^5$ clones.

S12.7. The yeast *Saccharomyces cerevisiae* has 16 chromosomes. All of them can be separated by pulse field gel electrophoresis. Strains with the following chromosome rearrangements were examined by pulse field electrophoresis along with DNA from a wildtype control:

a. A reciprocal translocation in which about one-third of chromosome IV (the largest chromosome) was exchanged with about one-third of chromosome I (the smallest chromosome).

b. An insertional translocation in which two-thirds of one chromosome was inserted into another chromosome.

c. A pericentric inversion in chromosome IV.

d. A paracentric inversion in chromosome IV.

What band pattern would you expect to see in each case?

ANS S12.7. a. The largest and the smallest bands would disappear and be replaced by two new bands of intermediate size; there is also the possibility that one or both of the new chromosomes would be similar in size to a wildtype chromosome and hence not result in a novel band; **b.** As compared with the wildtype pattern, one band would be smaller and one would be larger than expected; **c.** 16 bands identical to wildtype; **d.** 16 bands identical to wildtype.

S12.8. As a laboratory exercise, a friend is required to express a cloned *Drosophila* gene in bacteria to obtain large amounts of the recombinant protein. She is given a recombinant phage containing a 12-kb fragment of *Drosophila* genomic DNA, which, when introduced into the germline of a mutant fly, is able to rescue the mutant phenotype. Hence, the 12-kb fragment contains the entire gene. The fragment also hybridizes to a 4.7-kb RNA on Northern blots. (A Northern blot is one in which RNA is separated by electrophoresis and the bands are transferred to a filter and probed with a labeled complementary sequence). The protein encoded by the gene is approximately 110 amino acids in length and can be isolated by standard methods. Your friend excises the 12-kb fragment out of the phage and inserts it into a bacterial expression vector (a plasmid designed to allow transcription of inserts). Although molecular analysis indicates that the DNA was inserted correctly and that the insert is being transcribed, she is unable to isolate any of the gene product. She turns to you for advice. What explanations would you suggest and what would you recommend she do to obtain the protein?

ANS S12.8. There are several possible reasons for the failure. First, the genomic clone is likely to contain one or more introns that interrupt the coding sequence and cannot be removed properly in bacteria. Second, although the segment appears to contain all the sequences necessary for protein expression in the fly, eukaryotic promoter elements are not functional in bacteria, and the 330-bp coding sequence is not likely to be present so near the end of the insert to be fused in a proper orientation to the bacterial promoter elements and to preserve the correct open reading frame. It is most advisable to use a cDNA (DNA complementary to mRNA) instead of the genomic clone and to make sure that no frameshifts and in-frame stop codons occur between the ribosome-binding sequence and the translation start site in the expression vector.

S12.9. Aliquots of a 7.8-kilobase (kb) linear piece of DNA are digested with the restriction enzymes *Pvu*II, *Hinc*II, *Cla*I, and *Ban*II, alone and in pairs. The digestion products are separated by gel electrophoresis, and the size of each fragment is determined by comparison to size standards. The fragment sizes obtained, in kilobase pairs, are given below. Draw a diagram of the 7.8-kb fragment, showing the location of the restriction sites for each enzyme.

a. Digestion with *Pvu*II: 1.3 kb, 6.5 kb

b. Digestion with *Hinc*II: 0.5 kb, 3.3 kb, 4 kb

c. Digestion with *Cla*I: 1 kb, 6.8 kb

d. Digestion with *Ban*II: 1.3 kb, 6.5 kb

e. Digestion with *Pvu*II and *Cla*I: 1 kb, 5.5 kb, 1.3 kb

f. Digestion with *Pvu*II and *Hinc*II: 0.5 kb, 0.8 kb, 2.5 kb, 4 kb

g. Digestion with *Hinc*II and *Cla*I: 0.5 kb, 1 kb, 3 kb, 3.3 kb

h. Digestion with *Hinc*II and *Ban*II: 0.5 kb, 0.8 kb, 2.5 kb, 4 kb

i. Digestion with *Cla*I and *Ban*II: 1 kb, 1.3 kb, 5.5 kb

ANS S12.9. The restriction map is as shown below. The map is equivalent to one in which the orientation is reversed.

S12.10. A 3.3-kb size fragment created after the *Hinc*II digestion in the previous problem is inserted into a unique *Hinc*II site of the plasmid pUC18 and transformed into *E. coli*. Individual transformed colonies are isolated, and the recombinant plasmids from each colony are purified and mapped with the restriction enzyme *Pvu*II. To the surprise of a novice molecular geneticist, the plasmids do not all give the same pattern of restriction fragments on a gel. The plasmids fall into two distinct groups. Both groups yield the same number of bands in the gel, the aggregate size of which is the same, but two of the fragment sizes are different. Explain the reason for this difference.

ANS S12.10. The *Hinc*II fragment, which contains a *Pvu*II restriction site, is inserted in opposite orientations in the two types of clones.

S12.11. You have cloned a region of the genome of the nematode *C. elegans* that contains a mutation in a gene involved in controlling biorhythms. You make a restriction map of the cloned region and find that the following *Hin*dIII restriction map can be constructed:

```
   A        B        C           D
|_____|_____|_____|_____|
   4 kb     2 kb     5 kb            6 kb
```

Now you perform a *Hin*dIII digest of genomic DNA from individuals homozygous for the mutation and also from those that are homozygous for the wildtype allele. You subject both of these digests to electrophoresis in an agarose gel and transfer the DNA to a nylon membrane. When the membrane is probed with fragment A, B, or D, the probe hybridizes to fragments of 4, 2, and 6 kb, respectively, in both the mutant and the wildtype strain. When the membrane is probed with fragment C, the probe hybridizes to 11 different fragments in the mutant genome (including one fragment of 5 kb) and to 10 fragments in the wildtype genome (but not one of 5 kb). What could account for both the mutation and the pattern of bands seen with the C probe?

ANS S12.11. The mutation could be caused by the insertion of a transposable element, copies of which are also elsewhere in the genomes of both the wildtype and mutant worms. The transposon is inserted into region C; thus, when C is used as a probe, it detects all the sites in the genome at which the transposon resides.

S12.12. You are given a plasmid containing part of a gene of *D. melanogaster*. The gene fragment is 303 base pairs long. You would like to amplify it using the polymerase chain reaction (PCR). You design oligonucleotide primers 19 nucleotides in length that are complementary to the plasmid sequences immediately adjacent to both ends of the cloning site. What would be the exact size of the resulting PCR product?

ANS S12.12. The primer sequences are included in the PCR product at both ends of the gene fragment. The total length of the amplified piece of DNA is therefore $19 + 303 + 19 = 341$ base pairs.

S12.13. Suggest an experimental approach using a Southern blot that would allow one to estimate the number of copies of a particular transposable element present in the genomic DNA of an organism.

ANS S12.13. One approach would be to cleave the genomic DNA with a restriction enzyme that does not cut within the element. Each copy in the genome would be expected to have different distances between the ends of the element and the nearest restriction sites in the flanking genomic DNA. When probed with a fragment of the transposable element, each copy should yield a band of a different size, allowing the copies to be separated and counted.

S12.14. Suppose that you digest the genomic DNA of a particular organism with *Sau*3A (/GATC). Then you ligate the resulting fragments into a unique *Bam*HI (G/GATCC) cloning site of a plasmid vector. Would it be possible to isolate the cloned fragments from the vector using *Bam*HI? From what proportion of clones would it be possible?

ANS S12.12. Although the sticky ends of *Sau*3A and *Bam*HI are compatible, the *Bam*HI restriction site is reconstituted only if the genomic fragment has C next to the *Sau*3A site. The probability of a C at this position is 0.25, assuming equal amounts of four bases and their random distribution in the genome. The probability of recreating *Bam*HI sites at both ends of the cloned fragment (and, therefore, of being able to isolate the cloned fragment from the vector with *Bam*HI) is $0.25^2 = 0.0625$. Hence, only 6.25 percent of the cloned fragments would be flanked by *Bam*HI sites.

S12.15. Digestion of a DNA molecule with *Hind*III yields two fragments of 2.2 kb and 2.8 kb. *Eco*RI cuts the molecule, creating 1.8 kb and 3.2 kb fragments. When treated with both enzymes, the same DNA molecule produces four fragments of 0.8 kb, 1.0 kb, 1.2 kb, and 2.0 kb. Draw a restriction map of this molecule.

ANS S12.15. The only restriction map consistent with the data is a circular one:

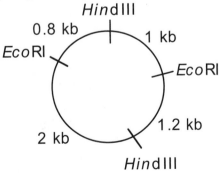

S12.16. What are the main differences between cDNA and genomic DNA libraries?

ANS S12.16. Genomic libraries contain all clonable sequences (including the untranscribed part of the genome) in the amounts theoretically proportional to their representation in the genome. cDNA libraries consist of sequences derived from mRNA and hence are without introns and other untranscribed regions; moreover, in cDNA libraries, infrequently transcribed genes are represented by fewer clones than highly expressed genes.

S12.17. You wish to amplify a unique 100-bp sequence from the human genome (3×10^9 bp) using the polymerase chain reaction. At the end of the amplification, you want the amount of amplified DNA to represent not less than 99 percent of all the DNA present. Assume that the amplification is exponential.

 a. How many cycles of amplification are necessary to achieve the 99 percent goal?

 b. How would the number of cycles change if you were to amplify a fragment of 1000 bp?

ANS S12.17. a. Let x be the amount of amplified DNA in base pairs, then $x/(x + 3 \times 10^9) = 0.99$ represents the minimum quantity for the 99 percent goal. Hence $x = 2.97 \times 10^{11}$ bp. This total amount of DNA represents $(2.97 \times 10^{11})/100 = 2.97 \times 10^9$ fragments, each of 100 base pairs. Because a PCR of n cycles yields 2^n amplified fragments, we set $2^n = 2.97 \times 10^9$. Hence, $n = 31.5$ cycles, so not less than 32 cycles are needed. **b.** In the case of a 1000 base pair target sequence, the number of amplified fragments is $(2.97 \times 10^{11})/1000$, from which $n = 28.1$; in this case, you would need at least 29 cycles to obtain the desired amount of product. (Because of the exponential amplification, the same relative quantity of a tenfold shorter fragment requires only ten percent more cycles.)

S12.18. You are given a DNA fragment containing the *Drosophila* developmental gene *fushi tarazu* (*ftz*) along with the restriction map shown below. The restriction sites are *Hin*dIII (5′ -A/AGCTT-3′), *Bcl*I (5′ -T/GATCA-3′), *Eco*RI (5′ -G/AATTC-3′), *Bam*HI (5′ -G/GATCC-3′). You are instructed to subclone the gene into a 3.8-kb plasmid vector having relevant restriction sites *Pst*I (5'-CTGCA/G-3'), *Bgl*II (5'-A/GATCT-3'), and *Bam*HI (5'-G/GATCC-3') positioned as follows: With what restriction enzymes should you cleave the *ftz*-containing region before ligating it with plasmid DNA that has been linearized with *Bgl*II?

ANS S12.18. Digestion of the plasmid with *Bgl*II creates a GATC overhang. This is compatible with the GATC overhangs created by either *Bam*HI or *Bcl*I, but not with the AATT overhang of *Eco*RI or the AGCT overhang of *Hin*dIII. *Bam*HI and *Bcl*I restriction sites also flank the *ftz* locus; therefore, you need to digest the *ftz* DNA with both *Bam*HI and *Bcl*I and ligate the resulting fragment into the plasmid linearized with *Bgl*II.

S12.19. Once you have subcloned the *ftz* region as in the previous problem, you want to determine the orientation in which the fragment is inserted in the resulting plasmid. You cleave the *ftz*-containing plasmid with *Bam*HI (5′ -G/GATCC-3′), *Pst*I (5′ -CTGCA/G-3′), and *Hin*dIII (5′ -A/AGCTT-3′), and observe fragments of sizes approximately 3 kb and 1 kb.

 a. Can you determine the orientation of the inserted fragment from this result?

 b. Would your answer change if the cloning site used in the plasmid were *Bam*HI rather than *Bgl*II? Explain.

ANS S12.19. a. It is important to remember that the *Bam*HI/*Bgl*II site created by the cloning procedure cannot be cut with *Bam*HI again. The two possible orientations of the insertion are shown below

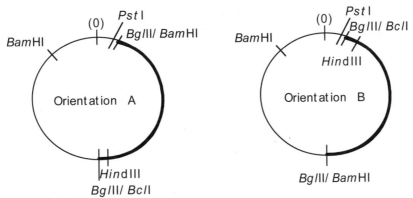

A restriction digest of a plasmid with orientation A with the enzymes *Bam*HI, *Pst*I, and *Hind*III would yield two approximately 3 kb fragments and one approximately 1 kb fragment. The same digest of a plasmid with orientation B would yield one 6 kb fragment and one 0.8 kb (plus a very small fragment unlikely to be detected). The results are thus compatible only with orientation A. **b.** If the cloning site in the plasmid were *Bam*HI rather than *Bgl*II, both orientations would yield two approximately 3 kb fragments and one approximately 1 kb fragment. Therefore, in this case, a digest with the three restriction enzymes would not be able to discriminate between the two possible orientations of *ftz* in the vector.

S12.20. You are given two strains of *E. coli* containing plasmids whose restriction maps are You are asked to subclone the gene for alcohol dehydrogenase (*Adh*) from plasmid B into plasmid A. Unsure of which cloning procedure would be the best, you try two different approaches.

 a. You digest both plasmids to completion with *Ppu*I (A/TGCAT) and *Sno*I (G/TGCAC), isolate the 4-kb *Ppu*I-*Sno*I *Adh* gene fragment and the 3.5-kb *Ppu*I-*Sno*I vector A fragment, carry out a ligation reaction containing both isolated DNA fragments, transform *E. coli* with the resulting DNA, and plate the transformed cells on medium containing tetracycline. The plates also contain Xgal and IPTG, which makes it possible to identify cells that contain the original plasmid A, because they turn blue as a result of the functional *lacZ* gene. Colonies with an insertion that interrupts the *lacZ* gene are white because of insertional inactivation.

 b. You follow the same procedure except that you use *Hind*III (A/AGCTT) instead of *Sno*I. Using approach **a.** you obtain many more blue colonies than using approach **b.** Explain why this is so.

ANS S12.20. In approach **a.**, the *Ppu*I and *Sno*I produce compatible sticky ends, so the vector plasmid (A) ends can religate onto themselves. Upon transformation into *E. coli*, such reconstituted vector molecules will produce blue colonies. In approach **b.**, the *Hind*III and *Ppu*I produce incompatible ends, so the only molecules that can recircularize are the ones that carry the *Adh* gene; transformants containing such plasmids are white.

S12.21. You purify plasmid DNA from white colonies obtained in both approaches in the previous problem. Predict the sizes of the resulting fragments when the isolated plasmids are digested with *Pst*I.

ANS S12.21. In approach (a), two different outcomes are possible, depending on the orientation in which the 4 kb *Ppu*I-*Sno*I fragment was inserted into the vector. One orientation yields fragments of 3 kb and 4.5 kb, the other orientation yields fragments of 1 kb and 6.5 kb. In approach (b), which illustrates directional cloning, the insertion is possible in only one orientation, which yields fragments of 1 kb and 6.5 kb.

Chapter 13: Genetic Control of Development
Answers to Chapter-end problems

Fill-ins

1. coordinate gene
2. blastoderm
3. ligand
4. meristem
5. flower ABC model
6. apoptosis
7. lineage diagram
8. maternal-effect gene
9. homeotic gene
10. zygotic gene

Analysis and Applications

ANS 13.1. Autonomous developmental fates are controlled by genetically programmed changes within cells. Fates determined by positional information are controlled by interactions with morphogens or with other cells. Cell transplantation and cell ablation (destruction) are two kinds of surgical manipulation that help distinguish between them.

ANS 13.2. Lineage mutations affect the developmental fates of one or more cells within a group of cells related by descent that normally undergo a defined pattern of development. Lineage mutations are detected by the occurrence of abnormal types or numbers of cells at characteristic positions within the embryo.

ANS 13.3. The *Drosophila* blastoderm is the flattened hollow ball of cells formed by cellularization of the syncytium formed by the early nuclear divisions. The fate map is a diagram of the blastoderm showing the locations of cells and their developmental fates. The existence of the fate map does not mean that development is autonomous, because many developmental decisions are made according to positional information in the blastoderm. In fact, most *Drosophila* developmental decisions are nonautonomous.

ANS 13.4. A female that is homozygous for a maternal-effect lethal produces defective eggs resulting in inviable embryos. However, the homozygous genotype itself is viable.

ANS 13.5. Carry out a complementation test. Cross two heterozygous genotypes and determine whether the female progeny have the maternal-effect lethal phenotype. If they are alleles, 1/4 of the progeny would be expected to have this phenotype. If they are not alleles, all of the progeny should be normal.

ANS 13.6. Cells normally destined to die adopt some other developmental fate, with the result that there are supernumerary copies of one or more cell types.

ANS 13.7. In a homeotic mutation, certain organs develop in a manner characteristic of that in neighboring segments, and therefore the lineage effect is one of transformation.

ANS 13.8. Yes, because mutations in these genes result in the wildtype floral organ identity being replaced by a different floral organ identity.

ANS 13.9. A sister-cell-segregation defect would lead to both daughter cells differentiating as B or to both differentiating as C. A parent-offspring-segregation defect would cause both daughter cells to differentiate as A.

ANS 13.10. Heterochronic mutations affect the timing of developmental events relative to each other; hence, a mutation that uniformly slows or accelerates development is not a heterochronic mutation.

ANS 13.11. Because the *Drosophila* oocyte contains all the transcripts needed to support the earliest stages of development; the mouse oocyte does not.

ANS 13.12. In a loss-of-function mutation, the genetic information in a gene is not expressed in some or all cells. In a gain-of-function mutation, the genetic information is expressed at inappropriate times or in inappropriate cells. Both mutations can occur in the same gene: some alleles may be loss of function and others gain of function. However, a particular allele must be one or the other (or neither).

ANS 13.13. Because the gene is necessary, a loss-of-function mutation will prevent the occurrence of the proper developmental fate. However, the allele will be recessive because a normal allele in the homologous chromosome will allow the developmental pathway to occur.

ANS 13.14. Because the gene is sufficient, a gain-of-function mutation will induce the developmental fate to occur. The allele will be dominant because a normal allele in the homologous chromosome will not prevent the developmental pathway from occurring.

ANS 13.15. Developmental abnormalities in gap mutations occur across contiguous regions, resulting in a gap in the pattern of normal development. Developmental abnormalities in pair-rule mutations are in even- or odd-numbered segments or parasegments, and so the abnormalities appear in horizontal stripes along the embryo.

ANS 13.16. The loss-of-function mutation results in the floral phenotype sepal–sepal–carpel–carpel; the gain-of-function mutation results in the floral phenotype petal–petal–stamen–stamen. The results imply that Ap3/Pi is necessary for petal development in whorl 2 and stamen development in whorl 3. In a wildtype genetic background, Ap3/Pi is sufficient for petal development in whorl 1 and stamen development in whorl 4.

ANS 13.17. The phenotype would resemble the *ap3* (or *pi*) and *ag* double mutant, namely, sepal–sepal–sepal–sepal.

ANS 13.18. Petal–petal–stamen–carpel.

ANS 13.19. The proteins required for cleavage and blastula formation are translated from mRNAs present in the mature oocyte, but transcription of zygotic genes is required for gastrulation.

ANS 13.20. The material required for rescue is either mRNA transcribed from the maternal o^+ gene or a protein product of the gene that is localized in the nucleus.

ANS 13.21. The transplanted nuclei respond to the cytoplasm of the oocyte and behave like the oocyte nucleus at each stage of development.

ANS 13.22. Look for embryos with a phenotype similar to *bicoid* mutants, lacking the head and thorax.

ANS 13.23. Whorls 1, 2, 3, and 4 yield leaf, petal, stamen, and carpel, repectively.

ANS 13.24. Whorls 1, 2, 3, and 4 yield sepal, petal, stamen, and leaf, repectively.

ANS 13.25. a. Because, in *agamous* mutants, whorls 1–4 yield sepals, petals, petals, and sepals, respectively, but petals and sepals require *apetala-1* expression. **b.** Because, in *apetala-1* mutants, whorls 1–4 yield carpels, stamens, stamens, and carpels, respectively, but carpels and stamens require *agamous* expression.

ANS 13.26. The phenotype of whorl 1 would probably be leaf, since that is the default state, but the phenotype of whorl 2 is not predicable because the result of *ap3* and *pi* expression alone is not evident from the model.

ANS 13.27. XDH activity is needed only at an early stage in development for the eyes to have wildtype pigmentation. The data are explained by a maternal effect in which the mal^+ / mal; ry / ry females in the cross transmit enough mal^+ gene product to allow brief activity of XDH in the ry^+ / ry embryos. In theory, the mal^+ product could be a transcription factor that allows ry^+ transcription, but in fact the mal^+ gene product participates in the synthesis of a cofactor that combines with the ry^+ gene product to make an active XDH enzyme.

ANS 13.28. a^+ is necessary for development of the medial and distal segments, b^+ is necessary for the development of the proximal segment, and c^+ is necessary for the development of the proximal and medial segments; when c^+ is missing from the medial segment, but a^+ is present in this segment, the segment is transformed to proximal, which implies that it is the interaction between a^+ and c^+ that yields the medial segment.

ANS 13.29. a. The results are consistent with the single mutants. **b.** The phenotypes of the double mutants indicate that a^+ alone is sufficient to produce the distal segment, that a^+ and c^+ are necessary to produce the medial segment, and that b^+ and c^+ are necessary to produce the proximal segment. **c.** The detailed model is shown in the accompanying diagram.

ANS 13.30.

Challenge Problems

ANS 13.31. First examine embryos of strains (c) and (d) to determine the wildtype expression patterns of *kni* and *ftz*. Next, cross strains (a) and (d) and strains (b) and (c). Intercross the F$_1$ heterozygotes from the cross (a) × (d) and examine the embryos to detect changes in *ftz* expression. Intercross the F$_1$ heterozygotes from the cross (b) × (c) and examine the embryos to detect changes in *kni* expression. Some of the F$_2$ embryos from the (a) × (d) cross will show abnormal expression of *ftz*, indicating that wildtype *kni* is required for proper *ftz* expression. The F$_2$ embryos of (b) × (c) will show normal expression of *kni*, indicating that *ftz* is not required for proper *kni* expression.

ANS 13.32.

ANS 13.33.

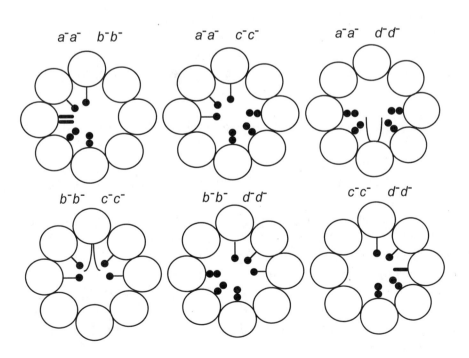

Supplemental problems with answers

S13.1. Define the following terms:
 a. Embryonic induction
 b. Gain-of-function mutation
 c. Fate map
 d. Pair-rule gene
 e. Segment-polarity gene
 f. Homeobox
 g. Homeotic mutation

ANS S13.1. a. Embryonic induction is a developmental process in which the fate of a group of cells is determined by interactions with nearby cells in the embryo. **b.** A gain-of-function mutation results in overexpression or inappropriate expression of a gene. **c.** A fate map is a diagram of the blastoderm of an organism identifying the regions from which particular adult structures derive. **d.** A pair-rule gene specifies the fate of alternating segments or parasegments in the early development of *Drosophila*. **e.** A segment-polarity gene determines the spatial pattern of development within the segments of *Drosophila* larvae. **f.** A homeobox is a DNA-sequence motif found in the coding regions of many regulatory genes; the amino acid sequence corresponding to the homeobox has a helix-loop-helix structure, a characteristic feature of many transcriptional activator proteins in both prokaryotes and eukaryotes. **g.** A homeotic mutation results in the replacement of one body structure by another body structure.

S13.2. What is the relationship between maternal-effect genes and zygotic genes?
ANS S13.2. The zygotic genes interpret and respond to the positional information laid out in the oocyte by the maternal-effect genes.

S13.3. In the early development of *C. elegans,* what is the role of the anchor cell in the differentiation of the vulva?
ANS S13.3. Five precursor cells participate in the development of the vulva. Each precursor has the capability of differentiating into one of three alternative fates. The fate adopted by each precursor cell depends on the concentration of an induction signal released by the anchor cell. The concentration of a signal experienced by each precursor depends on its distance from the anchor cell in the developing gonad.

S13.4. When in the development of most metazoan animals is the polarity of the embryo determined?
ANS S13.4. The polarity of the embryo is determined very early in the development, primarily through the expression of maternal-effect genes, the products of which create gradients in the oocyte.

S13.5. The same transmembrane receptor protein encoded by the *lin-12* gene is used in the determination of different developmental fates. What is the principal difference between the two types of target cells that develop differently in response to Lin-12 stimulation?
ANS S13.5. Distinct sets of genes are activated in the different target cells.

S13.6. Programmed cell death (apoptosis) is responsible in part for shaping many organs and tissues in normal development. If a group of cells in the duck leg primordium that are destined to die are

transplanted from their normal leg site to another part of the embryo just prior to the time they would normally die, they still die on schedule. The same operation performed a few hours earlier rescues the cells, and they do not die. How can you explain this observation?

ANS S13.6. The first experiment suggests that the genetic program of cell death is already activated and cannot be turned off. The second experiment shows that intercellular signaling must be responsible for inducing the cell-death fate because, when uninduced cells are transplanted to a new site, they do not die.

S13.7. A mutant of *C.elegans* has been isolated in which the gene for LET-23 receptor is deleted. What developmental fate would you expect cells P4.p – P8.p (precursors of vulva) to adopt?

ANS S13.7. The precursor cells normally differentiate into three cell types, 1°–2°–3°. The vulva is formed from the 1° and 2° cell lineages. In the absence of the LET-23 receptor, all precursor cells would be expected to adopt default 3° state, which would result in the complete absence of vulva.

S13.8. Classify each of the following mutations:

 a. A mutation in *C. elegans* in which a cell that normally produces two distinct daughter cells gives rise to two identical cells.

 b. A mutation in *Drosophila* that causes an antenna to appear at the normal site of a leg.

 c. A lethal mutation in *Drosophila* that is responsible for abnormal gene expression in alternating segments of the embryo

ANS S13.8. a. Cell-lineage mutation. **b.** Homeotic mutation. **c.** Pair-rule mutation.

S13.9. What causes induction of the morphogenic events in the *Drosophila* imaginal disks? When does this induction happen?

ANS S13.9. Morphogenesis is initiated by hormone ecdysone during the pupal stage of development.

S13.10. If a small amount of cytoplasm is removed from the posterior end of the *Drosophila* embryo before blastoderm formation, the mature fly that develops from this embryo is normal in every way except it does not have germ cells. How can you explain this finding?

ANS S13.10. Cytoplasm from the posterior end of the embryo contains some factor or factors that are necessary for the germ-cell differentiation.

S13.11. How would you prove that a newly discovered mutation has a maternal effect?

ANS S13.11. Perform reciprocal crosses. A maternal-effect gene results in phenotypically mutant progeny only when the mother is homozygous.

S13.12. A recessive mutation *smooth* is found in a species of flower in which hairs (trichomes) normally present on the leaf surface are missing. Another mutation in the same species, called *hairy,* results in the presence of trichomes on the flower petals, where they are not normally formed. Cloning and sequencing indicate that these mutations are different alleles of the same gene. Molecular analysis reveals that *smooth* is a frameshift mutation near the start of the coding sequence and that *hairy* has an upstream insertion of a transposable element that allows transcription of the gene in petal tissue. What features of these observations suggest that the gene in question is an important gene for the regulation of trichome formation?

ANS S13.12. The gene is both necessary and sufficient for the production of trichomes. The key observation is that loss-of-function and gain-of-function alleles in the gene have opposite phenotypic effects. The *smooth* allele is a recessive, loss-of-function mutation, resulting in absence of trichomes (in other words, the gene is necessary). The *hairy* allele is a (probably dominant) gain-of-function allele resulting in the presence of trichomes on petals (in other words, the gene is sufficient for producing trichomes wherever it is turned on).

S13.13. Two classes of genes involved in segmentation of the *Drosophila* embryo are gap genes, which are expressed in one region of the developing embryo, and pair-rule genes, which are expressed in seven stripes. Homozygotes for mutations in gap genes lack a continuous block of larval segments; homozygous mutations in pair-rule genes lack alternating segments. You examine gene expression by mRNA *in situ* hybridization and find that (1) the embryonic expression pattern of gap genes is normal in all pair-rule mutant homozygotes, and (2) the pair-rule gene expression pattern is abnormal in all gap gene mutant homozygotes. What do these observations tell you about the temporal hierarchy of gap genes and pair-rule genes in the developmental pathway of segmentation?

ANS S13.13. Gap genes act first in the hierarchy. In classical genetic terminology, they are epistatic to pair-rule genes.

S13.14. A paracentric inversion in *Drosophila* causes a dominant mutation that produces small wings. You mutagenize flies homozygous for this inversion with x rays and cross them to normal mates. Most progeny that arise have small wings, but a few rare progeny have normal wings. These rare progeny still have the original inversion but also contain a deletion spanning the more proximal of the two inversion breakpoints. (Proximal means closer to the centromere.) You correctly conclude from these observations that the dominant mutation is due to a genetic "gain of function" rather than to a reduction in gene activity. Explain how these results support this conclusion, and suggest an interpretation of how the gain-of-function phenotype arises.

ANS S13.14. Dominant mutations are generally gain of function; this conclusion is also supported by the observation that the phenotype can be reverted by a deletion. In this case, the gain-of-function phenotype may result from the inversion bringing a normal wing-development gene into proximity of an enhancer of an unrelated gene.

S13.15. One approach to the identification of important developmental genes in the mouse is to focus on genes whose DNA sequences are similar to those that have significant developmental roles in other organisms. Suppose that you want to study the mouse homolog of the *lin-3* gene of *C. elegans,* which is important in vulva formation in the worm. Homozygotes for a null mutation of *lin-3* lack a vulva. You propose that a homolog of *lin-3* exists in the mouse, and you want to examine the phenotype of a mutant mouse that lacks a functional form of this gene. Arrange the following steps in the order you would perform them to generate a mouse homozygous for a null mutation of the gene.

 a. Identify an open reading frame in a mouse cDNA that is similar to the *C. elegans lin-3* open reading frame.

 b. Create a deletion in a mouse genomic clone, and insert a gene resistant to the drug G418.

 c. Breed chimeric mice to donor strains to identify heterozygotes for a null mutation.

 d. Inject embryonic stem cells into differentially marked mouse blastocysts.

 e. Probe a mouse wildtype genomic library with a labeled mouse cDNA.

 f. Probe a mouse cDNA library with a labeled *C. elegans lin-3* cDNA.

g. Select for embryonic stem cells that can grow on G418.

h. Intercross null mutant heterozygotes to obtain a homozygous null mouse.

i. Identify chimeric mice.

j. Inject the DNA of an engineered mutation in the mouse *lin-3* homolog into embryonic stem cells.

k. Identify embryonic stem cells that have a null mutation in the mouse *lin-3* homolog.

ANS S13.15. The order should be **f--e--a--b--j--g--k--d--i--c--h**.

S13.16. Edward B. Lewis, Christianne Nüsslein-Volhard, and Eric Weichaus shared a 1995 Nobel Prize in Physiology or Medicine for their work on the developmental genetics of *Drosophila.* In their screen for developmental genes, Nüsslein-Volhard and Weichaus initially identified 20 lines bearing maternal-effect mutations that produced embryos lacking anterior structures but having the posterior structures duplicated. When Nüsslein-Volhard mentioned this result to a colleague, he was astonished to hear that mutations in 20 genes could give rise to this phenotype. Explain why his astonishment was completely unfounded.

ANS S13.16. The twenty mutations need not be mutations of twenty different genes; indeed, many of them proved to be alleles of one or another of a small set of genes.

S13.17. The gene *bicoid* exemplifies a maternal-effect gene that, when mutated, produces embryos that lack anterior structures but have the posterior structures duplicated. The Bicoid protein is a morphogen that establishes the domain of expression of the gap gene *hunchback* in a concentration-dependent manner. The Bicoid protein is usually present in an anterior-to-posterior gradient with the highest concentration at the anterior end of the early embryo. Diagrammed below is the major domain of expression of *hunchback* in an embryo from a wildtype mother.

What are the expected domains of *hunchback* expression in embryos from mothers with the following genotypes. Express your answers in the form of diagrams similar to the one here.

a. Homozygous mutant for *bicoid*

b. Homozygous for a duplication of a wildtype copy of *bicoid*

c. Homozygous for transgene that causes bicoid to be localized at both poles of the embryo

ANS S13.17. Answers in diagrammatic form.

S13.18. You are studying snowman development. Snowmen have three parts: Head, Torso, and Abdomen. Three genes are important in snowman development. Gene *A* is expressed in all three segments, gene *B* is active in Torso and Abdomen, and the product of gene *C* is present only in Abdomen. Three different mutants have been created with the following phenotypes

A^- No head; Torso; Abdomen

B^- Head; Head; Abdomen

C^- Head; Head; Torso

Predict the phenotype of a $B^- C^-$ double mutant.

ANS S13.18. The expected phenotype is Head; Head; Head

Chapter 14: Molecular Mechanisms of Mutation and DNA Repair
Answers to Chapter-end problems

Fill-ins

1. conditional mutation
2. base analog
3. cut-and-paste elements
4. replication slippage
5. mismatch repair
6. replica plating
7. frameshift mutation
8. pyrimidine dimer
9. synonymous mutation
10. depurination

Analysis and Applications

ANS S14.1. Such people are somatic mosaics and can be explained by somatic mutations in the pigmented cells of the iris of the eye or in their precursor cells.

ANS S14.2. Causes of a nonreverting mutation include (1) deletion of the gene, (2) multiple nucleotide substitutions in the gene, and (3) complex DNA rearrangement with more than one breakpoint in the gene. Deletions do not revert because the genetic information in the gene is missing, and the others do not revert because the nucleotide substitutions or DNA rearrangements are unlikely to be reversed precisely in one step.

ANS S14.3. Transitions are AT → GC, GC → AT, TA → CG, and CG → TA (total four). Transversions are AT → TA, AT → CG, GC → CG, GC → TA, TA → AT, TA → GC, CG → GC, and CG → AT (total eight).

ANS 14.4. The serine codon must be UCN, otherwise it could not change into an alanine in one step. The alanine codon must be GCN. Hence the amino acid change results from a U → G change in the codon, or an A → C base change in the transcribed strand of the *psbA* gene. It is therefore a transversion.

ANS 14.5. a. 2; **b.** 2; **c.** 3; **d.** 1.

ANS 14.6. If the +1 frameshift mutation shifts the reading frame to produce a nonsense codon, no −1 frameshift beyond the nonsense codon can prevent the termination of translation.

ANS 14.7. The genetic characteristic is instability. The mutation may revert at an unusually high rate as a result of excision of the transposable element. The mutant allele may also mutate to new alleles with different phenotypic effects if excision of the transposable element is imprecise and deletes flanking DNA sequences.

ANS 14.8. Any single nucleotide substitution creates a new codon with a random nucleotide sequence, and so the probability that it is a chain-termination codon (UAA, UAG, or UGA) is 3/64, or approximately 5 percent.

ANS 14.9. A frameshift mutagen will also revert frameshift mutations.

ANS 14.10. No, dominance and recessiveness are characteristics of the phenotype. They depend on the function of the gene and on which attributes of the phenotype are examined.

ANS 14.11. Photoreactivation and excision repair.

ANS 14.12. Because there are many ways in which an amino acid replacement can impair the activity of a wildtype protein, but very few ways that a mutant protein can regain wildtype activity other than restoration of the original amino acid.

ANS 14.13. Repeat-induced point mutation refers to hypermutation (largely G → A transitions) that takes place in sequences longer than a few hundred base pairs in haploid cells of *Neurospora* and related filamentous fungi. It is thought to be a defense mechanism against transposable elements because in most organisms these are the most common repetitive sequences.

ANS 14.14. Since each base pair contains one purine, the number of spontaneous depurinations per diploid cell per minute is $(3 \times 10^{-9})(6 \times 10^9) = 18$, or $18 \times 60 \times 24 = 26{,}000$ per diploid cell per day.

ANS 14.15. Solve $(1 \times 10^{-5}) \times x \times 2700 = 0.01$, where x is the proportion of X-linked genes capable of mutating to a recessive lethal. Then $x = 37$ percent.

ANS 14.16. a. 1:1 because the mutation is recessive and because males get their X chromosome from the mother. **b.** All females, because at 29°C the males (who in this case get their X chromosome from their father) die.

ANS 14.17. a. Development arrests at A at both the high and low temperatures. **b.** Development arrests at B at both the high and low temperatures. **c.** Development arrests at A at the high temperature and arrests at B at the low temperatures. **d.** Development arrests at B at the high temperature and arrests at A at the low temperature.

ANS 14.18. The mutation frequency in the Lac⁻ culture is at least $0.90 \times 10^{-8} = 9 \times 10^{-9}$. Because the mutation rate to a nonsense suppressor is independent of the presence of a suppressible mutation (in this case, the Lac⁻ mutation), the mutation rate in the original Lac⁺ culture is also at least 9×10^{-9}. The qualifier *at least* is important because not all nonsense suppressors may suppress the particular Lac⁻ mutation (that is, some suppressors may insert an amino acid that still results in a nonfunctional enzyme.)

ANS 14.19. a. 5×10^{-5} is the probability of a mutation per generation, and so $1 - (5 \times 10^{-5}) = 0.99995$ is the probability of no mutation per generation. The probability of no mutations in 10,000 generations equals $(0.99995)^{10,000} = 0.61$. **b.** The average number of generations until a mutation occurs is $1/(5 \times 10^{-5}) = 20,000$ generations.

ANS. 14.20.
```
5'-ATTAGTAGGG...AT...GGGAAAAAAAAAAAAAAAAACCC...AT...CCATTAGTA-3'
3'-TAATCATCCC...TA...CCCTTTTTTTTTTTTTTTTTGGG...TA...GGGTAATCAT-5'
```
(Note that the inversion also interchanges the strands.)

ANS 14.21. At 1 Gy, the total mutation rate is double the spontaneous mutation rate. Because a dose of 1 Gy increases the rate by 100 percent, then a dose of 0.5 Gy increases it by 50 percent and one of 0.1 Gy by 10 percent.

ANS 14.22. Amino acid replacements at many positions in the A protein do not eliminate its ability to function; only amino acid replacements at critical positions that do elminate tryptophan synthetase activity are detectable as Trp⁻ mutants.

ANS 14.23. The possible lysine codons are AAA and AAG, and the possible glutamic acid codons are GAA and GAG. Therefore, the mutation results from an AT → GC transition in the first position of the codon.

ANS 14.24. Six amino acid replacements are possible because the codons UAY (Y stands for either pyrimidine, C or U) can mutate in a single step to codons for Phe (UUY), Ser (UCY), Cys (UGY), His (CAY), Asn (AAY), or Asp (GAY).

ANS. 14.25.
a. Deletion plus a free circle.

b. Inversion

ANS 14.26. Single nucleotide substitutions that can account for the amino acid replacements are (1) Met (AUG) to Leu (UUG), (2) Met (AUG) to Lys (AAG), (3) Leu (CUN) to Pro (CCN), (4) Pro (CCN) to Thr (ACN), (5) Thr (ACR) to Arg (AGR), in which R stands for any purine (A or G) and N for any nucleotide. The substitutions in 1, 2, 4, and 5 are transversion and that in 3 is a transition. Because 5-bromouracil primarily induces transitions, the Leu → Pro replacement is expected to be the most frequent.

ANS 14.27. The sectors are explained by a nucleotide substitution in only one strand of the DNA duplex. Replication of this heteroduplex yields one daughter DNA molecule with the wildtype

sequence and another with the mutant sequence. Cell division produces one Lac$^+$ and one Lac$^-$ cell, located side by side. Since the cells do not move on the agar surface, the Lac$^+$ cells form a purple half-colony and the Lac$^-$ cells form a pink half-colony.

ANS 14.28. The *a* and *b* gene products may be subunits of a multimeric protein. A few proteins with compensatory amino acid replacements can interact to give wildtype activity, but most mutant proteins cannot interact in this way with each other or with wildtype.

ANS. 14.29.
a. Ectopic recombination results in a reciprocal interchange of chromosome parts (called a reciprocal translocation).

b. Ectopic recombination results in a chromosome with two centromeres (a dicentric chromosome) and in one with no centromere (an acentric chromosome).

ANS 14.30. a. All progeny would be able grow in the absence of arginine. **b.** The genotype of the diploid is Su^+ / Su^- arg^+ / arg^-, where Su^+ indicates the ability to suppress and Su^- indicates inability to suppress. The resulting haploid spores are 1/4 Su^+ arg^+, 1/4 Su^+ arg^-, 1/4 Su^- arg^+, and 1/4 Su^- arg^-. The first three are Arg$^+$ and the last Arg$^-$, and so the ratio is 3 Arg$^+$: 1 Arg$^-$. **c.** The diploid genotype is Su^+ arg^- / Su^- arg^+. The haploid spores are in the proportions 0.05 Su^+ arg^+, 0.45 Su^+ arg^-, 0.45 Su^- arg^+, and 0.05 Su^- arg^-. Therefore, 95 percent of the progeny are Arg$^+$ and 5 percent are Arg$^-$.

Challenge Problems

ANS 14.31. a. The homologous chromosomes in a heterozygous genotype carry *A* and *a*. After replication, there are two *A* copies from one homolog and two *a* copies from the other. Chromosome pairing and segregation during meiosis lead to the 2 *A* : 2 *a* expectation. This is not a "statistical" expectation, since each individual ascus should have 2 *A* and 2 *a* ascospores. **b.** The statistical expectation of 1 : 1 is observed among random spores because any particular heterozygous gene is very unlikely to be present in the heteroduplex region formed by the genetic exchange. In tetrad analysis, usually fewer that one percent of all asci show gene conversion. Even so, if the direction of gene conversion is unbiased, an average segregation ratio of 1 : 1 will still be expected.

ANS 14.32. Asci C, D and F might arise from gene conversion at the *m* locus as follows. Branch migration through *m* results in two regions of heteroduplex DNA. In ascus type C, one region is replicated before repair, leaving + and *m* alleles intact; the other region is repaired before replication (+ to *m*), yielding two *m* alleles (therefore a 3 : 5 ratio). In ascus type D, both heteroduplex regions are replicated before repair, leaving all alleles intact, but changing their order in the ascus (therefore

a 3 : 1 : 1 : 3 ratio). In ascus type F, both heteroduplex regions are repaired (+ to *m*) before replication, yielding four *m* alleles (therefore a 2 : 6 ratio).

ANS 14.33. a. The wildtype anticodon is 5'-CAG-3'; The mutant anticodon is 5'-CAC-3'. **b.** The mutational event was a CG to GC transversion. **c.** Val. **d.** Leu.

Supplemental problems with answers

S14.1. Define the following terms:
 a. Gene conversion
 b. Mismatch repair
 c. Silent mutation
 d. Photoreactivation
 e. Transversion mutation

ANS S14.1. a. Gene conversion is the phenomenon in which the products of a meiotic division in a heterozygous genotype are found in a ratio different from the expected 2:2, for example, 5:3; 3:5; 3:1, or 1:3. **b.** Mismatch repair refers to the removal of an improperly paired nucleotide from a DNA and its replacement with one that can pair properly. **c.** A silent mutation has no phenotypic effect. **d.** Photoreactivation is the enzymatic splitting of a pyrimidine dimer in DNA that has been damaged by ultraviolet light; the process requires visible light and a photoreactivation enzyme. **e.** A transversion mutation is the substitution of a purine nucleotide for a pyrimidine nucleotide or vise versa.

S14.2. If a deletion eliminates a single amino acid in a protein, how many base pairs are missing?
ANS S14.2. Exactly three. Otherwise, there would be a frameshift and all downstream amino acids would be different.

S14.3. Do all nucleotide substitutions in the second position of a codon necessarily produce an amino acid replacement?
ANS S14.3. All nucleotide substitutions in the second codon position result in either an amino acid replacement or a terminator codon.

S14.4. Do all nucleotide substitutions in the first position of a codon necessarily produce an amino acid replacement? Do all of them necessarily produce a nonfunctional protein?
ANS S14.4. Both UUR and CUR code for leucine, and both CGR and AGR code for arginine (R stands for any purine, either A or G). Hence, in each of these codons, one of the possible substitutions in the first codon position does not result in an amino acid replacement. Even when an amino acid replacement does occur, the mutant protein may still be functional because more than one amino acid at a given position in a protein molecule may be compatible with normal or nearly normal function.

S14.5. If base substitutions were random, what ratio of transversions to transitions would be expected?
ANS S14.5. There are eight possible transversions (A →T, A → C, G → T, G → T, T → A, T → G, C → A, C → G) but only four possible transitions (A → G, G→ A, T → C, C → T), hence the expected ratio is 2:1.

S14.6. In the real world, spontaneous base substitutions are biased in favor of transitions. What is the consequence of this bias for base substitutions in the third position of codons?

ANS S14.6. Examination of the standard genetic code shows that, in all codons with a pyrimidine in the third position, the particular pyrimidine present does not matter; the same is true for all but two codons ending in a purine. This feature of the code means that most transitions mutations in the third position are silent.

S14.7. How many different mutations can result from a single base substitution in the unique tryptophan codon TGG? Classify each as silent, missense, or nonsense.

ANS S14.7. There are nine different mutations: (1) TGG → AGG, (2) TGG → GGG, (3) TGG → CGG, (4) TGG → TAG, (5) TGG → TTG, (6) TGG → TCG, (7) TGG → TGA, (8) TGG → TGT, (9) TGG → TGC. Numbers (4) and (7) are nonsense, the rest are missense. There are no silent mutations of this codon because it is unique.

S14.8. How many amino acids can replace tyrosine by a single-base substitution in the DNA? (Do not assume that you know which tyrosine codon is being used.)

ANS S14.8. Six amino acid replacements are possible because the codons UAY (Y stands for either pyrimidine, C or U) can mutate in a single step to codons for Phe (UUY), Ser (UCY), Cys (UGY), His (CAY), Asn (AAY), or Asp (GAY). A change from Y to R results in a termination codon, not an amino acid replacement.

S14.9. What is the minimum number of single-nucleotide substitutions that would be necessary for each of the following amino acid replacements?

 a. Met → Val

 b. Lys → Gly

 c. His → Met

 d. Phe → Pro

ANS S14.9. a. 1; **b.** 2; **c.** 3; **d.** 2.

S14.10. Every human gamete contains, very approximately, 80,000 genes. If the forward mutation rate is between 10^{-5} and 10^{-6} new mutations per gene per generation, what percentage of all gametes will carry a gene that has undergone a spontaneous mutation?

ANS S14.10. Somewhere in the range between $80,000 \times 10^{-5} = 0.80 = 80$ percent and $80,000 \times 10^{-6} = 0.08 = 8$ percent. In other words, roughly speaking, between 8 and 80 percent of all sperm or eggs may carry at least one new mutation.

S14.11. If a mutation rate is between 10^{-5} and 10^{-6} per gene per generation, what does this imply in terms of the number of mutations of a particular gene per million gametes per generation?

ANS S14.11. It means that every million copies of the gene include from 1 to 10 new mutations (because $10^{-5} \times 10^{6} = 10$ and $10^{-6} \times 10^{6} = 1$).

S14.12. If the spontaneous mutation rate of a gene is 10^{-6} mutations per generation, and a dose of ionizing radiation of 10 grays doubles the rate of mutation, what mutation rate would be expected

with 1 gray of radiation? Assume that the rate of induced mutation is proportional to the radiation dose.

ANS S14.12. Because 10 grays adds 10^{-6} to the mutation rate, then, assuming proportionality, each 1 gray adds 100/1000 as much, or 0.1×10^{-6}; hence, the expected rate is $1.0 \times 10^{-6} + 0.1 \times 10^{-6} = 1.1 \times 10^{-6}$.

S14.13. A population of 1×10^6 bacterial cells undergoes one round of DNA replication and cell division. If the forward mutation rate of a gene is 1×10^{-6} per replication:
 a. What is the expected number of mutant cells after cell division?
 b. What is the probability that the population contains no mutant cells?

ANS S14.13. a. There are 1×10^6 replications and a rate of mutation of 1×10^{-6} new mutants per replication, so the expected number of new mutants is $(1 \times 10^6) \times (1 \times 10^{-6}) = 1$. **b.** The total number of cells after division is 2×10^6. The probability of any one cell being a mutant is therefore $1/(2 \times 10^6) = 5 \times 10^{-7}$. The probability that any cell is a nonmutant is therefore $1 - (5 \times 10^{-7})$, and the probability that each of the cells in the population is nonmutant is this quantity raised to the power of 2×10^6. The answer is $P = 0.368$. (Students familiar with the Poisson distribution may recognize this as $e^{-1} = 0.368$, the "Poisson zero term.")

S14.14 In theory, deamination of both cytosine and 5-methylcytosine results in a mutation. However, nucleotide substitutions produced by loss of the amino group from cytosine are rarely observed, although those produced by loss of the amino group from 5-methylcytosine are relatively frequent. What is a possible explanation for this phenomenon?

ANS S14.14 Loss of the amino group from cytosine yields uracil, which is specifically removed from DNA by a special repair enzyme. On the other hand, deamination of 5-methylcytosine produces thymine which, being a normal base in DNA, is not removed, resulting in a mutation.

S14.15. The mismatch repair system can detect mismatches that occur in DNA replication and can correct them after replication. In *E. coli*, how does the system use DNA methylation to determine which base in a pair is the incorrect one?

ANS S14.15 To distinguish the template strand from the newly synthesized strand, the system takes advantage of the normal delay in methylation after replication. During an interval of several minutes, the new strand remains undermethylated, which allows the mismatch repair system to identify and correct mistaken base.

S14.16. If one of the many copies of the tRNA gene for Glu underwent a mutation in which the anticodon became CUA instead of CUC, what would be the result? (*Hint*: The key is that only one of many tRNA copies is mutated.)

ANS S14.16. A 5'-CUA-3' anticodon recognizes the 5'-UAG-3' codon in the mRNA molecule. Since UAG is one of the three termination codons, this mutation is an example of a nonsense suppressor. Because of the mutant tRNA, some proteins with the UAG stop codon will not be terminated properly but will instead have the amino acid Glu inserted and continue being translated into the normally untranslated 3' region of the mRNA, until eventually another stop codon is reached. The result is the production of a polypeptide chain with additional amino acids at the carboxyl end.

Because only one copy of the tRNA gene is mutant, the normal GAG will still be recognized as Glu by the nonmutant tRNA.

S14.17. A strain of *E. coli* contains a mutant tRNAAsn. Instead of recognizing the codon 5′-AAU-3′, as it does in nonmutant cells, the mutant tRNA now recognizes the codon 5′-AGU-3′. A missense mutation of another gene, affecting amino acid number 6 along the chain, is suppressed in cells with the mutant tRNAAsn.

 a. What are the anticodons of the wildtype and mutant tRNAAsn molecules?

 b. What kind of mutation is present in the mutant tRNAAsn gene?

 c. What amino acid would be inserted at position 6 of the mutant polypeptide chain if the missense mutation were not suppressed?

 d. What amino acid is inserted at position 6 when the missense mutation is suppressed?

ANS S14.17. a. The wildtype anticodon is 5'-AAU-3', whereas the mutant anticodon is 5'-ACU-3'. **b.** The mutational event was an AT to GC transision. **c.** Ser. **d.** Asn.

S14.18. A mutation is selected after treatment with a particular mutagen, and organisms containing the mutation are then mutagenized to find revertants.

 a. Can a mutation caused by hydroxylamine be induced to revert to the wildtype sequence by re-exposure to hydroxylamine?

 b. Can a mutation caused by hydroxylamine be induced to revert by nitrous acid? (Hydroxylamine reacts specifically with cytosine and causes GC R AT transitions; nitrous acid causes deamination of A and C).

ANS S14.18. a. No, because the AT base pair is stable to the hydroxylamine treatment. **b.** Yes, because deamination of A yields hypoxanthine, which pairs with C, yielding an AT $\rightarrow$ GC transition.

S14.19. The tryptophan synthase of *E. coli* is a tetrameric enzyme formed by the polypeptide products of *trpB* and *trpA* genes. The wildtype subunit encoded by *trpB* has a glycine in position 38, whereas two mutants, B13 and B32, have Arg and Glu at this position, respectively. Plating these mutants on minimal medium sometimes yields spontaneous revertants to prototrophy. Four independent revertants of B13 have Ile, Thr, Ser, and Gly in position 38, and three independent revertants of B32 have Gly, Ala, and Val in the same position. What codon is in position 38 in the wildtype *trpB* gene?

ANS S14.19. Glycine has the codon formula GGN. The only glycine codons that can mutate to either arginine or glutamic acid in one step have the formula GGR, where R means either A or G. Mutation B13 has arginine and can mutate in a single step to isoleucine. The only arginine codon that can mutate in this manner is AGA (mutating to AUA). Mutation B13 must therefore be a GGN-to-AGA mutation and, because it is a single-step mutation, the original glycine codon must be GGA. You should verify that this interpretation is consistent with the other mutational data as well.

S14.20. In the *rIIB* gene of bacteriophage T4, there is a small coding region near the beginning of the gene in which the particular amino acid sequence that is present is not essential for protein function. (Single-base insertions and deletions in this region were used to prove the triplet nature of the genetic code.) Under what condition would a -1 frameshift mutation at the beginning of this region not be suppressed by a +1 frameshift mutation at the end of the region?

ANS S14.20. If the -1 frameshift mutation shifts the reading frame to produce a nonsense codon, no +1 frameshift beyond the nonsense codon can prevent the termination of translation.

S14.21. *E. coli* mutation *lacZ-1* was induced by acridine treatment, whereas *lacZ-2* was induced by 5-bromouracil. What kind of mutations are they likely to be? What sort of mutant β-galactosidase will these mutations produce?

ANS S14.21. Acridine is an intercalating agent, and can be expected to produce frameshift mutations. 5-bromouracil is incorporated in place of T, but is sometimes read as C by DNA polymerase. Thus , 5-bromouracil-induced mutations would be expected to be point mutations, usually TA to CG transitions. If these expectations were realized in these two mutations, *lacZ-1* would be expected to be a frameshift mutatiosn and *lacZ-2* would probably contain a single amino acid difference from the normal β-galactosidase. (Alternatively, *lacZ-2* could produce a truncated polypeptide due to a nonsense mutation.)

S14.22. In molecular evolutionary studies, biologists often regard serine as though it were two different amino acids, one type of "serine" corresponding to the fourfold-degenerate UCN codon and the other type of "serine" corresponding to the twofold-degenerate AGY codon. Why does it make sense to regard serine in this way but not the other amino acids encoded by six codons: leucine (UUR and CUN) and arginine (AGR and CGN)? (In this symbolism for the nucleotides, Y is any pyrimidine, R any purine, and N any nucleotide.)

ANS S14.22. It makes sense for serine because two mutations are required to change UCN into AGY or the other way around. Because it's unlikely for two point mutations to occur simultaneously in the same codon, an organism couldn'tt change from one serine codon class to the other in a single step. There would have to be an intermediate stage in which serine was replaced by a different amino acid. However, for leucine and arginine, it is possible to change from UUR to CUN or from AGR to CGN (even through two consecutive steps) without ever changing the amino acid.

S14.23. A *Drosophila* female is heterozygous for an X-linked temperature-sensitive recessive allele that is viable at 18°C but lethal at 29°C. What sex ratio would be expected among the progeny if the progeny were reared at:

 a. 18°C.
 b. 29°C.

ANS S14.23. a. 1 : 1; half the males inherit the temperature-sensitive mutation, but it is viable at 18°C. **b.** 2 female : 1 male, because the half of the males that inherit the temperature-sensitive mutation die at 29°C.

S14.24 You carry out a large-scale cross of genotypes *A m B* × *a + b* of two strains of *Neurospora crassa* and observe a number of aberrant asci, some of which are shown below.

(1)	(2)	(3)	(4)	(5)
A m B	A m B	A m B	A m B	A m B
A m B	A m B	A m B	A m B	A m B
A m b	A m b	A m b	A m b	A + b
A + b	A m b	A + b	A m b	A + b
a m B	a m B	a + B	a m B	a + B
a + B	a + B	a + B	a m B	a + B
a + b	a + b	a + b	a + b	a + b
a + b	a + b	a + b	a + b	a + b

158

Your colleague who provided the strains insists that they are both deficient in the same gene in the DNA mismatch repair pathway. The results of your cross seem to contradict this assertion.

a. Which of the asci depicted above would you exhibit as evidence that your colleague is incorrect?

b. Which ascus (or asci) would you exhibit as definitive evidence that DNA mismatch repair in these strains is not 100 percent efficient?

c. Among all asci resulting from meioses in which heteroduplexes form across the $m/+$ region, what proportion of asci will be tetratype for the A and B markers and also show $4 : 4$ segregation of $m : +$, under the assumption that 30 percent of heteroduplexes in the region are not corrected, 40 percent are corrected to m, and 30 percent are corrected to $+$?

ANS S14.24. a. Acsi of types (4) and (5) show typical $3 : 1$ patterns of segregation expected with gene conversion, strongly suggesting that mismatch repair does take place. The ratios of $m : +$ in these asci are $6 : 2$, and $2 : 6$, respectively. Asci (2) and (3) also show evidence of mismatch repair because the segregation ratios are, respectively, $5 : 3$ and $3 : 5$. **b.** In asci of types (1), (2), and (3), adjacent pairs of ascospores, which result from post-meiotic mitosis, do not have the same genotype; this result implies that the immediate product of meiosis was a heteroduplex, resulting in genetically different ascospores after the mitotic division. The persistence of the heteroduplexes implies that mismatch repair is not 100 percent efficient. **c.** Half the asci with a heteroduplex across the $m/+$ region will have recombination of the outside markers. Among these, $4 : 4$ segregation of $m : +$ will be found if either (1) neither heteroduplex was corrected or (2) both heteroduplexes were corrected but in opposite directions. The probability of neither heteroduplex being corrected is $(0.30)^2 = 0.09$ and of both being corrected is $(0.70)^2 = 0.49$. Among those in which both are corrected, the proportion that are corrected in opposite directions is $2 \times 0.40 \times 0.30 = 0.24$. Putting all this together, the required answer is $0.50 \times (0.09 + 0.24) = 0.165$, or 16.5 percent.

Chapter 15: Molecular Genetics of the Cell Cycle and Cancer
Answers to Chapter-end problems

Fill-ins

1. tumor-suppressor gene
2. oncogene
3. gene fusion
4. loss of heterozygosity
5. apoptosis
6. DNA damage checkpoint
7. processivity
8. retinoblastoma (RB) protein
9. spindle assembly checkpoint
10. anaphase-promoting complex (APC/C)

Analysis and Applications

ANS 15.1. a. A normal phenotype. **b.** The mother cell and daughter cell are unable to separate; they remain attached through a small cytoplasmid bridge, and successive divisions form clumps of interconnected cells, each cell attached to its mother and its own daughters through such cytoplasmic bridges.

ANS 15.2. At the G1/S checkpoint, because of the unrepaired double-stranded DNA breaks caused by the X rays.

ANS 15.3. They transfer phosphate groups to their target protein; the counterparts that reverse phosphorylation are phosphatases.

ANS 15.4. It binds to and sequesters the transcription factor *E2F,* which is needed for transcription of the genes required for DNA synthesis.

ANS 15.5. Pds1p and cyclin B are important targets of the anaphase promoting complex. This complex is a ubiquitin-protein ligase that ubiquitinates the proteins and tags them for destruction in the proteasome. Destruction of Pds1p allows disjunction of the sister chromatids and is associated with the metaphase/anaphase transition; destruction of cyclin B is associated with the mitosis/G1 transition.

ANS 15.6. A DNA damage checkpoint, which responds to double-stranded breaks or other damage to DNA; a centrosome duplication checkpoint, which is activated unless the centrosome has duplicated and the products have moved into position; and a spindle checkpoint, which is activated when the spindle is not completely assembled or when one or more chromosomes is unattached to the spindle or improperly aligned on the spindle.

ANS 15.7. The p53 protein is the major player. Normally p53 does not accumulate in the nucleus because it is continuously exported by Mdm2. In the presence of DNA damage, p53 is

phosphorylated and acetylated, which reduces its binding by Mdm2; the protein accumulates in the nucleus and activates transcription of (among other proteins) p21, GADD45, and 14-3-3σ, which are associated with a block in the G1/S transition, prolongation of S phase, and a block in the G2/M transition, respectively.

ANS 15.8. A decrease in processivity means that the polymerase complex detaches from the template after a smaller number of nucleotides have been replicated. More frequent reinitiation of DNA synthesis is therefore required, which prolongs the time spent in DNA replication. The prolongation allows greater time for repair enzymes to repair damaged DNA.

ANS 15.9. Bax and Bcl2 are normally present as heterodimers. Overproduction of Bax results in Bax homodimers that activate the apoptosis pathway. The p53 protein plays a role in apoptosis because p53 is a transcription factor for the gene encoding Bax. Certain cellular oncogenes result in overproduction of Bcl2, which counteracts the effect of Bax overproduction by sequestering Bax subunits in Bax/Bcl2 heterodimers.

ANS 15.10. It is a "genetic disease" in that genetic mutations take place in cells that make them undergo uncontrolled growth and division. However, most cancers are caused by somatic mutations in the cells of affected individuals, hence they are not inherited from the parents (familial) but rather due to new somatic mutations.

ANS 15.11. a. Test for genetic linkage of the segregating cancer gene to DNA markers very near the *p53* gene. If there is tight linkage between the disease gene and a DNA marker at *p53*, then it is likely that the disease is *p53*-related. If the disease gene is not genetically linked to *p53*, another gene is probably involved. **b.** Possible sites for change include: promoter changes that reduce expression of the *p53* gene, changes in introns that correspond to essential splice sites, or a deletion that removes the whole gene (so that the sequence of *p53* from a heterozygous individual is that of the wildtype *p53*$^+$ homolog). **c.** Anything that can mimic loss of *p53* function could underlie the phenotype. A mutation that causes overexpression of Mdm2 is one possibility. Other possibilities are mutations that abrogate the ability of a protein kinase that phosphorylates p53 (if there is a crucial one) or a protein acetylase that acetylates p53, so long as lack of either modification results in failure of p53 levels to rise in response to DNA damage (presumably because Mdm2 can still bind to p53). For all three suggestions, the syndrome should show dominant inheritance but loss of heterozygosity should be required for expression at the cellular level.

ANS 15.12. Since the tumors are sporadic in origin, the DNA of the normal cells is not informative, since the changes occurred clonally in somatic cells. In patient 1, there is no indication of a change in DNA structure. The mutation is likely to be a missense or nonsense mutation. In patient 2, the DNA fragment that hybridizes to *p53* cDNA in tumor cells is smaller in size than the wildtype fragment; a partial deletion of the *p53* gene has occurred. In patient 3, there is no DNA present in tumor cells that is homologous to the *p53* gene; the entire gene seems to have been deleted. In patient 4, the DNA homologous to the *p53* gene is present in two fragments rather than one. A chromosomal aberration that disrupts function of p53 must have occurred. The most likely candidates are translocation or inversion. One breakpoint in the aberration must have occurred within the *p53* gene.

ANS 15.13. Because the normal G1/S checkpoint serves to allow DNA damage (such as broken chromosomes) to be repaired prior to entering the S period. In the absence of a normal G1/S checkpoint, the cell transitions into S even when there are broken chromosomes and other abnormalities.

ANS 15.14. Because p53 plays a key role in monitoring DNA damage through transcriptional activation of *p21*, *GADD*, and *14-3-3σ*, and in activating the pathway of apoptosis through transcriptional activation of *Bax*.

ANS 15.15. Ras–GTP is a central step in transmitting a growth signal in response to activation of certain tyrosine kinase receptors. Constitutive Ras–GTP transmits the growth signal continuously.

ANS 15.16. The accompanying diagram shows how mitotic recombination can cause loss of heterozygosity. The diagram also shows that all genetic markers distal to (toward the telomere side of) the site of recombination also lose heterozygosity.

ANS 15.17. It means that most individuals who inherit a mutant *RB1* allele from either parent develop retinoblastoma, so in families the mutant allele behaves as a dominant with respect to the retinoblastoma phenotype. However, somatic cells in heterozygous individuals do not become cancerous unless they undergo a loss of heterozygosity, making them effectively homozygous for the mutation, so at the cellular level the mutation is recessive.

ANS 15.18. 3 tumors/$(4 \times 10^6$ cells$) = 0.75 \times 10^{-6} = 7.5 \times 10^{-7}$ per cell. This is not exactly a "mutation" rate because it includes such events as chromosome loss, mitotic recombination, and so forth, which are not, strictly speaking, "mutations."

ANS 15.19. Since the rate of loss of heterozygosity per cell is 7.5×10^{-7} and there are 4×10^6 cells at risk in both eyes together, the probability of no loss of heterozygosity in any cell is $(1 - 7.5 \times 10^{-7})$ raised to the power of 4×10^6, which equals 0.05, or 5 percent. The penetrance of familial retinoblastoma is therefore 95 percent. (Students familiar with the Poisson distribution can use the fact that the mean number of tumors per heterozygous individual is 3, from which the Poisson distribution implies that the number of individuals with no tumors is $e^{-3} = 0.05$.)

ANS 15.20. a. The smaller band should be associated with the mutant *RB1* allele, the larger with the nonmutant allele. **b.** The loss of heterozygosity is independent in different tumors, hence the mechanism need not be the same in both cases. **c.** In this case the wildtype allele has undergone a new mutation (or perhaps a small deletion or insertion), which inactivates the gene but does not detectably change the size of the band.

ANS 15.21. They might be the same by chance, but may often be different. The reason is that the event leading to loss of heterozygosity in any one tumor is independent of that leading to loss of heterozygosity in any other tumor, in particular, a tumor in the opposite eye.

ANS 15.22. The son's genotype is *AL p53⁻ BL/AS p53⁺ BS*. **a.** The bands AS p53⁺ and BS are lost. **b.** *AL p53⁻* and *BL* all become homozygous. **c.** *p53⁻* and *BL*, but *AL/AS* remains heterozygous. **d.** No apparent change in banding pattern from noncancerouos cells. **e.** *p53⁻* is replaced *p53⁺*. The expected band patterns are shown in the illustration.

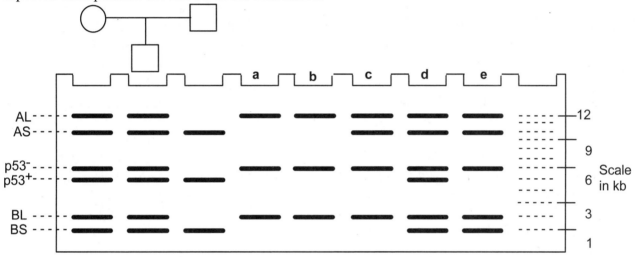

ANS 15.23. Inspection of the pedigree indicates that the band c from the mother in generation I (individual 9) derives from a mutant allele, since all of her affected offspring, and none of her normal offspring, inherit this allele. Thus individual 5 carries the mutant allele associated with band c, and among her offspring individuals 2 and 7 are at high risk, the others not. The individual 20 also carries the mutant allele yielding band c, hence among his offspring individuals 16, 21, and 22 are at high risk, the others not. The remaining individual 13 in generation III is not at risk, even though her DNA yields a band that comigrates with c. The reason is that this band was derived from an allele in her father, who is unrelated to any of the affected individuals in the pedigree; hence the band c in this case marks a nonmutant allele.

ANS 15.24. a. The cells should stop dividing at 37°C because they would no longer sense and propagate a growth stimulatory signal (probably the presence of nutrients rather than growth factors in this example). **b.** Recessive. The Ras produced from the wildtype gene in the same cell would still propagate the signal. **c.** Such a mutant cell would continue to divide even when nutrients are exhausted. Such a mutant will die when starved, rather than cease growing. **d.** The mutation would be dominant. The mutant Ras will remain in the GTP-bound form regardless of what wildtype Ras is doing and will ceaselessly propagate a signal to grow.

ANS 15.25. One approach is first to determine whether genes for T cell receptor or the heavy chain of immunoglobulins map near the translocation site. If either is near the breakpoint, one would expect a promoter fusion to be present. As conformation, it should be determined whether the mRNA of the gene next to the breakpoint is the normal size, as it would be expected to be in a promoter fusion. If there is no suggestion that the T cell receptor or IgH genes are at the site of the translocation, one would expect a gene fusion. To test this, make DNA probes from DNA flanking the site of the translocation and use them to probe RNA blots from normal and leukemic cells (the probes have to be long enough to extend into exons or they will not hybridize to mRNAs). For a gene fusion, the mRNA in the leukemic cell should be a chimera, and one would expect a single mRNA from the leukemic cells to hybridize with both flanking DNAs; for wildtype cells, the two probes should hybridize to mRNAs of different sizes. A more refined analysis would tell whether the gene fusion took place in introns.

ANS 15.26. Effectively, HPV removes all the brakes on cellular proliferation, turns on all the stimuli, and removes the infected cell's ability to induce apoptosis to kill itself. The cell will effectively be *p53⁻*, since E6 is present to ensure that levels of p53 do not rise. This means that synthesis of Bax will not be induced, and cells will not undergo apoptosis. In addition, synthesis of p21, GADD45, and 14-3-3σ will not be accelerated, so the cells will not arrest in the cell cycle. Because E7 disables RB, E2F will be active at all times, resulting in new rounds of DNA synthesis and continued cellular proliferation.

ANS 15.27. a. Six genes. The complementation groups are: 1; (2, 6); 3; (4, 5, 8); (7, 9); 10. **b.** Mutants 4, 5, and 8 carry new *cdc13* alleles and mutants 7 and 9 carry new *mob1* alleles. The other four genes remain unidentified.

ANS 15.28. I-1 or I-2, III-3

ANS 15.29. The newly synthesized DNA of the *cdc9* mutant cells remains unligated if synthesized at 37°C. The DNA checkpoint detects the damage and arrests the cells at the G2/M boundary. Upon return to 23°C, ligase activity returns and seals the nicks; the cells live because their DNA is intact. The *rad9 cdc9* double mutants also make DNA that contains nicks at 37°C. However, because the checkpoint is nonfunctional, the cells proceed through mitosis without sealing the nicks. The genome becomes fragmented. Upon return to 23°C, the cells are unable to form colonies because they do not have intact genomes. Incubation in benzimidazole at 37°C prevents the double mutants from continuing into mitosis, effectively introducing an artificial checkpoint. Once the cells are returned to 23°C, they can seal the nicks and will survive.

ANS 15.30. *RAD9* is probably not involved in the G1/S DNA checkpoint, since the *cdc28*, *cdc6*, and *cdc8 rad9* double mutants survive incubation at 36°C, implying that the G1/S checkpoint is intact in the *rad9* mutant.
RAD9 is also probably not involved in the centrosome duplication checkpoint, since the *cdc7 rad9* double mutant survives incubation at 36°C. *RAD9* is involved in the S phase DNA checkpoint since *cdc2*, *cdc13* and *cdc17 rad9* (as well as *cdc9 rad9*) double mutants die at 36°C. *RAD9* is probably not involved in the spindle or in the exit from mitosis checkpoints, since *cdc16*, *cdc20*, *cdc23*, and *cdc15 rad9* double mutants survive incubation at 36°C.

Challenge Problems

ANS 15.31. Because the 1/100 dilution has the same intensity of hybridization as the control DNA, the cancer cells must contain 100 copies of *MYC* for every copy of *MYC* present in normal cells. Apparently some type of amplification of the *MYC* gene took place in the origin of the cancer cells, since the gene is present in about 200 copies per cell (versus 2 copies per cell in the noncancer cells).

ANS 15.32. Using gene knockout technology, delete one of the two copies of the *CLB2* gene in a diploid cell homozygous for the *his3* and *ura3* mutations. For example, replace the *CLB2* gene sequences in a plasmid vector with the *HIS3* sequence, PCR the fragment containing *HIS3* and the sequences that normally flank *CLB2* upstream and downstream (including the promoter) from the plasmid, and use this fragment to transform a diploid homozygous for the *his3* marker to His$^+$. Transform this diploid with a centromere-containing plasmid that carries *URA3* and the cDNA encoding human cyclin B (or D). Sporulate the diploid and dissect the resulting asci. If meiotic spore clones that are His$^+$ Ura$^+$ grow faster than spore clones that are His$^+$ Ura$^-$, human cyclin B is able to substitute for Clb2. If the His$^+$ Ura$^-$ and His$^+$ Ura$^+$ spore clones grow equally slowly, human cyclin B cannot replace Clb2. The test can be made more stringent and conclusive if the diploid strain is also made homozygous for *clb1*, because Clb1 partially substitutes for Clb2. Since the *clb1 clb2* mutant is inviable, the doubly mutant segregants will only survive if human cyclin B (or D) is able to substitute for Clb2.

ANS 15.33. a. One would expect the strain to continue through mitosis whether or not each chromosome is attached to a spindle fiber. Aneuploid cells should therefore be generated. Monosomic strains would be detected as Canr Ura$^-$/Foar His$^-$ derivatives of the parental strain. Loss of the homolog carrying the wildtype alleles uncovers the three markers. **b.** One would expect the strain to fail to correct replication errors, including mismatched bases. This would be most readily detected as an increase in the rate of mutation. For this strain, one should detect at higher frequencies Canr or Foar derivatives of the parental strain that remain wildtype for the other two markers.

Supplemental problems with answers

S15.1. Define the following terms:
 a. Apoptosis
 b. Contact inhibition
 c. Cell cycle
 d. Loss of heterozygosity
 e. Processivity of a DNA polymerase

ANS S15.1. a. Apoptosis is genetically programmed cell death. **b.** Contact inhibition is a phenomenon of suppression of cell growth and division by cell-to-cell contact. **c.** Cell cycle is the growth cycle of a cell; in eukaryotes, it is subdivided into G_1 (Gap 1), S (DNA synthesis), G_2 (Gap 2) and M (mitosis). **d.** Loss of heterozygosity is uncovering of the recessive allele by various mechanisms, such mutations, chromosome loss or deletion. **e.** The processivity of a DNA polymerase refers to the number of consecutive nucleotides in the template strand that are replicated before the polymerase detaches from the template.

S15.2. Is the cell cycle reversible?

ANS S15.2. The cell cycle is not reversible. The cycle is propelled forward by a process of protein degradation that complements the periodic activation of cyclin–CDK complexes. Proteolysis eliminates proteins that were used in the preceding phase as well as proteins that would inhibit progression into the next phase. In the early stages of the cell cycle, progression requires the sequential activation of cyclin–CDKs. Entry into each new phase also requires the destruction of the cyclins used in the preceding phase. In the later stages of the cell cycle, progression is propelled by proteolysis alone.

S15.2. At what stage in the cell cycle are histones produced? What general feature of cell division does the timing of histone synthesis exemplify?

ANS S15.2. In the S phase as DNA synthesis takes place and the new histones are needed to form nucleosomes with the newly replicated DNA. The general principle is that gene products used in the cell division cycle are usually synthesized when they are needed.

S15.3. Inside the cell, what key events are monitored during the cell cycle?

ANS S15.3. They are: DNA damage and replication completion, centrosome duplication, and assembly of the spindle and attachment of the kinetochores to the spindle.

S15.4. Why were "cyclin" proteins given that name? What assures their orderly appearance during the cell division cycle?

ANS S15.4. Because their abundance goes up and down in accordance with the phase of the cell cycle. They appear in an orderly manner because the transcription of each cyclin is activated by the appearance of a previous cyclin, and they disappear relatively rapidly because of protein degradation.

S15.5. The function of some cyclin-dependent protein kinases (CDKs) has been remarkably conserved in evolution. Indeed, coding sequence for the human protein Cdc2 is able to substitute for the *CDC28* gene in *S.cerevisae*, and allow the yeast cell to grow and mate essentially normally. The following sequence near the NH$_2$-end of the molecule is identical in both proteins: Gly-Glu-Gly-Thr-Tyr-Gly-Val-Val-Tyr-Lys-Ala. Does this mean that nucleotide sequences of the two genes coding for this region of the polypeptide are also identical? Explain your answer.

ANS S15.5. No, they are not necessarily identical because the genetic code is redundant. The third position in each codon might be different in two organisms. Therefore, despite the fact that two amino acid sequences are 100% identical, the DNA sequences might be only 67% identical (11 out of 33 base pairs may be different). In reality, two DNA sequences are 76% identical (25 out of 33 base pairs are exactly the same).

S15.6. How many different nucleotide sequences may encode the amino acid sequence mentioned in the previous problem?

ANS S15.6. There are 4 different codons for each of Gly, Thr, Val and Ala, 3 for Glu, and 2 for each of Tyr and Lys. Hence, there are $4^7 \times 3 \times 2^3 = 393216$ different sequences that can code for this amino acid sequence.

S15.7. What genes are often involved in cancer progression?

ANS S15.7. Genes that function in cell cycle regulation or checkpoint control.

S15.8. When is phosphorylation of the RB protein completed during the cell cycle? How does this affect the RB protein? And what are the consequences of RB phosphorylation?

ANS S15.8. The RB phosphorylation is completed late in G1 when cells become committed to DNA replication. Phosphorylation of RB inactivates the protein and frees the bound E2F transcription factor, which results in transcription of the genes and translation of the enzymes responsible for DNA replication. The cells begin to accumulate the precursors and enzymes required for DNA synthesis. E2F also activates transcription of the gene for E2F itself (positive autoregulation), as well as those for the cyclins E and A and the Cdk2 kinase subunit.

S15.9. How does decrease in the processivity of DNA polymerase help the cell to repair DNA damage?

ANS S15.9. The processivity of a DNA polymerase refers to the number of consecutive nucleotides in the template strand that are replicated before the polymerase detaches from the template. Decreasing the processivity of DNA polymerase therefore slows down DNA synthesis, in effect buying time for the cell to repair DNA damage.

S15.10. The *rad9* mutant was isolated as a mutant more sensitive to UV damage than the wildtype, and subsequent studies showed that the gene product is involved in the S phase DNA checkpoint. Does this finding account for the radiation-sensitive phenotype? Explain.

ANS S15.10. Both wildtype and *rad9* mutants are capable of repairing DNA damage provided they have the time to do so. However, the *rad9* mutant does not arrest in response to DNA damage, hence any DNA repair that takes place must occur "on the fly" as cells are continuing through the cycle. Inevitably, some damage must remain unrepaired that kills the cell containing it. The wildtype cells arrest at G2/M, repair DNA damage, and only then resume passage through the cell cycle.

S15.11. In case of DNA damage, what would happen to a cell that lacks p21 protein?

ANS S15 11. If DNA damage were properly sensed, and p53 functioned as usual to increase levels of 14-3-3σ and GADD45, cells would accumulate in G2 and be unable to undergo mitosis. However, DNA would continue to be synthesized. In addition, lacking p21 protein, the cells would have a defective G1/S checkpoint and so could embark on additional rounds of DNA synthesis. The expected result of p21 malfunction would therefore be polyploid cells.

S15.12. Explain why Mdm2 is considered the product of a proto-oncogene, whereas p53 is considered the product of a tumor-suppressor gene.

ANS S15.12. Mdm2 acts normally to promote cell proliferation by transporting p53 from the nucleus. Overexpression of Mdm2 due to a gain-of-function mutation can overcome p53 activation in the presence of DNA damage, resulting in uncontrolled proliferation. The p53 protein normally acts to inhibit cell division in the presence of DNA damage; in this case a loss-of-function mutation in the gene for p53 results in uncontrolled proliferation.

S15.13. Most mutagens are also carcinogens, and most carcinogens are also mutagens. Explain why this is the case.

ANS S15.13. Because cancer cells result from somatic mutations.

S15.14. With regard to the appearance of cancer as a function of age, distinguish between "one-hit" kinetics and "two-hit" kinetics. Which type of kinetics is found in sporadic cancers? Which in familial cancers? Explain why.

ANS S15.14. One-hit kinetics means that a fraction of the total number of cases observed goes up at a constant rate per year, as if one mutation alone were sufficient to cause the disease; two-hit kinetics means that the fraction of the total number of cases observed goes up at an increasing rate per year, as if two mutations, one after the other, were required. Two-hit kinetics characterizes sporadic cancers, one-hit familial cancers. The familial cancers are one-hit because one of the "hits" (mutations) is inherited through the germ line.

S15.15. A gene for hereditary prostate cancer has been mapped to chromosomal location 1q25; it shows autosomal dominant inheritance. How would you go about identifying the mutant gene?

ANS S15.15. Genetically map the gene to high resolution using molecular markers to identify several closely linked molecular markers on each side of the disease gene. Then obtain overlapping YAC, BAC and PAC clones spanning the entire region between the flanking markers. The next step could be any of several. One could look for transcripts that are expressed from the region that was narrowly defined by mapping, or look for transcripts that are expressed in prostate gland that are encoded in this region, or use the clones to probe Southern blots to look for differences in fragments between normal and tumor tissue. The best candidate gene/region would be one that encodes a prostate specific transcript or one altered in a Southern blot. These would be highest priority for further investigation. One could also look for single strand conformational polymorphisms within the region. Ultimately, one would sequence the DNA in the narrowly defined region and try to identify a sequence difference that segregates in the family that is associated 100 percent with the affected phenotype.

S15.16. Yeast mutants defective in various DNA repair processes have been isolated as UV and/or X-ray sensitive strains. Included among these are *rad1* mutants, which are defective in excision repair, *rad27* mutants, which are defective in mismatch repair, and *rad52* mutants, which are defective in repair of double strand breaks.

 a. Would you expect the *rad1 rad9*, *rad27 rad9* and *rad52 rad9* double mutants to be viable?

 b. If viable, would you expect them to be more, as, or less sensitive to radiation than the single *rad1*, *rad27* and *rad52* mutants?

 c. Would you expect the mutants to be altered for other characteristics?

ANS S15.16. a. Although each double mutant has two defective repair pathways, several others remain intact. The double mutants would therefore be expected to be viable, but "sick": it is likely that more than the normal fraction of cells would die. **b.** One would expect the double mutants to be more sensitive to radiation than the single mutants because they would not arrest and buy time to repair lesions, since they have a defective DNA damage checkpoint. **c.** One would expect the double mutants to show elevated mutation rates, even when compared to the *rad1*, *rad27* or *rad52* strains, since they would lack adequate time to repair replication errors.

S15.17. The gene for the human AP endonuclease has been identified and mapped to chromosomal location 14q11.2-12. How would you find out whether loss of function of the AP endonuclease predisposes an individual to cancer?

ANS S15.17. First investigate families showing inherited cancer syndromes and determine whether the gene segregating maps to 14q11-12. If such a family or families were identified, then determine

the DNA sequence of the AP endonuclease gene in family members to see whether a mutation cosegregates with the cancer phenotype. If it does, then determine whether tumors are homozygous for the mutation due to loss of heterozygosity. As confirmation, clone the mutant cDNA, express this in *E. coli* (preferably in an AP endonuclease deficient mutant), recover the protein, and test in vitro for AP endonuclease activity. The enzyme produced from the wildtype cDNA would serve as the positive control. If no dominant gene for a syndrome associated with 14q11-12 is identified, study of families segregating for recessive genes would be warranted. The expectations would be somewhat different. Affected people should be homozygous, not heterozygous, for the mutation, and all carriers should be heterozygous. Normal and tumor tissue in afflicted individuals should both be homozygous for the mutation, and loss of heterozygosity should play no role in expression of the cancer phenotype.

S15.18. What would be the effect of a mutation in the *RAS* gene that inactivates its GTPase function?

ANS S15.18. Without GTPase function Ras is unable to hydrolyze the GTP and return itself to the inactive state of Ras–GDP. It remains in its active form of Ras–GTP, whether or not the cell is receiving signals from growth-factor receptors. A signal for growth is therefore transmitted constitutively, and unrestrained growth and division takes place.

Chapter 16: Mitochondrial DNA and Extranuclear Inheritance
Answers to Chapter-end problems

Fill-ins

1. extranuclear inheritance
2. heteroplasmy
3. RNA editing
4. petite mutant
5. maternal inheritance
6. maternal effect
7. symbiosis
8. segregational petite
9. fertility restorer
10. kappa particle

Analysis and Applications

ANS 16.1. Because mitrochondria are the major sites of energy production (ATP) in eukaryotic cells.

ANS 16.2. Because the severity depends on the proportion of defective mitochondria that are present in the affected individual.

ANS 16.3. Yes, it is true in the human mitochondrial code. In the standard code the exceptions to the rule are AUA and AUG, which code for isoleucine and methionine, respectively, and UGA and UGG, which code for "stop" and tryptophan, respectively.

ANS 16.4. UGA should not be used for Trp and AUA should not be used for Ile. To encode a polypeptide of the same length, neither AGA nor AGG should be used for termination, otherwise these would be translated in the cytoplasm as Arg and yield a longer polypeptide chain.

ANS 16.5. Most likely nuclear; the corresponding amino acid sequence is Met–Arg–His–Asn–Asp–Arg–Gly–Arg–Pro–Asn–Arg. In mitochondria, the translation would be Met–stop–His–Asn–Asp–stop–Gly–stop–Pro–Asn–Arg. The stop codons in the first 11 codons is incompatible with an open reading frame.

ANS 16.6. All transition mutations in the third position are synonymous. Among 128 possible transversion mutations, 56 are synonymous, or a fraction 56/128 = 43.8 percent.

ANS 16.7. Inheritance is strictly maternal, and so yellow is probably inherited cytoplasmically. A reasonable hypothesis is that the gene for yellow is contained in chloroplast DNA.

ANS 16.8. Pollen is not totally devoid of cytoplasm, and occasionally it contains a chloroplast that is transmitted to the zygote.

ANS 16.9. The Y-chromosomal DNA is inherited only by male offspring, whereas the organelle DNA is inherited by both sexes of offspring.

ANS 16.10. This trait is maternally inherited, and so the phenotype is that of the mother. The progeny are **a.** green; **b.** white; **c.** variegated, green or white, depending on segregation of chloroplasts; **d.** green.

ANS 16.11. With X-linked inheritance, half of the F_2 males (1/4 of the total progeny) would be white. The observed result is that all of the F_2 progeny are green.

ANS 16.12. If the daughter chloroplasts segregate at random, both of them will go to the same pole half the time. For all four products to contain a descendant chloroplast, the segregation has to be perfect in three divisions, which occurs with probability $(1/2)^3 = 1/8$. Therefore, the probability that at least one cell lacks a descendant chloroplast equals $1 - 1/8 = 7/8$.

ANS 16.13. The cluster of four restriction sites suggests an inverted-repeat sequence. Recombination between the inverted repeats inverts the segment between them, yielding the two different restriction maps. They are both present in single individuals because one is derived from the other by recombination, which must take place at a sufficiently high rate that each individual has both types of mtDNA.

ANS 16.14. The inheritance is not Mendelian because there is no evidence of segregation. The bands corresponding to the two largest DNA fragments are mutually exclusive and show maternal inheritance; the bands corresponding to the two smallest DNA fragments are mutually exclusive and show paternal inheritance. One possibility is that the smaller bands derive from mitochondrial DNA and the larger from chloroplast DNA; another is that the smaller bands derive from chloroplast DNA and the larger from mitochondrial DNA. In any event the larger and smaller bands are respectively maternally and paternally derived, respectively.

ANS 16.15. The chloroplast from the m^- strain is preferentially lost and the m alleles segregate 1 : 1. The expected result is $1/2\ a^+\ b^-\ m^+$ and $1/2\ a^+\ b^-\ m^-$.

ANS 16.16. a. All *cpl-r*, because the chloroplast comes from the mt^+ parent. **b.** All *mit-s* because the mitochondria come from the mt^- parent. **c.** Resistant : sensitive in a ratio of 2 : 2 because a nuclear gene undergoes Mendelian segregation.

ANS 16.17. a. *cpl-r mit-r nuc-r* : *cpl-r mit-r nuc-s* in a ratio of 2 : 2. **b.** *cpl-s mit-s nuc-r* : *cpl-s mit-r nuc-s* in a ratio of 2 : 2.

ANS 16.18. The *klv-r* versus *klv-s* difference segregates as 1 : 1, consistent with their being alleles of a gene in the nucleus. The association with mating type can be explained by linkage: the *klv* and *mt* loci are genetically linked with a frequency of recombination of $r = 20/200 = 10$ percent (10 map units).

ANS 16.19. Because the petite phenotype results from a mutant nuclear gene that undergoes normal 2 : 2 segregation meiosis, yielding 2 petite : 2 nonpetite progeny from a cross.

ANS 16.20. Petite, because neither parent contributes functional mitochondria.

ANS 16.21. Because every tetrad shows uniparental inheritance, it is likely that the trait is determined by factors transmitted through the cytoplasm, such as mitochondria. The 4 : 0 tetrads result from diploids containing only mutant factors, and the 0 : 4 tetrads result from diploids containing only wildtype factors.

ANS 16.22. In autogamy, one product of meiosis becomes a homozygous diploid nucleus, and so half of the *Aa* cells that undergo autogamy become *AA* and half become *aa*.

ANS 16.23. The mating pairs are 1/4 *AA* × *AA*, 1/2 *AA* × *aa*, and 1/4 *aa* × *aa*. These produce only *AA*, *Aa* and *aa* progeny, respectively, and so the progeny are 1/4 *AA*, 1/2 *Aa*, and 1/4 *aa*. In autogamy, the *Aa* genotypes become homozygous for either *A* or *a*, and so the expected result of autogamy is 1/2 *AA* and 1/2 *aa*.

ANS 16.24. Begin by considering the situation without cytoplasmic exchange. In this case the *KK* killer exconjugant becomes *Kk* (kappa), where (kappa) means that the kappa bacterium is present in the cytoplasm, and the *kk* nonkiller exconjugant becomes *Kk* (no kappa). Immediately after autogamy, the ratios become 1/4 *KK* (kappa), 1/4 *kk* (kappa), 1/4 *KK* (no kappa), and 1/4 *kk* (no kappa). The kappa bacterium cannot be maintained in the *kk* (kappa) strain, hence the overall ratio of killer : nonkiller is that of (kappa) : (no kappa), which is 1 : 3. On the other hand, with cytoplamic exchange, the 1/4 *KK* (no kappa) and 1/4 *kk* (no kappa) become 1/4 *KK* (kappa) and 1/4 *kk* (kappa). The latter cannot maintain kappa, but the former can, so the overall ratio of killer : nonkiller with cytoplasmic exchange is 1 : 1. The cytoplasmic exchange is necessary to obtain the 1 : 1 ratio because, while the *K* allele is necessary to maintain kappa, it cannot create kappa. The kappa bacterium must be transferred from the killer partner.

ANS 16.25. The F$_1$ nuclear genotype is *Rsf/rsf*, and all the progeny receive male-sterile cytoplasm (restored to male fertility by the *Rsf* allele). In the next generation, 3/4 of the plants are *Rsf/–* and are both female and male fertile, but 1/4 of the plants are *rsf/rsf*, which are female fertile but male sterile.

ANS 16.26. The only functional pollen is *a B*. All the progeny of the *AA bb* plants are *Aa Bb* and those of the *aa BB* plants are *aa BB*.

ANS 16.27. The most likely possibility is maternal transmission of a factor, possibly a virus or bacteria, which results in a high pre-adult mortality among the male offspring.

ANS 16.28. The result excludes hypothesis (1) but doesn't distinguish between hypotheses (2) and (3).

ANS 16.29. Because the progeny coiling is determined by the genotype of the mother, the rightward coiling snail has genotype *ss*. To explain the rightward coiling, the mother of this parent snail would have had the + allele, and must in fact have been + / *s*.

ANS 16.30. The adjoining table shows the percent of restriction sites shared between each pair of mitochondrial DNA molecules.

	1	2	3	4	5
1	100	0	80	10	0
2		100	0	10	100
3			100	11	0
4				100	10
5					100

The entries in the table may be explained by example. Molecules 3 and 4 together have 9 restriction sites, of which 1 is shared, and so the entry in the table is 1/9 = 11%. The diagonal entries of 100 mean that each molecule shares 100% of the restriction sites with itself. The two most closely related molecules are 2 and 5 (in fact, they are identical), and so these must be grouped together. The two next closest are 1 and 3, and so these also must be grouped together. The 2–5 group shares and average of 10 percent restriction sites with molecule 4, and the 1–3 group shares an average of 10.5 percent restriction sites [that is, (10 + 11)/2] with molecule 4. Therefore, the 2–5 group and the 1–3 group

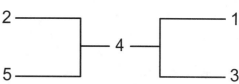

are about equally distant from molecule 4. The diagram shows the inferred relationships among the species. Data of this type do not indicate where the "root" should be positioned in the tree diagram.

Challenge Problems

ANS 16.31. No, because in mitochondrial DNA each tRNA is encoded in a unique gene. In nuclear DNA, most tRNAs are present in two or more copies, allowing one copy to mutate to a nonsense suppressor without compromising the translation of the normal codon. In mitochondrial DNA, such a mutation would change the translation of every open reading frame and would probably be lethal.

ANS 16.32. Among Africans, the average time traversed in tracing the ancestry from a present-day mitochondrial DNA back to a common ancestor and forward again to another present-day mitochondrial DNA is between 78×1500 years and 78×3000 years, or 117,000 to 234,000 years; the backward and foward times are equal, and so the person having the common ancestor of the mitochondrial DNA lived between 117,000/2 = 58,500 years ago and 234,000/2 = 117,000 years ago. Among Asians, similar calculations result in a range of 43,500 to 87,000 years for the common ancestor of mitochondrial DNA. Among Caucasians, the calculated range is 30,000 to 60,000 years.

ANS 16.33. a. This is a segregational petite; the nuclear mutation that causes it is unlinked to the *ade6* locus. **b.** This is a neutral petite, since it fails to be recovered in the progeny. **c.** This is a segregational petite, the nuclear mutation for which is linked to *ade6* with a recombination frequency of $r = 15/100 = 15$ percent (15 map units).

Supplemental problems with answers

S16.1. Define the following terms:

a. Maternal inheritance

b. Maternal effect

c. Cytoplasmic male sterility

d. Heteroplasmy

e. RNA editing

f. Phylogenetic tree

ANS S16.1. a. Maternal inheritance refers to uniparental transmission through the mother. **b.** Maternal effect is the influence of the mother's nuclear genotype on the phenotype of the progeny. **c.** Cytoplasmic male sterility is a condition in which the plant does not produce functional pollen, but the female reproductive organs and fertility are normal. **d.** Heteroplasmy is the condition in which two or more genetically different types of organelles are present in the same cell. **e.** RNA editing is post-transcriptional modification of RNA. **f.** A phylogenetic tree is a diagram showing the genealogical relationships among a set of genes or species.

S16.2. A woman with the mild form of a mitochondrial disease, Leber's hereditary optic neuropathy (LHON), has four children: two with severe disease expression, one unaffected, and one with the same level of expression as the mother. Explain this pattern of inheritance.

ANS S16.2. The woman has a mixture of normal and abnormal mitochondria. Her children inherited both types of mitochondria but in different ratios. Those who are affected severely have the lowest ratio of normal : abnormal mitochondria, whereas the unaffected child received primarily normal mitochondria.

S16.3. How do mitochondrial and nuclear genomes interact at the functional level?

ANS S16.3. Most polypeptide chains encoded in mitochondrial genes form complexes with polypeptide chains encoded in nuclear genes in order to create the active proteins that function in mitochondria.

S16.4. A dwarfed corn plant is crossed as a female parent to a normal plant, and the F_1 progeny are found to be dwarfed. The F_1 plants are self-fertilized, and the F_2 plants are found to be normal. Each F_2 plant is self-fertilized, and 3/4 of F_3 generation are found to be normal whereas 1/4 of the plants are dwarfed. Which of the following hypotheses are consistent with these results? Explain your reasoning.

 a. Cytoplasmic inheritance

 b. Nuclear inheritance

 c. Maternal effect

 d. Cytoplasmic inheritance plus mutation in a nuclear gene

ANS S16.4. The data are most readily explained by the action of a recessive nuclear gene with a maternal effect. The crosses are:

Parents *dd* dwarf female × *DD* normal male

F_1 *Dd*, all dwarf because the mother is *dd*

F_2 3/4 *D–* : 1/4 dd all normal because the mother is *Dd*

F_3 3/4 normal because the mother is *D–* : 1/4 dwarf because the mother is *dd*

S16.5. A strain of yeast with a mutation *ery-r* conferring resistance to the antibiotic erycetin is crossed with a strain of opposite mating type with the genotype *ery-s*. After meiosis and sporulation, three tetrads are isolated. The spores have the following genotypes:

I	II	III
a ery-r	α ery-s	α ery-r
a ery-r	α ery-s	**a** ery-r
α ery-r	**a** ery-s	**a** ery-r
α ery-r	**a** ery-s	α ery-r

 a. What genetic hypothesis can explain these results?

 b. If an *ery-r* strain were used to generate petites, would you expect some of the petites to be sensitive to erycetin? Explain.

ANS S16.5. a. Each tetrad shows uniparental inheritance for the antibiotic resistance, suggesting cytoplasmic inheritance of this gene. In contrast, the mating type alleles segregate in Mendelian fashion, as expected for nuclear genes. **b.** Because *ery-r* is most likely mitochondrial, and petites result from deletions in mitochondrial DNA, some of the petites may very well lose their resistance.

S16.6. In a fungal organism closely related to *Saccharomyces cerevisiae*, a strain resistant to three antibiotics is used to induce petite colonies. The antibiotics are erycetin, chlorpromanin, and paralysin, and the resistance genes are denoted *ery-r, chl-r,* and *par-r,* respectively. Each of the resistance genes is known to be present in mitochondrial DNA. Each row in the accompanying table is the result of an experiment in which petite colonies selected for loss of genetic marker A (one of the antibiotic resistances) were tested for simultaneous loss of genetic marker B (another of the antibiotic resistances).

Marker A	Marker B	Loss of marker A only	Loss of markers A and B
ery-r	*chl-r*	170	19
ery-r	*par-r*	54	81
chl-r	*par-r*	116	8

From these data, deduce the order of the genes and the relative distances between them in the mitochondrial DNA.

ANS S16.6. This problem is solved much like one involving cotransduction, except that the revertants result from deletions in the mitochondrial DNA that eliminate one or more anmtibiotic-resistance genes. The first row of the table implies that 19/189 = 10 percent of the petites that had lost *ery-r* also had lost *chl-r*. The second row implies that 81/135 = 60 percent of the petites that had lost *ery-r* also had lost *par-r*. The third row implies that 8/124 = 6 percent of the petites that had lost *chl-r* also had lost *par-r*. The low frequency of simultaneous loss in the last case means that *chl-r* and *par-r* are the most distant genes, which implies that *ery-r* is in the middle. The comparison of 10 percent with 60 percent means that *ery-r* is closer to *par-r* than it is to *chl-r*. The genetic map is therefore:

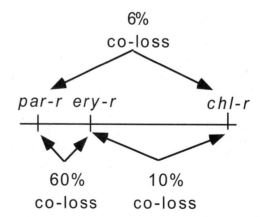

175

S16.7. Two haploid strains of *Neurospora* are isolated that have genetic defects in the ATPase complex. The mutants are designated $A1^-$ and $A2^-$. The crosses $A1^- \times A1^+$ and $A2^- \times A2^+$ were carried out, and one ascus was analyzed from each cross. The cross $A1^- \times A1^+$ yielded a 4 : 4 ratio of $A1^+ : A1^-$ ascospores, whereas the cross $A2^- \times A2^+$ yielded an 8 : 0 ratio of $A2^+ : A2^-$ ascospores.

a. What difference between the mutations can explain these discordant results?

b. What other types of tetrads would one expect from these crosses?

ANS S16.7.a. The 4 : 4 segregation indicates a mutation in a nuclear gene. The 8 : 0 ratio implies mitochondrial inheritance. **b.** The nuclear gene should always segregate 1 : 1 (except for an occasional gene conversion). The mitochondrial mutation might also be expected to produce some ascospores that are $A2^-$ owing to occasional loss of sufficient numbers of wildtype mitochondria to counteract the defective ones.

S16.8. Mothers addicted to cocaine who use the drug during pregnancy can give birth to babies who are also addicted. Suggest a mechanism for this maternal effect.

ANS S16.8. The drug in the mother's blood passes through placenta, enters the baby's system, and causes the addiction.

S16.9. If organelles were originally symbionts, why don't we call them symbionts instead of organelles?

ANS S16.9. Because organelles have evolved a long way from being symbionts, including the loss of most of their genome. Symbionts contain all, or almost all, genes necessary for their own existence. Organelles are indispensable entities in the cell and have no free-living state. Their genomes are relatively small and encode few proteins, and most of their functions are encoded by nuclear genes.

S16.10. How would you prove the existence of RNA editing in mitochondria?

ANS S16.10. One way would be to create cDNA and genomic libraries and compare the nucleotide sequences of corresponding clones. Another, more difficult, way would be to compare the predicted amino acid sequence of a polypeptide based on the coding region of the gene with the amino acid sequence of an actual polypeptide.

S16.11. What might prevent a cloned mitochondrial gene from humans to yield a functional protein in a bacterial host?

ANS S16.11. The genetic code in mitochondria is different from that in prokaryotes. For instance, in mitochondria UGA is not a stop codon but encodes tryptophan. Therefore, the polypeptide chain in bacterial cell would be always terminated at the position normally occupied in mitochondrial protein by tryptophan.

S16.12. What is controversial about the hypothesis of a mitochondrial Eve who lived in Africa? Is the controversial part the conclusion that there is a common ancestor of human mitochondrial DNA, or is it the inference of the geographical location of the common ancestor? Explain.

ANS S16.12. The difficulty is not with postulating a common ancestor of human mitochondrial DNA. It is a mathematical certainty that all human mitochondrial DNA must, eventually, trace back to a single ancestral woman. This principle is true because there is differential reproduction and,

therefore, each mitochondrial lineage has a chance of becoming extinct in every generation; hence, given enough time, all lineages except one must eventually become extinct. The question is whether the woman who was the common ancestor of all mitochondria lived in Africa, because the inferred phylogenetic tree of mitochondrial DNA does not point unambiguously to an African origin.

S16.13. How would you prove that a newly discovered mutation in a nuclear gene has a maternal effect?

ANS S16.13. Perform reciprocal crosses. A maternal-effect gene results in phenotypically mutant progeny only when the mother is homozygous for mutation.

S16.14. The product of the maternal-effect gene *dorsal* (*dl*) in *Drosophila* is required for the development of the normal dorsal-ventral pattern of the embryo. Females homozygous for the dl^2 allele produce eggs that are unable to support normal embryonic development, irrespective of the genotype of the zygote. What kind of crosses is necessary to produce dl^2/dl^2 females?

ANS S16.14. Although embryos from dl^2/dl^2 females are abnormal, those from heterozygous females have normal embryonic development because the wildtype allele of *dorsal* supplies of the oocyte with sufficient product for embryogenesis. Therefore, homozygous females can be obtained in the cross of heterozygous females with either dl^2/dl^+ or dl^2/dl^2 males. The first cross produces 1/4 homozygous females, the second 1/2

S16.15. In *Drosophila*, the maternal-effect gene *snake* belongs (together with the gene *dorsal* mentioned in the problem **S16.14**) to the dorsal group of genes that are required for the development of the normal dorsal-ventral pattern of the embryo. Females homozygous for the snk^4 allele produce embryos unable to survive, irrespective of the their own genotype. However, embryos can be rescued by injecting oocytes from snk^4/snk^4 females with cytoplasm from either snk^+/snk^+ or snk^+/ank^2 eggs. Injections of the extract from nuclei are ineffective. Embryos of dl^2/dl^2 females, on the contrary can be rescued by injections of nuclei extracts from both dl^+/dl^+ or dl^+/dl^2 oocytes. Suggest the explanation for these results.

ANS S16.15. The product of *snake* functions in cytoplasm. The product of *dorsal* is localized and active in the nucleus.

S16.16. Searching for genes affecting posterior development in the *Drosophila* embryo, you identified 34 lines bearing maternal-effect mutations that result in the embryos lacking pole cells and sterile adults. When you mentioned this result to a colleague, she was surprised to hear that mutations in 34 genes could give rise to this phenotype. Explain why her bewilderment was completely unfounded.

ANS S16.16. The thirty four mutations need not to be mutations of thirty four different genes; indeed, many of them proved to be alleles of a small set of nine genes.

Chapter 17: Molecular Evolution and Population Genetics
Answers to Chapter-end problems

Fill-ins

1. random mating
2. gene tree
3. natural selection
4. random genetic drift
5. neighbor joining
6. equilibrium
7. inbreeding coefficient
8. paralogous genes
9. selectively neutral mutation
10. molecular clock

Analysis and Applications

ANS 17.1. Adults 2/3 *Aa* and 1/3 *aa*. It is not necessary to assume random mating because the only fertile matings are *Aa* × *Aa*. These produce 1/4 *AA*, 1/2 *Aa*, and 1/4 *aa* zygotes, but the *AA* zygotes die, leaving 2/3 *Aa* and 1/3 *aa* adults.

ANS 17.2 The numbers of alleles of each type are *A*, 2 + 2 + 5 + 1 = 10; *B*, 5 + 12 + 12 + 10 = 39; *C*, 10 + 5 + 5 + 1 = 21. The total number is 70, so the allele frequencies are *A*, 10/70 + 0.14; *B*, 39/70 + 0.56; and *C*, 21/70 + 0.30.

ANS 17.3. a. Two bands indicate heterozygosity for two different VNTR alleles. **b.** A person who is homozygous for a VNTR allele will have a single VNTR band. (An alternative explanation is also possible: some VNTR alleles are present in small DNA fragments that migrate so fast that they are lost from the gel; a heterozygote for one of these alleles will have only one band—the one corresponding to the larger DNA fragment—because the band corresponding to the smaller DNA fragment will not be detected. **c.** VNTR alleles are codominant because both are detected in heterozygotes. **d.** Because none of the bands in the four pairs of parents have the same electrophoretic mobility, the parents of each child can be identified as the persons who share a single VNTR band with the child. Child A has parents 7 and 2; child B has parents 4 and 1; child C has parents 6 and 8; and child D has parents 3 and 5.

ANS 17.4. Each individual has a pattern of bands exactly like his or her mother, so the most likely explanation is mitochondrial inheritance. The Hardy-Weinberg principle is not relevant to mitochondrial inheritance because the genotype of the progeny is not determined by the genotypes of both parents but only by the genotype of the mother.

ANS 17.5. Allele 6.5 frequency = (2 × 9 + 21 + 15 + 6)/200 = 0.30; allele 6.2 frequency = (2 × 12 + 21 + 18 + 7)/200 = 0.35; allele 6.0 frequency = (2 × 6 + 15 + 18 + 5)/200 = 0.25; allele 5.7 frequency = (2 × 1 + 6 + 7 + 5)/200 = 0.10.

ANS 17.6. Hardy-Weinberg frequencies imply that $P = p^2$, $Q = 2pq$, and $R = q^2$. Substituting, $Q^2/4 = p^2q^2$ and $PR = p^2q^2$ also, hence $Q^2/4 = PR$.

ANS 17.7. If the genotype frequencies satisfy the Hardy-Weinberg principle, they should be in the proportions p^2, $2pq$, and q^2, respectively. In each case, p equals the frequency of AA plus one-half the frequency of Aa, and $q = 1 - p$. The allele frequencies and expected genotype frequencies with random mating are **a.** $p = 0.50$, expected: 0.25, 0.50, 0.25; **b.** $p = 0.635$, expected: 0.403, 0.464, 0.133; **c.** $p = 0.7$, expected : 0.49, 0.42, 0.09; **d.** $p = 0.775$, expected: 0.601, 0.349, 0.051; **e.** $p = 0.5$, expected: 0.25, 0.50, 0.25. Therefore, only **a.** and **c.** fit the Hardy-Weinberg principle.

ANS 17.8. The total number of individual equals 1000. Letting A_1, A_2, and A_3 be the alleles associated with the single DNA fragments, from largest to smallest, the allele frequencies are $p_1 = (2 \times 18 + 68 + 115)/2000 = 0.1095$, $p_2 = (2 \times 90 + 68 + 360)/2000 = 0.3040$, and $p_3 = (2 \times 349 + 115 + 360)/2000 = 0.5865$. The expected genotype frequencies (given in the same left-to-right order as shown in the gel) are 11.99, 66.58. 92.42, 128.44, 356.59, and 343.98. The chi-squared value works out to 4.62. There are 3 degrees of freedom because there are 6 classes of data, and two allele frequencies have been estimated from the data (only two, because the third could have been deduced by subtracting the others from 1), and $6 - 1 - 2 = 3$. The P value is about 0.25, so the fit to the genetic hypothesis is satisfactory.

ANS 17.9. The frequency of the recessive allele is $q = (1/14,000)^{1/2} = 0.0085$. Hence, $p = 1 - 0.0085 = 0.9915$, and the frequency of heterozygotes is $2pq = 0.017$ (about 1 in 60).

ANS 17.10. Because the frequency of homozygous recessives is 0.10, the frequency of the recessive allele q is $(0.10)^{1/2} = 0.316$. This means $p = 1 - 0.316 = 0.684$, and so the frequency of heterozygotes is $2 \times 0.316 \times 0.684) = 0.43$. Because the proportion 0.90 of the individuals are nondwarfs, the frequency of heterozygotes among nondwarfs is $0.43/0.90 = 0.48$.

ANS 17.11. a. Since the proportion 0.60 can germinate, the proportion 0.40 that cannot are the homozygous recessives. Thus, the allele frequency q of the recessive is $(0.4)^{1/2} = 0.63$. This implies that $p = 1 - 0.63 = 0.37$ is the frequency of the resistance allele. **b.** The frequency of heterozygotes is $2pq = 2 \times 0.37 \times 0.63 = 0.46$. The frequency of homozygous dominants is $(0.37)^2 = 0.14$, and the proportion of the surviving genotypes that are homozygous is $0.14/0.60 = 0.23$.

ANS 17.12. $I^A I^A$, $(0.16)^2 = 0.026$; $I^A I^O$, $2(0.16)(0.74) = 0.236$; $I^B I^B$, $(0.10)^2 = 0.01$; $I^B I^O$, $2(0.10)(0.74) = 0.148$; $I^O I^O$, $(0.74)^2 = 0.548$; $I^A I^B$, $2(0.16)(0.10) = 0.032$. The phenotype frequencies are: O, 0.548; A, $0.026 + 0.236 = 0.262$; B, $0.01 + 0.148 = 0.158$; AB, 0.032.

ANS 17.13. a. There are 17 A and 53 B alleles, and the allele frequencies are: A, $17/70 = 0.24$; B, $53/70 = 0.76$. **b.** The expected genotype frequencies are: AA, $(0.24)^2 = 0.058$; AB, $2(0.24)(0.76) = 0.365$; BB, $(0.76)^2 = 0.578$. The expected numbers are 2.0, 12.8, and 20.2, respectively.

ANS 17.14. The frequency in males implies that $q = 0.2$. The expected frequency of the trait in females is $q^2 = 0.0004$. The expected frequency of heterozygous females is $2pq = 2(0.98)(0.02) = 0.0392$.

ANS 17.15. The frequency of the yellow allele y is 0.2. In females, the expected frequencies of wildtype ($+/+$ and $y/+$) and yellow (y/y) are $0.8^2 + 2(0.8)(0.2) = 0.96$ and $(0.2)^2 = 0.04$, respectively. Among 1000 females, there would be 960 wildtype and 40 yellow. The phenotype frequencies are very different in males. In males, the expected frequencies of wildtype ($+/Y$) and yellow (y/Y) are 0.8 and 0.2, respectively, where Y represents the Y chromosome. Among 1000 males, there would be 800 wildtype and 200 yellow.

ANS 17.16. The frequency of heterozygotes is smaller by the amount $2pqF$, in which F is the inbreeding coefficient.

ANS 17.17. Inbreeding is suggested by a deficiency of heterozygotes relative to $2pq$ expected with random mating. The suggestive populations are **d.** with expected heterozygote frequency 0.349 and **e.** with expected heterozygote frequency 0.5.

ANS 17.18. The allele frequency is the square root of the frequency of affected offspring among unrelated individuals, or $(8.5 \times 10^{-6})^{1/2} = 2.9 \times 10^{-3}$. With inbreeding, the expected frequency of homozygous recessives is $q^2(1 - F) + qF$, in which F is the inbreeding coefficient. When $F = 1/16$, the expected frequency of homozygous recessives is $(2.9 \times 10^{-3})^2(1 - 1/16) + (2.9 \times 10^{-3})(1/16) = 1.9 \times 10^{-4}$; when $F = 1/64$, the value is 5.3×10^{-5}.

ANS 17.19. a. Note that $1/(2.6 \times 10^6) = 3.846 \times 10^{-7}$; set $q^2 = 3.846 \times 10^{-7}$, hence $q = 0.000620$. **b.** $q^2(15/16) + q(1/16) = 3.912 \times 10^{-5}$, or 1 in 25,561. **c.** $0.99 \times 3.846 \times 10^{-7} + 0.01 \times 3.912 \times 10^{-5} = 7.720 \times 10^{-7}$. **d.** $(0.01 \times 3.912 \times 10^{-5})/(7.720 \times 10^{-7}) = 50.7$ percent. Although only 1 percent of the matings are between first-cousins, they account for more than half of the homozygous recessives for this gene.

ANS 17.20. a. B, H, and I. **b.** JHE<u>B</u>FIK, JIF<u>B</u>EHK, J<u>H</u>K, J<u>I</u>K. **c.** Respective contributions to the inbreeding coefficient of L are $(1/2)^7(1 + F_B) + (1/2)^7(1 + F_B) + (1/2)^3 + (1/2)^3 = (1/2)^6 1 + F_B) + (1/2)^2$. **d.** If $F_B = 0$, this reduces to $17/64 = 0.266$.

ANS 17.21. For each pair of taxa, the UPGMA distance is the sum of the branch lengths connecting them. The distance matrix is therefore

	B	C	D
A	17.4	6.4	12.6
B		17.4	17.4
C			12.6

ANS 17.22. a. Here, $F = 0.66$, $p = 0.43$, and $q = 0.57$. The expected genotype frequencies are: AA, $(0.43)^2(1 - 0.66) + (0.43)(0.66) = 0.347$; AB, $2(0.43)(0.57)(1 - 0.66) = 0.167$; BB, $(0.57)^2(1 - 0.66)$

+ (0.57)(0.66) = 0.487. **b.** With random mating, the expected genotype frequencies are: AA, $(0.43)^2$ = 0.185; AB, $2(0.43)(0.57)$ = 0.490; BB, $(0.57)^2$ = 0.325.

ANS 17.23. Use Equation 15-11 with $n = 40$, $p_0/q_0 = 1$ (equal amounts inoculated), and p_{40}/q_{40} = 0.35/0.65. The solution for w is $w = 0.9846$, which is the fitness of strain B relative to strain A, and the selection coefficient against B is $s = 1 - 0.9846 = 0.0154$.

ANS 17.24. Let p_t be the frequency of the mutant X chromosomes in generation t, with $p_0 = 1$. **a.** p_1 = $p_0(1 - 0.05) = 0.95$. **b.** $p_{10} = p_0(1 - 0.05)^{10} = 0.599$. **c.** $p_{10} = p_0(1 - 0.05)^{20} = 0.358$. **d.** Solve p_t = $p_0(1 - 0.05)^t = 0.01$, hence $t = 90$ generations.

ANS 17.25. $10^{-4}/(10^{-4} + 10^{-7}) = 0.999$.

ANS 17.26. a. $q = \sqrt{(\mu/s)}$, where $\mu = 10^{-6}$ and $s = 1$; $q = 0.001$. **b.** $q = \mu/hs$, where μ is as before and $hs = 0.01$; in this case $q = 0.0001$. **c.** The equilibrium frequency of a is reduced by $(0.001 - 0.0001)/0.0001 = 90$ percent.

ANS 17.27. a. $2 \times 0.00005 \times 0.99995 = 10^{-4}$, or 1 in 10,000. **b.** Because $q = \mu/hs$, where q = 0.00005 and $hs = 0.20$ are given, $\mu = 0.00005 \times 0.20 = 1 \times 10^{-5}$.

ANS17.28.

	A	B
[CD]	17	17
A		8

ANS 17.29. a. A rare beneficial dominant, because the heterozygous genotypes are exposed to the selection favoring it. **b.** Note that this is the same case as in part **a**, because the allele of a rare beneficial dominant is a common deleterious recessive, and the other way around. Hence, the frequency of the common deleterious recessive changes faster, because the beneficial selection acts on the rare heterozygous genotypes.

ANS 17.30. a. $q = 0.10/(0.50 + 0.10) = 0.167$. **b.** $2pq = 28.8$ percent. **c.** $q = 0.10/(1.00 + 0.10) =$ 0.091. **d.** 16.5 percent.

Challenge Problems

ANS 17.31. The frequency of each allele is $1/n$ and there are n possible homozygotes. Therefore, the total frequency of homozygotes is $n \times (1/n)^2 = 1/n$, which implies that the total frequency of heterozygotes is $1 - 1/n$.

ANS 17.32. The frequencies are calculated as in the Hardy-Weinberg principle except that, for apparently homozygous alleles, $2p$ is used instead of p^2. With regard to the genotype (6, 9.3) for *HUMTHO1*, (10, 11) for *HUMFES*, (6, 6) for *D12S67*, and (18, 24) for *D1S80*, the calculation is $2 \times$ $0.230 \times 0.310 \times 2 \times 0.321 \times 0.373 \times 2 \times 0.324 \times 2 \times 0.293 \times 0.335 = 0.0043$, or about one in 230

people. With regard to the genotype (8, 10) for *HUMTH01*, (8, 13) for *HUMFES*, (1, 2) for *D12S67*, and (19, 19) for *D1S80*, the calculation is $2 \times 0.105 \times 0.002 \times 2 \times 0.007 \times 0.066 \times 2 \times 0.015 \times 0.005 \times 2 \times 0.011 = 1.28 \times 10^{-12}$, or about one in 8×10^{11} people. The point is that DNA typing is at its most powerful at discriminating among people who carry rare alleles.

ANS 17.33. a. $F_E = (1/2)3 + (1/2)3 = 1/4$, and $F_F = 1/4$ also. **b.** $F_I = (1/2)^5 + (1/2)^5 + (1/2)^5 + (1/2)^5 + (1/2)^3 + (1/2)^3 = 3/8$.

Supplemental problems with answers

S17.1. Define the following terms:
 a. Population
 b. Natural selection
 c. Random genetic drift
 d. Polymorphic gene
 e. Selectively neutral mutation
 f. Selection-mutation balance

ANS S17.1. a. A population is a group of organisms of the same species within which the individual organisms usually find their mates. **b.** Natural selection is the process proposed by Charles Darwin whereby species become progressively more adapted to their environments through the disproportionate survival and reproduction of the best-adapted genotypes. **c.** Random genetic drift is the change in allele frequency from one generation to the next owing to the finite size of natural populations. **d.** A polymorphic gene is one at which there are two or more relatively common alleles in the population. **e.** A selectively neutral mutation has no effect on the survival or reproduction of the genotype that carries it. **f.** Selection-mutation balance is the equilibrium allele frequency of a harmful allele attained when the loss of the harmful allele through impaired survival and reproduction is exactly offset by the gain of harmful alleles through new mutations.

S17.2. In a large, randomly mating herd of cattle, 16 percent of the newborn calves have a certain type of dwarfism because of a homozygous recessive allele. Assume Hardy-Weinberg frequencies.
 a. What is the frequency of the recessive dwarfing allele?
 b. What is the frequency of heterozygous carriers in the herd?
 c. Among the cattle that are nondwarfs, what is the frequency of carriers?

ANS S17.2. a. $q = \sqrt{(0.16)} = 0.40$; **b.** $2pq = 2 \times 0.6 \times 0.4 = 48$ percent; **c.** the frequency of nondwarf cattle is $p^2 + 2pq = 0.36 + 0.48 = 0.84$, among which $2pq = 0.48$ are carriers, hence the frequency of carriers among nondwarfs equals $2pq/(p^2 + 2pq) = 0.57$. Note that this is substantially greater than the frequency of carriers among all the cattle, dwarfs and nondwarfs together.

S17.3. A population of fish includes 1 percent albinos resulting from a homozygous recessive allele that eliminates the normal pigmentation. Assuming Hardy-Weinberg proportions, determine the frequency of heterozygous genotypes.

ANS S17.3. $q = 0.01$, hence $q = 0.1$, $p = 1 - q = 0.9$, and $2pq = 0.18$.

S17.4. Hereditary hemochromatosis, a defect in iron metabolism resulting in impaired liver function, arthritis, and other symptoms, is one of the most common genetic diseases in northern Europe. The

disease is relatively mild and easily treated when recognized. About one person in 400 is affected. Assuming Hardy-Weinberg proportions, determine the expected frequency of carriers.

ANS S17.4. Set $q^2 = 1/400$, whence $q = \sqrt{(1/400)} = 0.05$, and $2pq = 0.095$.

S17.5. For an X-linked recessive allele maintained by mutation-selection balance, would you expect the equilibrium frequency of the allele to be greater or smaller than that of an autosomal recessive allele, assuming that the relative fitnesses are the same in both cases? Why?

ANS S17.5. The harmful recessive allele will have a smaller equilibrium frequency in the X-linked case because the allele is exposed to selection in hemizygous males.

S17.6. How many *A* and *a* alleles are present in a sample of organisms that consists of 10 *AA*, 15 *Aa*, and 4 *aa* individuals? What are the allele frequencies in this sample?

ANS S17.6. The 10 *AA* individuals have 20 *A* alleles, the 15 *Aa* have 15 *A* and 15 *a*, and the 4 *aa* have 8 *a*. Altogether there are 35 *A* and 23 *a* alleles, for a total of 58. The allele frequency of *A* is 35/58 = 0.603 and that of *a* is 23/58 = 0.397.

S17.7. An inherited defect in a certain receptor protein confers resistance to infection with HIV1 (human immunodeficiency virus 1, the cause of AIDS). Resistant people are homozygous recessive and are found at a frequency of 1 percent in the population. Assuming Hardy-Weinberg proportions, determine the frequency of heterozygous genotypes.

ANS S17.7. Set $q^2 = 0.01$ or $q = 0.1$. The frequency of heterozygous genotypes equals $2 \times 0.9 \times 0.1 = 0.18$.

S17.8. Organisms were sampled from three different populations polymorphic for the alleles *A* and *a* and yielded these observed numbers of each of the possible genotypes:

	AA:		*Aa*:		*aa*:		Total:	
a.	5		60		75		140	
b.	10		50		80		140	
c.	15		40		85		140	

In terms of the magnitude of the chi-square obtained in a test of goodness of fit to Hardy-Weinberg proportions, which of these samples is closest to Hardy-Weinberg proportions? Do any of the samples deviate significantly from Hardy-Weinberg proportions?

ANS S17.8. In each case the allele frequency of *A* is 0.25 and the expected numbers of the three genotypes are 8.75, 52.50, and 78.75, respectively. The chi-square values are: **a.** 2.86, **b.** 0.32, and **c.** 7.94. Sample **b.** yields the closest fit to Hardy-Weinberg proportions. Sample **a.** also fits, but not so closely. Sample **c.** deviates significantly at the 1 percent level.

S17.9. In a population in Hardy-Weinberg equilibrium for a recessive allele at frequency *q*, what value of *q* is necessary for the ratio of carriers to affected organisms to equal each of the following?

 a. 10

 b. 100

 c. 1000

ANS S17.9. The ratio of carriers to homozygous recessives equals $2pq/q^2 = 2p/q = (2/q) - 2$; hence, for any ratio, *x*, the allele frequency *q* equals $2/(x + 2)$. The answers are therefore: **a.** 2/12 = 0.167, **b.** 2/102 = 0.020, and **c.** 2/1002 = 0.002.

S17.10. A man is known to be a carrier of the cystic fibrosis allele. He marries a phenotypically normal woman. In the general population, the incidence of cystic fibrosis at birth is approximately one in 1700. Assume Hardy-Weinberg proportions.

 a. What is the probability that the wife is also a carrier?

 b. What is the probability that their first child will be affected?

ANS S17.10. a. The probability that the wife is a carrier is the probability that a phenotypically normal person is a carrier. This probability is $2pq/(p^2 + 2pq)$, where $q = \sqrt{(1/1700)} = 0.024$ and $p = 0.976$. The numerator $2pq = 0.047$ and the denominator $p^2 + 2pq = 0.999$ (close enough to 1 that it can be ignored). Hence, the probability that the wife is a carrier equals 0.047. **b.** If she is a carrier, the probability that the first child will be affected is 1/4, and hence the overall probability that the first child will be affected equals $0.047 \times 1/4 = 0.012$, or about one in 84.

S17.11. A man with normal parents whose brother has phenylketonuria marries a phenotypically normal woman. In the general population, the incidence of phenylketonuria at birth is approximately one in 10,000. Assume Hardy-Weinberg proportions.

 a. What is the probability that the man is a carrier?

 b. What is the probability that the wife is also a carrier?

 c. What is the probability that their first child will be affected?

ANS S17.11. a. 2/3; **b.** $2pq/(p^2 + 2pq) = 0.0198$ because $q = \sqrt{(1/10,000)} = 0.01$; **c.** $2/3 \times 0.0198 \times 1/4 = 0.0033$, or approximately one in 300.

S17.12. What genotype frequencies constitute the Hardy-Weinberg principle for a gene in a large, randomly mating allotetraploid population with two alleles at frequencies p and q?

ANS S17.12. Just as the Hardy-Weinberg principle yields the genotype frequencies in a diploid as the successive terms in the expansion of $(p + q)^2$, the analogous expression in an allotetraploid population is $(p + q)^4$, and so the genotype frequencies are given by p^4 (*AAAA*), $4p^3q$ (*AAAa*), $6p^2q^2$ (*AAaa*), $4pq^3$ (*Aaaa*) and q^4 (*aaaa*).

S17.13. A large population includes 10 alleles of a gene. The ratio of the allele frequencies forms the arithmetic progression $1 : 2 : 3 : \ldots : 8 : 9 : 10$. The genotypes are in Hardy-Weinberg proportions.

 a. What ratio is formed by the frequencies of the homozygous genotypes?

 b. Among all heterozygous genotypes that carry the most common allele, what ratio is formed by the frequencies of the heterozygous genotypes?

ANS S17.13. a. $1^2 : 2^2 : 3^2 : \ldots : 8^2 : 9^2 : 10^2 = 1 : 4 : 9 : \ldots : 64 : 81 : 100$. **b.** $2 : 3 : \ldots : 8 : 9 : 10$.

S17.14. For an X-linked gene with two alleles in a large, randomly mating population, the frequency of carrier females equals one-half of the frequency of the males carrying the recessive allele. What are the allele frequencies?

ANS S17.14. Set $q/2 = 2pq$, so that $q = 2 \times 2pq$; therefore, $p = 1/4$, and $q = 3/2$.

S17.15. If the frequency of a homozygous dominant genotype in a randomly mating population is 0.09, what is the frequency of the dominant allele? What is the combined frequency of all the other alleles of this gene?

ANS S17.15. $p^2 = 0.09$, and so $p = (0.09)^{1/2} = 0.30$. All other alleles have a combined frequency of $1 - 0.30 = 0.70$.

S17.16. In Caucasians, the M-shaped hairline that recedes with age (sometimes to nearly complete baldness) was once thought to be due to an allele that is dominant in males but recessive in females. If this were true, and if the frequency of the baldness allele were 30 percent, what frequencies of the bald and nonbald phenotypes would be expected in males and females under random mating?

ANS S17.16. The bald and nonbald alleles would have frequencies of 0.3 and 0.7, respectively. Bald females are homozygous and would occur in the frequency $(0.3)^2 = 0.09$; nonbald females would occur with frequency 0.91. Bald males are homozygous or heterozygous and would occur with frequency $(0.3)^2 + 2(0.3)(0.7) = 0.51$; nonbald males would occur with frequency 0.49.

S17.18. A trait due to a harmful recessive X-linked allele in a large, randomly mating population affects one male in 50. What is the frequency of carrier females? What is the expected frequency of affected females?

ANS S17.18. Set $q = 1/50 = 0.02$. Then the frequency of carrier females equals $2pq = 2 \times 0.02 \times 0.98 = 0.0392$, or about two times the frequency of affected males. The expected frequency of affected females equals $q^2 = 0.0004$, or one in 2500.

S17.19. B For two alleles in Hardy-Weinberg proportions in a random mating population, show that the proportion of heterozygous children from a heterozygous mother is 1/2, irrespective of the allele frequencies. Explain why this is true.

ANS S17.19. An Aa mother has $1/2$ A and $1/2$ a gametes. The probability that the former is fertilized by an a-bearing sperm is q and the latter by an A-bearing sperm is p, hence the probability of a heterozygous offspring is $(1/2)q + (1/2)p = (1/2)(p + q) = 1$. The truth of the assertion depends on the fact that, because there are only two alleles, $p + q = 1$.

S17.20. In DNA typing, how many genes must be examined to prove that evidence left at a crime scene comes from a suspect? How many genes must be examined to prove that the evidence does not come from a suspect?

ANS S17.20. In principle, one can never prove that evidence does come from a suspect, no matter how many genes are examined; one can, however, examine a sufficiently large number of genes to make it extremely unlikely that a match could be coincidental. On the other hand, it is possible to exclude a suspect as the source of the evidence; all that is needed is one band resulting from one allele that is a mismatch.

S17.21. The DNA type of a suspect and that of blood left at the scene of a crime match for each of n genes, and each gene is heterozygous and so yields two bands. The frequency of each of the bands in the general population is 0.1. Use the product rule to calculate:

 a. The number of genes for which the probability of a match by chance is less than one in a million.

 b. The number of genes for which the probability of a match by chance is less than one in ten billion.

ANS S17.21. According to the product rule, the chance of a random match is $(2 \times 0.1 \times 0.1)^n$, where n is the number of genes. **a.** Set $(2 \times 0.1 \times 0.1)^n = 1 \times 10^{-6}$, so that $n = 3.5$ (hence, 4 loci are required). **b.** Set $(2 \times 0.1 \times 0.1)^n = 1 \times 10^{-10}$, so that $n = 5.9$ (hence, 6 loci are required).

S17.22. The ABO blood groups are determined by three alleles, I^A, I^B, and I^O, where I^{Av} and I^B are codominant and I^O is recessive. In a random mating population in which the allele frequencies of I^A, I^B, and I^O are 0.4, 0.1, and 0.5, respectively:

 a. What are the expected frequencies of the 6 possible genotypes?

 b. What are the expected frequencies of blood types A, B, AB, and O?

 c. What fraction of type B individuals is heterozygous?

ANS S17.22. a. $I^A I^A$, 0.16; $I^B I^B$, 0.01; $I^O I^O$, 0.25; $I^A I^B$, 0.08; $I^A I^O$, 0.40; $I^B I^O$, 0.10. **b.** A, 0.56; B, 0.11; AB, 0.08; O, 0.25. **c.** 0.10/0.11 = 90.9 percent.

S17.23. Interacting with the ABO blood groups is another, genetically unlinked locus known as secretor, which has two alleles. Genotypes *Se/Se* and *Se/se* secrete the A and B antigens into sweat, saliva, and other body fluids, whereas the homozygous recessive genotype *se/se* does not secrete these antigens. If the frequency of secretors in a population is 67 percent, what are the estimated allele frequencies of the *Se* and *se* alleles? Does the estimation require the assumption of Hardy-Weinberg proportions? Explain why or why not.

ANS S17.23. If we set $q^2 = 1 - 0.67$, then $q = 0.5475$ is the frequency of the *se* allele and $1 - q = 0.4255$ the frequency of the *Se* allele. The estimation requires Hardy-Weinberg proportions, because only then is the frequency of homozygous recessive genotypes equal to q^2.

S17.24. Consider the population in Problem **17-00** in light of the secretor frequencies in Problem **17-00**. If individuals were typed by examining saliva for the A and B antigens, rather than the red blood cells, what would the apparent frequencies of the blood groups A, B, AB, and O become?

ANS S17.24. Apparent frequencies: A, $0.67 \times 0.56 = 0.375$; B, $0.67 \times 0.11 = 0.074$; $0.67 \times 0.08 = 0.054$; and O, 0.498.

S17.25. Two strains of bacteria, A and B, are placed into direct competition in a chemostat. A is favored over B. What is the value of the selection coefficient (s) if, after one generation, the ratio of the number of A cells to the number of B cells:

 a. Increases by 10 percent?

 b. Increases by 90 percent?

 c. Increases by a factor of 2?

ANS S17.25. After one generation of selection, $p_1/q_1 = (p_0/q_0)(1/w)$, where w is the fitness of B relative to A (and $s = 1 - w$), p is the frequency of A and q the frequency of B. **a.** The result implies that $p_1/q_1 = 1.10 \times p_0/q_0$, hence the equation to solve is $1.10 = (1/w)$ or $w = 0.909$; hence, $s = 1 - 0.9091 = 0.0909$ is the selection coefficient against B in competition with A. **b.** Here $p_1/q_1 = 1.90 \times p_0/q_0$ and so $w = 0.5263$ or $s = 0.4737$ is the selection coefficient. **c.** In this case, $p_1/q_1 = 2.00 \times p_0/q_0$ and so $w = 0.5000$, whence $s = 0.5000$.

S17.26. Two strains of bacteria, A and B, are placed into direct competition in a chemostat. A is favored over B. If the selection coefficient per generation is constant, what is its value if, in an interval of 100 generations:

 a. The ratio of A cells to B cells increases by 10 percent?

 b. The ratio of A cells to B cells increases by 90 percent?

 c. The ratio of A cells to B cells increases by a factor of 2?

ANS S17.26. To obtain the selection coefficient s, use $p_n/q_n = (p_0/q_0)(1/1 - s)^n$, where $n = 100$, p is the frequency of A and q the frequency of B. **a.** The result implies that $p_n/q_n = 1.10 \times p_0/q_0$, hence the equation to solve is $1.10 = (1/1 - s)^{100}$, or rearranging and taking logarithms, $s = 0.00095$. **b.** In this case, $s = 1 - \exp[1/100 \times \ln(1/1.90)] = 0.00640$. **c.** Here, $s = 1 - \exp[1/100 \times \ln(1/2)] = 0.00691$.

S17.27. A strain of pathogenic bacteria undergoes cell division exactly two times as often as a nonpathogenic mutant strain of the same bacteria. What is the relative fitness of the pathogenic strain compared to the nonpathogenic strain? You may regard the generation time as the length of time for one division of a nonpathogenic cell.

ANS S17.27. It makes intuitive sense that, if the pathogenic strain divides twice as often, then it should be twice as fit. To derive this result more quantitatively, note that, if the pathogenic strain divides two times for every one division of the nonpathogenic strain, then, with successive divisions of the nonpathogenic strain, the cell numbers of the pathogenic and nonpathogenic strains are 1 vs 1 (no division yet), 4 vs 2 (one division), 16 vs 4 (two divisions), 64 vs 8 (three divisions), and so forth (in general, the ratio is $2^{2n}/2^n$, where n is the number of generations of the nonpathogenic strain). Using the formula $p_1/q_1 = (p_0/q_0)(1/w)$, where w is the fitness of the nonpathogenic strain relative to the pathogenic strain, we have, in any two successive generations, $p_1/q_1 = 2 \times p_0/q_0$, and therefore $w = 1/2$ is the relative fitness of the nonpathogenic strain relative to the pathogenic strain. The relative fitness of the pathogenic strain is $1/w = 2$.

S17.28. An allele A undergoes mutation to the allele a at the rate of 10^{-5} per generation. If a very large population is fixed for A (generation 0), what is the expected frequency of A in the following generation (generation 1)? What is the expected frequency of A in generation 2? Deduce the rule for the frequency of A in generation n.

ANS S17.28. Let p_n be the allele frequency of A in generation n and, for convenience, set $\mu = 10^{-5}$. The probability of a particular A allele not mutating in any one generation is $1 - \mu$, hence $p_1 = (1 - \mu)p_0$ but, because $p_0 = 1$, $p_1 = 1 - \mu = 0.99999$. The relation between p_2 and p_1 is the same as that between p_1 and p_0, and so $p_2 = (1 - \mu)p_1 = (1 - \mu)(1 - \mu)p_0 = (1 - \mu)^2 p_0 = (1 - \mu)^2 = 0.99998$. In general, the rule is $p_n = (1 - \mu)^n p_0$, which, in this example, is $(0.99999)^n$.

S17.29. A three alleles with allele frequencies p_1, p_2, and p_3 in Hardy-Weinberg proportions in a random mating population, what is the proportion of heterozygous offspring expected from a heterozygous mother?

ANS S17.29. $p_1 p_2 (1 - p_1)(1 - p_2) + p_1 p_3 (1 - p_1)(1 - p_3) + p_2 p_3 (1 - p_2)(1 - p_3)$

S17.30. Large samples are taken from a single population of each of four related species of the flowering plant *Phlox*. The genotype frequencies for a gene with two alleles are estimated from each of the samples, and this yields the genotype frequencies in the accompanying table. For each species, calculate the allele frequencies and the genotype frequencies expected using the Hardy-Weinberg principle. Identify which of the populations give evidence of inbreeding, and for each apparently inbreeding population, calculate the inbreeding coefficient.

Genotype frequency

Species	AA	Aa	aa
a	0.0720	0.2560	0.6720

b	0.0400	0.3200	0.6400
c	0.0080	0.3840	0.6080
d	0.0880	0.2240	0.6880

ANS S17.30. In each species, the allele frequency p is estimated from the genotype frequencies as Freq(AA) + $1/2 \times$ Freq(Aa) and turns out to equal 0.2, hence $q = 0.8$ in all species. The expected genotype frequencies are therefore 0.0400, 0.3200, and 0.6400, which is observed in species **b.** The other species deviate from Hardy-Weinberg proportions, but only species **a.** and **d.** have a deficiency of heterozygous genotypes, which is characteristic of inbreeding. With inbreeding, the frequency of heterozygotes is given by $2pq(1 - F)$ and so F can be estimated from the ratio of observed to expected heterozygote frequencies. In species **a**, $1 - F = 0.2560/0.3200 = 0.8$, whence $F = 0.2$; and, in species **d**, $1 - F = 0.2240/0.3200 = 0.7$, whence $F = 0.3$.

S17.31. The considerations in this problem illustrate the principle that for a rare, harmful, recessive allele, matings between relatives can account for a majority of affected individuals even though they account for a small proportion of all matings. Suppose that the frequency of the rare homozygous recessive genotype among the progeny of nonrelatives is one in 4 million and that first-cousin matings constitute 1 percent of all matings in the population.

 a. What is the frequency of the homozygous recessive among the offspring of first-cousin matings?

 b. Among all homozygous recessive genotypes, what proportion comes from first-cousin matings?

ANS S17.31. Set $q = \sqrt{(1/4{,}000{,}000)} = 0.0005$. For first-cousin matings, the inbreeding coefficient of the offspring is $F = 1/16 = 0.0625$. **a.** $q^2(1 - F) + qF = 2.5 \times 10^{-7} \times 0.9375 + 0.0005 \times 0.0625 = 0.00003148$, or one in 31, 766. **b.** $0.01 \times 0.00003148/(0.99 \times 2.5 \times 10^{-7} + 0.01 \times 0.00003148) = 0.56$. In other words, first-cousin matings account for 56 percent of all affected individuals but only 1 percent of all matings. (Note, however, that the trait is very rare in the first place.)

S17.32. If the frequency of a harmful recessive allele in a population is 0.01:

 a. What is the expected frequency of homozygous recessive genotypes among the offspring of nonrelatives?

 b. What is the expected frequency of homozygous recessive genotypes among the offspring of first-cousin matings?

 c. What is the relative risk (ratio of answer in **b** to answer in **a**)?

ANS S17.32. a. $(0.01)^2 = 0.0001$, or 1 in 10,000; **b.** $(0.01)^2(15/16)+(0.01)(1/16) = 0.000719$, or 1 in 1391. **c.** The relative risk is 637.4.

S17.33. A diploid population consists of 50 breeding organisms, of which one organism is heterozygous for a new mutation. If the population is maintained at a constant size of 50, what is the probability that the new mutation will be lost by chance in the first generation as a result of random genetic drift? (You may assume that the species is monoecious.) What is the answer in the more general case in which the breeding population consists of N diploid organisms?

ANS S17.33. The next generation is formed from 100 gametes drawn at random from the breeding organisms in the previous generation. Among these organisms, the frequency of the mutant allele is $1/50 \times 1/2 = 1/100$. (The 1/2 is necessary because the organism with the mutation is heterozygous.) Hence, the probability that the mutant allele will not be represented in the next generation is $(1 - 1/100)^{100} = 0.366$. (This number is approximately e^{-1}, which might be expected from the properties

of the Poisson distribution.) In the more general case, the answer is $(1 - 1/2N)^{2N}$, which equals approximately e^{-1}. (Try calculating it for a few special values of N.)

S17.34. A population segregating for the alleles A and a is sampled, and genotypes are found in the proportions 1/3 AA, |1/3 Aa, and 1/3 aa. These are not Hardy-Weinberg proportions. How big would the size of the sample have to be for the resulting P value to equal 0.05 in a chi-square test for goodness of fit?
ANS S17.34. The allele frequency of A is 0.5. Let N be the sample size. The chi-square value equals $(0.3333N - 0.25N)^2/0.25N + (0.3333N - 0.50N)^2/0.50N + (0.3333N - 0.25N)^2/0.25N = 0.1111N$. To make the P value equal 0.05, the chi-square must equal 4.0, hence $N = 4/0.1111 = 36$. The observed numbers would then be 12, 12, and 12, respectively.

S17.35. An allele A mutates to an allele a at a rate of 10^{-6} per generation, and homozygous aa genotypes are lethal. What is the equilibrium allele frequency of a, and the frequency of aa in zygotes at the time of fertilization, if:
 a. The a allele is completely recessive?
 b. The a allele is overdominant and confers a selective advantage of 2 percent on the heterozygous genotypes?
ANS S17.35. a. $q = \sqrt{[(1 \times 10^{-6})/1]} = 1 \times 10^{-3}$; frequency of homozygous $aa = q^2 = 1 \times 10^{-6}$, or 1 in 1,000,000. **b.** The fitnesses of AA, Aa, and aa are given as 1.00 : 1.02 : 0, which, relative to the heterozygous genotype, are 1.00/1.02 : 1.02/1.02 : 0/1.02, or 0.9804 : 1 : 0. Then at equilibrium $q = 0.0196/(0.0196 + 1) = 0.0192$; the frequency of homozygous $aa = q^2 = (0.0192)^2 = 0.0003698$, or 1/2704. (Note that the overdominance increases the frequency of homozygous recessives at equilibrium by a factor of 370.)

S17.36. An observed sample of a gene with two alleles from a population conforms almost exactly to the genotype frequencies expected for a population with an inbreeding coefficient F and allele frequencies 0.2 and 0.8. What is the smallest value of F that will lead to rejection of Hardy-Weinberg proportions at the 5 percent level of significance in each of the following cases? (*Hint*: Set chi-square equal to 4.0.)
 a. A sample size of 200 organisms.
 b. A sample size of 500 organisms.
 c. A sample size of 1000 organisms.
ANS S17.36. In a case with sample size N, the observed numbers of the genotypes are given by $[p^2(1 - F) + pF]N$, $2pq(1 - F)N$, and $[q^2(1 - F) + qF]N$, respectively, because they are said to conform to the expected values with inbreeding. In this case, $p = 0.2$ and $q = 0.8$, but it is actually easier to consider the more general case. The expected numbers with Hardy-Weinberg are p^2N, $2pqN$, and q^2N, respectively. The terms in the chi-square are (*observed - expected*)2/*expected*. In the case at hand, the (*observed - expected*) terms are $pqFN$, $-2pqFN$, and $pqFN$, respectively, and so the chi-square works out to be $q^2F^2N + 2pqF^2N + p^2F^2N = F^2N$. (Note how neatly the allele frequencies disappear.) To obtain a value just barely significant at the 5 percent level, we need chi-square $= 4.0$, hence the minimal value of F is given by $F^2 = 4/N$ or $F = 2/\sqrt{N}$. The answers are therefore: **a.** F = 0.1414, **b.** F = 0.0894, and **c.** F = 0.0632.

Chapter 18: The Genetic Basis of Complex Inheritance
Answers to Chapter-end problems

Fill-ins

1. quantitative-trait locus (QTL)
2. hybrid vigor
3. genotype-by-environment interaction
4. standard deviation
5. truncation point
6. broad-sense heritability
7. narrow-sense heritability
8. inbreeding depression
9. liability
10. selection limit

Analysis and Applications

ANS 18.1. Genotype-environment interaction.

ANS 18.2. Since the variance equals the square of the standard deviation, the only possibilities are that the variance equals either 1 or 0.

ANS 18.3. a. The mean or average. **b.** The one with the greater variance is broader. **c.** 68 percent within one standard deviation of the mean, 95 percent within two.

ANS 18.4. Broad-sense heritability is the proportion of the phenotypic variance attributable to differences in genotype, or $H^2 = \sigma_g^2/\sigma_t^2$, which includes dominance effects and interactions between alleles. Narrow-sense heritability is the proportion of the phenotypic variance due only to additive effects, or σ_a^2/σ_t^2, which is used to predict the resemblance between parents and offspring in artificial selection. If all allele frequencies equal 1 or 0, both heritabilities equal zero.

ANS 18.5. The F_1 generation provides an estimate of the environmental variance. The variance of the F_2 generation is determined by the genotypic variance and the environmental variance.

ANS 18.6. For fruit weight, $\sigma_e^2/\sigma_t^2 = 0.13$ is given. Because $\sigma_t^2 = \sigma_g^2 + \sigma_e^2$, then $H^2 = \sigma_g^2/\sigma_t^2 = 1 - \sigma_e^2/\sigma_t^2 = 1 - 0.13 = 0.87$. Therefore, 87% is the broad-sense heritability of fruit weight. The values of H^2 for soluble-solid content and acidity are 91% and 89%, respectively.

ANS 18.7. Estimates as follows: mean, $104/10 = 10.4$; variance, $24.4/(10 - 1) = 2.71$; standard deviation $(2.71)^{1/2} = 1.65$.

ANS 18.8. a. Phenotypes 0, 2, 4, and 6 with frequencies 0.015625, 0.140625, 0.421875, and 0.421875, respectively. **b.** Mean 4.50, variance 2.25, standard deviation 1.50. c. Phenotypes 0, 1, 2, 3, 4, 5, and 6 with frequencies 0.0156, 0.0938, 0.2344, 0.3125, 0.2344, 0.0938, and 0.0156, respectively. Mean 3.00, variance 1.50, standard deviation 1.22.

ANS 18.9. An IQ of 130 is two standard deviations above the mean, and so the proportion greater equals $(1 - 0.95)/2 = 2.5$ percent; 85 is one standard deviation below the mean, and so the proportion smaller equals $(1 - 0.68)/2 = 16$ percent; the proportion above 85 equals $1 - 0.16 = 84$ percent, which can be calculated alternatively as $0.50 + 0.68/2 = 0.84$.

ANS 18.10. a. To determine the mean, multiply each value for the pounds of milk produced (using the midpoint value) by the number of cows and divide by 304 (the total number of cows) to obtain a value of the mean of 4032.9. The estimated variance is 693,633.8, and the estimated standard deviation, which is the square root of the variance, is 832.8. **b.** The range that includes 68 percent of the cows is the mean minus the standard deviation and the mean plus the standard deviation, or 4033 − 833 = 3200 to 4033 + 833 = 4866. **c.** Rounding to the nearest 500 yields 3000–5000. The observed number in this range is 239; the expected number is $0.68 \times 304 = 207$. **d.** For 95 percent of the animals, the range is within two standard deviations or 2367–5698. Rounding off to the nearest 500 yields 2500–6000. The observed number is 296, which compares well to the expected number of $0.95 \times 304 = 289$.

ANS 18.11. a. Because 15 to 21 is the range of one standard deviation from the mean, the proportion is 68 percent. **b.** Because 12 to 24 is the range of two standard deviations from the mean, the proportion is 95 percent. **c.** A phenotype of 15 is one standard deviation below the mean; because a normal distribution is symmetric about the mean, the proportion with phenotypes more than one standard deviation below the mean is $(1 - 0.68)/2 = 0.16$. **d.** Those with 24 leaves or greater are more than two standard deviations above the mean, and so the proportion is $(1 - 0.95)/2 = 0.025$. **e.** Those with 21 to 24 leaves are between one and two standard deviations above the mean, and the expected proportion is $0.16 - 0.025 = 0.135$ (because 0.16 have more than 21 leaves and 0.25 have more than 24 leaves).

ANS 18.12. a. The genotypic variance is 0 because all F_1 mice have the same genotype. **b.** With additive alleles, the mean of the F_1 generation will equal the average of the parental strains.

ANS 18.13. Among the F_1 the total variance equals the environmental variance, which is given as 1.46. Among the F_2, the total variance, given as 5.97, is the sum of the environmental variance (1.46) and the genotypic variance, and so the genotypic variance equals $5.97 - 1.46 = 4.51$. The broad-sense heritability is the genotypic variance (4.51) divided by the total variance (5.97), or $4.51/5.97 = 0.76$.

ANS 18.14. From the F_1 data, $\sigma_e^2 = (2)^2 = 4$; from the F_2 data, $\sigma_g^2 + \sigma_e^2 = (3)^2 = 9$; hence $\sigma_g^2 = 9 - 4 = 5$, and so $H^2 = 5/9 = 56$ percent.

ANS 18.15. The maternal affect would increase the mother–offspring correlation relative to the father–offspring correlation. An estimate of the narrow-sense heritability would therefore be larger if estimated from the mother–offspring correlation than if estimated from the father–offspring correlation, but the latter is a better estimate because maternal effects are not genetically transmitted.

ANS 18.16. The offspring are genetically related as half-siblings, and Table 18-3 says that the theoretical correlation coefficient is $h^2/4$.

ANS 18.17. Table 18-3 gives the correlation coefficient between first cousins as $h^2/8$, and so $h^2 = 8 \times 0.09 = 72$ percent.

ANS 18.18. a. Because *Difflugia* is an asexual organism, parent and offspring have the same genetic relationship as monozygotic twins, hence the broad-sense heritabilities are 0.956 and 0.287, respectively. **b.** The environmental component of the variance for length of longest spine is larger than for tooth number.

ANS 18.19. Using Equation 18-4, the minimum number of genes affecting the trait is $D^2/8\sigma_g^2 = (17.6)^2/(8 \times 0.88) = 44$.

ANS 18.20. $\sigma_g^2 = 0.0570 - 0.0144 = 0.0426$ and $D = 1.689 - (-0.137) = 1.826$. The minimum number of genes is estimated as $n = (1.826)^2/(8 \times 0.0426) = 9.8$.

ANS 18.21. Use Equation 18-6 with $M^* - M = 50$ grams in each generation of selection, with M initially 700 grams. The expected gain in each generation of selection is $0.8 \times 50 = 40$ grams, and so after five generations the expected mean weight is $700 + 5 \times 40 = 900$ grams.

ANS 18.22. $h^2 = (2.33 - 2.26)/(2.37 - 2.26) = 63.6$ percent.

ANS 18.23. a. $12 + (0.2)(16 - 12) = 12.8$ g. **b.** $12 + (0.2)(8 - 12) = 11.2$ g.

ANS 18.24. Use Equation 18-6 with $M = 10.8$, $M^* = 5.8$, and $M' = 8.8$. The narrow-sense heritability is estimated as $h^2 = (8.8 - 10.8)/(5.8 - 10.8) = 0.40$.

ANS 18.25. a. In this case, $M = 10.8$, $M^* = 5.8$, and $M' = 9.9$. The estimate of h^2 is $(9.9 - 10.8)/(5.8 - 10.8) = 0.18$. **b.** The result is consistent with the earlier result because of the differences in the variance. In the previous case, the additive variance was $0.4 \times 4 = 1.6$. In the present case, the phenotypic variance is 9. If the additive variance did not change, then the expected heritability would be $1.6/9 = 0.18$, which is that observed. This problem has been idealized somewhat in that, in real examples, the additive variance would also be expected to change with a change in environment.

ANS 18.26. The mean weaning weight of the 20 individuals is 81 pounds, and the standard deviation is 13.8 pounds. The mean of the upper half of the distribution can be calculated using the relationship given in the problem, which says that the mean of the upper half of population is 81 +

$0.8 \times 13.8 = 92$ pounds. Using Equation 18-6, the expected weaning weight of the offspring is $81 + 0.2(92 - 81) = 83.2$ pounds.

ANS 18.27. a. For each locus the mean phenotype is $(1/4)(0) + (1/2)(1) + (1/4)(2) = 1$, hence for 20 independent and additive loci the mean phenotype is 20. **b.** 40. **c.** $(1/4)^{20} = 9.1 \times 10^{-13}$. **d.** $N = 1.1 \times 10^{12}$.

ANS 18.28. a. 1.0, 0.67, 0.18, 0.10, 0.02, 0.01, and 0.002, respectively. **b.** With rare recessive alleles, most homozygous offspring come from matings between heterozygous genotypes, so there is essentially no parent-offspring correlation in phenotype.

ANS 18.29. By successive substitutions, $M_1 = M_0 + h^2S$, $M_2 = M_1 + h^2S = (M_0 + h^2S) + h^2S = M_0 + 2h^2S$, $M_3 = M_2 + h^2S = (M_0 + 2h^2S) + h^2S = M_0 + 3h^2S$, and so forth, yielding $M_t = M_0 + th^2S$.

ANS 18.30. Successive substitutions in this case yields $M_t = M_0 + h^2(S_1 + S_2 + S_3 + ... + S_{t-1})$.

ANS 18.31. One approach is to use Equation 18-4 with $D = 2n - 0 = 2n$, from which $n = (2n)^2/8\sigma_g^2$, or $\sigma_g^2 = n/2$. A more-direct approach uses the fact that, with unlinked, additive genes, the total genetic variance is the summation of the genetic variance resulting from each gene. With one gene, the genetic variance equals 1/2, and so with n genes the total genetic variance equals $n/2$.

Challenge Problems

ANS 18.32. a. The mean of the random mating population is 3. **b.** The selected parents consist of 6/7 that have a phenotype of 5 and 1/7 that have a phenotype of 6, so their mean phenotype is 36/7. **c.** At each locus, 6/7 for the favorable allele and 1/7 for the unfavorable allele. **d.** With random mating, each locus contributes $(6/7)^2 \times 2 + 2(6/7)(1/7) \times 1 = 12/7$ to the phenotype, so all three loci together yield a mean phenotype of 36/7. **e.** Yes, because $M' = 36/7$, $M^* = 36/7$, and $M = 21/7$, with $h^2 = 1$. **f.** $h^2 = 1$ is expected because the genetic effects are completely additive and because there is no environmental variation effecting the trait.

ANS 18.33. a. This is a nonrecombinant class and so should have the genotype Q / q for the QTL affecting egg lay; the average should be $(300 + 270)/2 = 285$ eggs per hen. **b.** This is a crossover class of progeny. In view of the relative distances of the two intervals of 0.07 : 0.03, 7/10 of the crossovers should occur in the region Cx—Q and 3/10 in the region Q—Dx. The expected genotypes with respect to the QTL are 7/10 q / q (crossing-over in the Cx—Q region) and 3/10 Q / q (crossing-over in the Q—Dx region). The average phenotype is expected to be $(7/10) \times 270 + (3/10) \times 285 = 274.5$ eggs per hen. **c.** This is also a crossover class, but the reciprocal of that in the previous part. In this case the expected genotypes with respect to the QTL are 7/10 Q / q (crossing-over in the Cx—Q region) and 3/10 q / q (crossing-over in the Q—Dx region). The expected average egg lay is $(7/10) \times 285 + (3/10) \times 270 = 280.5$ eggs per hen. **d.** These are again nonrecombinants with QTL genotype q / q, and the expected egg lay is 270 eggs per hen.

ANS 18.34. a. The rare genetic disease is transmitted as a simple Mendelian dominant. Genotype Q / q is affected and q / q is not. Because the disease is rare, the frequency of Q / Q homozygous genotypes is negligible. **b.** Male IV-2 has the genotype Q / q, and so the probability that he has an affected daugher is 1/2. **c.** Male IV-2 has the genotype H / H for gene 2; with random mating, the probability that his daughter will have the genotype H / F is equal to the probability that an randomly chosen egg contains the F allele, which is given in the population-frequency table as 0.05, or 5 percent. **d.** The genotypes of the individuals in the pedigree are as follows. At this stage in the analysis, we do not yet know anything about linkage, but we can, in some cases, specify the linkage phase in terms of which alleles were transmitted together in a single gamete. When known, the alleles transmitted in a single gamete are grouped together in parentheses. Also, the order in which the genes are listed is arbitrary. (The two columns on the right are referred to in the next part of the analysis.)

Genotypes of individuals in pedigree

I-1	$(q A E) / (q A E)$		
I-2	Q / q ; C / D ; F / G		
II-1	$(q A E) / (Q D F)$	NRC	
II-2	$(q A H) / (q B H)$		
II-3	$(q A E) / (q C G)$	NRC	
II-4	$(q A G) / (q A H)$		
II-5	$(q A E) / (Q D G)$	NRC	
II-6	$(q A H) / (q B H)$		
II-7	$(q A E) / (Q D F)$	NRC	
II-8	$(q A E) / (q C G)$	NRC	
II-9	q / q ; A / B ; E / G		
III-1	$(q B H) / (q B H)$		
III-2	$(q B H) / (Q D E)$	NRC	REC
III-3	$(q A H) / (Q D E)$	NRC	REC
III-4	$(q A H) / (q A F)$	NRC	REC
III-5	$(q A G) / (q A E)$		NRC
III-6	$(q A H) / (q A G)$		REC
III-7	$(q B H) / (q A E)$	NRC	NRC
III-8	$(q A H) / (Q D G)$	NRC	NRC
III-9	q / q ; B / C ; E / H		
III-10	$(q B H) / (q A G)$	NRC	REC
III-11	$(q A E) / (q A E)$		NRC
III-12	$(q B G) / (q A G)$		REC
III-13	q / q ; B / C ; E / G	Undeterminable	
IV-1	$(q B H) / (Q D E)$	NRC	NRC
IV-2	$(q B H) / (Q D H)$	NRC	REC
IV-3	$(q B H) / (q B E)$	NRC	REC
IV-4	$(q B E) / (Q D G)$	NRC	NRC
IV-5	$(q C H) / (q A H)$	NRC	NRC
IV-6	$(q C H) / (Q D G)$	NRC	NRC

e. There is evidence of linkage between genes 1 and 3. In particular, the allele Q is always transmitted with allele D, starting with male I-2 at the top of the pedigree. If we assume that this

male has the genotype $(Q\ D) / (q\ C)$, then, throughout the pedigree, there are 17 individuals in which recombination between genes 1 and 3 could have been detected. These cases are identified in the third column of the foregoing table. All 17 are nonrecombinant, and so the recombination fraction between genes 1 and 3 in these data is 0/17. As far as one could discern from the pedigree alone, the Q and D alleles could be identical. However, the population-frequency table gives the allele frequency of D as 5 percent and the text says that the Q allele is rare, hence most D alleles in the population must be on chromosomes carrying q, so that D and Q are separable. Turning to genes 1 and 2, there are 17 people in whom recombination could be detected. These are identified in the fourth column in the foregoing table. Among the 17 cases, one is undeterminable and 8 are recombinant and 8 nonrecombinant. Genes 1 and 2 are therefore unlinked. Most likely that are on different chromosomes, but they could also be very far apart on the same chromosome.

Supplemental problems with answers

S18.1. Define the following terms:
 a. Multifactorial trait
 b. Quantitative-trait locus (QTL)
 c. Threshold trait
 d. Individual selection
 e. Broad-sense heritability
 f. Genotype-environment association
ANS S18.1. a. A multifactorial trait is determined by the joint action of "many factors," including the alleles of two or more genes and in most cases multiple environmental influences. **b.** A QTL is a gene whose allele contribute to variation in a quantitative trait. **c.** A threshold trait is one that is either present or absent according to the value of an underlying liability or risk, which is itself a multifactorial trait. **d.** Individual selection is selection among individual organisms based on their own phenotype (rather than, for example, the mean phenotype of the sibship from which the come). **e.** Broad-sense heritability is the ratio of the genotypic variance to the total variance of a trait in a population. **f.** Genotype-environment association takes place when the genotypes and environmental factors affecting a trait are not combined at random.

S18.2. After several generations of selection for maze-learning ability in rats, the maze-bright rats were superior to maze-dull rats in learning the maze when motivated by hunger (the condition of the selection). However, the maze-dull rats were superior to the maze-bright rats in learning the maze when motivated by escape from water. Is this an example of genotype-environment interaction? Explain.
ANS S18.2. It is an example of genotype-environment interaction because the relative performance of the two populations is reversed merely by changing the environment in which the test is carried out.

S18.3. Although most behaviors are complex traits influenced by several genes, some behavioral differences among individuals can be ascribed to alleles of a single gene (for example, the *period* gene in *Drosophila*). Mice that are mutant for the *waltzer* gene run around in circles, shake their heads both horizontally and vertically, and are very irritable. Four matings among animals isolated from a small population containing *waltzer* yielded the following litters:

 wildtype × waltzer 3 wildtype, 2 waltzer

wildtype × wildtype	7 wildtype
wildtype × wildtype	6 wildtype, 2 waltzer
waltzer × waltzer	5 waltzer

Judged on the basis of these data, do you think it is likely that the *waltzer* allele is dominant or recessive to the wildtype allele?

ANS S18.3. The waltzer allele is recessive to the wildtype allele.

S18.4. The mammalian visual system is very complex, but the ability to detect colors is under relatively simple genetic control. The genes that are defective in color blindness code for a family of photoreceptor proteins known as opsins. Normal people have four opsin genes that code for four different photoreceptor proteins: an opsin (called rhodopsin) constituting the major visual pigment, an opsin that is sensitive to blue light, an opsin that is sensitive to green light, and an opsin that is sensitive to red light. Under what conditions might a simple genetic trait, such as color blindness, affect a person's behavior?

ANS S18.4. Under conditions in which behavioral choices are strongly influenced by the ability to distinguish among different colors—for example, the ability to distinguish red and green in obeying traffic lights.

S18.5. Recurring behavioral disorders were observed in some male members of a large pedigree extending over several generations. The males were mildly mentally retarded and, especially when under stress, were prone to repeated acts of aggression-including sex offenses, attempted murder, and arson. An X-linked gene, *MAO,* coding for the enzyme monoamine oxidase, which participates in the breakdown of neurotransmitters, was found to be defective in the affected men in this pedigree. Other researchers found abnormal levels of monoamine oxidase in some unrelated men with similar disorders, even though the *MAO* gene was not defective in these cases. Does this evidence support the hypothesis that defective monoamine oxidase is responsible for the behavioral disorder? Explain.

ANS S18.5. This example illustrates some of the complexities of behavior genetics in human beings. The correlation between the *MAO* gene and the behavioral disorder in the large pedigree is suggestive. However, single pedigrees may be misleading because a correlation with a genetic marker may result from chance. Even if the disorder in this example is genetically determined, the cause need not be *MAO*. The disorder may result from a different gene that is genetically linked to *MAO,* or the large pedigree may also contain other genes influencing the disorder and the *MAO* mutation may be only a contributing factor. The finding that unrelated men with similar behavioral disorders may have abnormal levels of monoamine oxidase is also suggestive. However, without data on the distribution of enzyme levels among normal men and among those with the behavioral disorder, the strength of the evidence is impossible to evaluate.

S18.6. Huntington disease is an autosomal-dominant neurodegenerative disease marked by motor disturbance, cognitive loss, and psychiatric disorders; it has a typical age of onset of between 30 and 40 years. The function of the wildtype gene product is not known. However, the gene shares an interesting feature with a number of other disease genes in human beings. It undergoes "trinucleotide expansion." The gene contains a region with several repeats of the trinucleotide CAG. Wildtype alleles of the gene typically have 11 to 34 CAG repeats; among mutant alleles, the number of CAG repeats ranges from 40 to 86. What molecular test could be used to detect the mutant Huntington disease allele in the child of a person who develops the disease at the age of 39? If the affected

person's spouse is homozygous normal for the gene, what proportion of their children would be expected to be affected?

ANS S18.6. The test would take advantage of the size differences between the wildtype and mutant alleles. The DNA of parents and child would be digested with a restriction enzyme that cleaves the DNA at sites flanking the CAG repeat. The resulting fragments would be separated by size with electrophoresis and the fragments of interest identified by hybridization using a radioactive probe for the CAG-containing fragment. The mutant allele should be longer than the wildtype allele owing to the greater number of CAG repeats. Because the mutant allele is dominant, any mating between heterozygous mutant and homozygous wildtype is expected to result in 50% affected offspring.

S18.7. A population of sweet clover includes 20 percent with two leaves, 70 percent with three leaves, and 10 percent with four leaves. What are the mean and variance in leaf number in this population?

ANS S18.7. The mean equals $0.2 \times 2 + 0.7 \times 3 + 0.1 \times 4 = 2.90$. The variance equals $0.2 \times (2 - 2.9)^2 + 0.7 \times (3 - 2.9)^2 + 0.1 \times (4 - 2.9)^2 = 0.2900$. The standard deviation is therefore $\sqrt{(0.2900)} = 0.5385$.

S18.8. In an experimental population of the flour beetle *Tribolium castaneum,* the pupal weight is distributed normally with a mean of 2.0 mg and a standard deviation of 0.2 mg. What proportion of the population is expected to have a pupal weight between 1.8 and 2.2 mg? Between 1.6 and 2.4 mg? Would you expect to find an occasional pupa weighing 3.0 mg or more? Explain your answer.

ANS S18.8. The range 1.8 to 2.2 mg is the mean $\pm$ 1 standard deviation, and 68 percent of the population is expected to fall within this range. Similarly, the range 1.6 to 2.4 mg is the mean $\pm$ 2 standard deviations, within which 95 percent of the population is expected to fall. A beetle with a pupal weight of 3.0 mg or more deviates by more than $+$ 5 standard deviations from the mean. Since only 0.15 percent of the population deviates by more than $+$ 3 standard deviations, animals with pupae weighing more than 3.0 mg are expected to be exceedingly rare and, in practice, not found. (The expected proportion weighing $\geq$ 3.0 mg actually equals 3×10^{-7}, or roughly one in 3 million animals.)

S18.9. Tabulated below are the numbers of eggs laid by 50 hens over a 2-month period. The hens were selected at random from a much larger population. Estimate the mean, variance, and standard deviation of the distribution of egg number in the entire population from which the sample was drawn.

<div align="center">

48 50 51 47 54 45 50 38 40 52

58 47 55 53 54 41 59 48 53 49

51 37 31 47 55 46 49 48 43 68

59 51 52 66 54 37 46 55 59 45

44 44 57 51 50 57 50 40 63 33

</div>

ANS S18.9. $\Sigma x_i = 2480$ and so the estimated mean equals $2480/50 = 49.60$ eggs. To estimate the variance, subtract the mean from each value, square, sum these together, and divide by 49, or, in symbols, $s^2 = \Sigma(x_i - 49.60)^2/49 = 60.3265$. The standard deviation is the square root of the variance, hence $s = \sqrt{(60.3265)} = 7.76702$. (Note: An alternative method of calculating the estimate of the variance is to use the sum of the values and the sum of the squares as follows: $s^2 = N/(N - 1) \times$

$[\Sigma x^2/N - (\Sigma x/N)^2]$. In the present example, this expression evaluates to $(49/50) \times [125,964/50 - (49.60)^2] = 60.3265$, the same as calculated earlier.

S18.10. Suppose that the 50 hens in the previous problem constituted the entire population of hens present in a flock instead of a sample from a larger flock. What are the mean, variance, and standard deviation of egg number in the population? Why are some of these numbers different from those calculated in the previous problem?

ANS S18.10. In this case, the entire population is represented and so there is no need to make inferences about a larger population from a representative sample. In other words, the mean and variance are identical to the true mean μ and variance σ^2 in the population. The mean is therefore $\mu = 49.60$ eggs, the same as before. However, the variance is $\sigma^2 = \Sigma(x_i - 49.60)^2/50 = 59.1200$. The denominator is 50 rather than 49 because the latter is a correction necessary only when estimating the variance from a sample of individuals, not when studying the entire population. For the same reason, the standard deviation equals $\sigma = 7.6890$. As this problem illustrates, the differences are very small when the sample size is reasonably large.

S18.11. Two homozygous genotypes of *Drosophila* differ in the number of abdominal bristles. In genotype *AA,* the mean bristle number is 20 with a standard deviation of 2. In genotype *aa,* the mean bristle number is 23 with a standard deviation of 3. Both distributions conform to the normal curve, in which the proportions of the population that have a phenotype within an interval defined by the mean $\pm 1, \pm 1.5, \pm 2,$ and ± 3 standard deviations are 68, 87, 95, and 99.7 percent, respectively.

 a. In genotype *AA,* what is the proportion of flies with a bristle number between 20 and 23?
 b. In genotype *aa,* what is the proportion of flies with a bristle number between 20 and 23?
 c. What proportion of *AA* flies have a bristle number greater than the mean of *aa* flies?
 d. What proportion of *aa* flies have a bristle number greater than the mean of *AA* flies?

ANS S18.11. a. Note that 23 is the mean + 1.5 standard deviations. The problem says that 87 percent of the population falls within $20 \pm 1.5 \times 2 = 17$ to 23 bristles. Since the distribution is symmetrical around 20, then 43.5 percent of the population falls in the range 20 to 23. **b.** In this case, 20 is the mean - 1 standard deviation, and we are told that 68 percent of the population falls in the range $23 \pm 3 = 20$ to 26. Since the distribution is symmetrical around 23, then 34 percent of the population falls in the range 20 to 23. **c.** The mean of *aa* flies is 1.5 standard deviations greater than the mean of *AA* flies; since we know from part (a) that 87 percent of the flies are in the range 17 to 23, and the distribution is symmetrical, 6.5 percent have less than 17 bristles and 6.5 percent have more than 23 bristles. The latter is the desired answer. **d.** The mean of *AA* flies is 1 standard deviation below the mean of *aa* flies. Since 68 percent of *aa* flies have a bristle number in the range 20 to 26, and the distribution is symmetrical, then 16 percent have a bristle number greater than 26 and 16 percent have a bristle number less than 20. The proportion with a bristle number greater than 20 is therefore 84 percent.

S18.12. If the genotypes in the previous problem were crossed and the F_1 flies mated to produce an F_2 generation, would you expect the distribution of bristle number among F_2 flies to show segregation of the *A* and *a* alleles? Explain your answer.

ANS S18.12. No. The distribution of bristle number in *AA* and *aa* overlaps to such an extent that single flies could not be classified correctly in regard to genotype. The presence of *Aa* heterozygotes in the F_2 generation would make matters even worse.

S18.13. A meristic trait is determined by a pair of alleles at each of four unlinked loci: *A, a* and *B, b* and *C, c* and *D, d.* The alleles act in an additive fashion such that each capital letter adds one unit to the phenotypic score. Thus the phenotype ranges from a score of 0 (genotype *aa bb cc dd*) to 8 (genotype *AA BB CC DD*). What is the expected distribution of phenotype score in the F_2 generation of the cross *aa bb cc dd* × *AA BB CC DD*? Draw a histogram of the distribution.

ANS S18.13. The distribution is given by successive terms in the expansion of $[(1/2\,X + 1/2\,x)^2]^4$, where, in the expansion, each X adds one additional unit to the phenotypic score and each x adds none. In this expression, the X and x are placeholders for the capital and small letters of each of the genes. The result of the multiplication is $(1/2\,X + 1/2\,x)^8 = (1/2)^8 \times [X^8 + 8X^7x + 28X^6x^2 + 56X^5x^3 + 70X^4x^4 + 56X^3x^5 + 28X^2x^6 + 8Xx^7 + x^8]$. The distribution of phenotypes is therefore 1/256 (phenotypic score of 8), 8/256 (score of 7), 28/256 (score 6), 56/256 (score 5), 70/256 (score 4), 56/256 (score 3), 28/256 (score 2), 8/256 (score 1), 1/256 (score 0). The histogram is:

S18.14. With respect to the trait in the previous problem, what is the expected distribution of phenotypes in a randomly mating population in which the frequency of each allele indicated with a capital letter is 0.8 and in which the alleles of the different loci are combined at random to produce the genotypes?

ANS S18.14. In this case the distribution is given by successive terms in the expansion of $[(4/5\,X + 1/5\,x)^2]^4$ because the allele frequencies are given by 0.8 and 0.2, respectively. The successive terms are therefore $(1/5)^8 \times [4^8X^8 + 4^78X^7x + 4^628X^6x^2 + 4^556X^5x^3 + 4^470X^4x^4 + 4^356X^3x^5 + 4^228X^2x^6 + 4^18Xx^7 + 4^0x^8]$, and the distribution of phenotypes is as follows:

Phenotypic score	Proportion of population
0	$1/5^8 = 0.00000256$
1	$32/5^8 = 0.00008192$
2	$448/5^8 = 0.00114688$
3	$3584/5^8 = 0.00917504$
4	$17920/5^8 = 0.04587520$
5	$57344/5^8 = 0.14680064$
6	$114688/5^8 = 0.29360128$
7	$131072/5^8 = 0.33554432$
8	$65536/5^8 = 0.16777216$

Note that a phenotypic score of 8 is not the most frequent phenotype in the population even though the allele denoted by the capital letter is the most frequent at each locus.

S18.15. The F_1 generation of a cross between two inbred strains of maize has a standard deviation in mature plant height of 15 cm. When grown under the same conditions, the F_2 generation produced by the $F_1 \times F_1$ cross has a standard deviation in plant height of 25 cm. What are the genotypic variance and the broad-sense heritability of mature plant height in the F_2 population?

ANS S18.15. The variance in mature plant height in the F_1 generation is 225 cm^2, which equals the environmental variance. The variance in the F_2 generation is 625 cm^2, which equals the genotypic plus the environmental variance, hence the genotypic variance equals 400 cm^2. The broad-sense heritability is therefore 400 cm^2/625 cm^2 = 64 percent.

S18.16. Two inbred strains of *Drosophila* are crossed and the F_1 generation is brother-sister mated to produce a large, genetically heterogeneous F_2 population that is split into two parts. One part is reared at a constant temperature of 25°C, and the other part is reared under conditions in which the temperature fluctuates among 18°C, 25°C, and 29°C. The broad-sense heritability of body size at the constant temperature is 45 percent, but under fluctuating temperatures it is 15 percent. If the genotypic variance is the same under both conditions, by what factor does the temperature fluctuation increase the environmental variance?

ANS S18.16. Let *V(G)* be the genotypic variance, *V(EC)* be the environmental variance under constant conditions, and *V(EF)* be the environmental variance under fluctuating conditions. The problem stipulates that *V(G)/[V(G) + V(EC)]* = 0.45, hence *V(EC)* = 0.55*V(G)*/0.45. *V(G)/[V(G) + V(EF)]* = 0.15, and hence *V(EF)* = 0.85*V(G)*/0.15. Consequently, *V(EF)/V(EC)* = 4.64. Therefore, the temperature fluctuations increase the environmental variance for body size by a factor of 4.64.

S18.17. The narrow-sense heritability of withers height in a population of quarterhorses is 30 percent. (Withers height is the height at the highest point of the back, between the shoulder blades.) The average withers height in the population is 17 hands. (A "hand" is a traditional measure equal to the breadth of the human hand, now taken to equal 4 inches.) From this population, studs and mares with an average withers height of 16 hands are selected and mated at random. What is the expected withers height of the progeny? How does the value of the narrow-sense heritability change if withers height is measured in meters rather than hands?

ANS S18.17. The expected average height of the progeny equals 17 + 0.30 × (16 - 17) = 16.7 hands. The heritability is a ratio of variances and is independent of the unit of measurement. Hence, measuring withers height in meters makes no difference in the heritability.

S18.18. The narrow-sense heritability of adult stature in people is about 25 percent. What does this value imply about the correlation coefficient in adult height between father and son?

ANS S18.18. $r = h^2/2$. Therefore, a narrow-sense heritability of 25 percent implies a father-son correlation coefficient of 12.5 percent.

S18.19. Suppose that the narrow-sense heritability of adult stature in people equals 25 percent. A man whose height is 5 cm above the average height for men marries a woman whose average height equals that for women. Among their progeny, what is the expected average deviation from the mean adult height in the entire population?

ANS S18.19. The formula to use is *M' - M* = h^2 × (*M* - M*) but, in this case, the values given are *M* - M* for the male and female and the desired answer is *M' - M*. Because *M* - M* differs in the parents, the appropriate value to use is the average, or (5 + 0)/2 = 2.5 cm. Therefore, *M' - M* = 0.25 × 2.5 cm = 0.625 cm is the average deviation from the population mean expected in the progeny.

S18.20. From a population of *Drosophila* with an average abdominal bristle number of 23.2, flies with an average bristle number of 27.6 were selected and mated at random to produce the next

generation. The average bristle number among the progeny was 25.4. What is the realized heritability? Is this a narrow-sense or a broad-sense heritability? Explain your answer.

ANS S18.20. The realized heritability is $h^2 = (25.4 - 23.2)/(27.6 - 23.2) = 50$ percent. This is a narrow-sense heritability because it expresses the relation between the average phenotype of parents and their progeny.

S18.21. In human beings, there is about a 90 percent correlation coefficient between identical twins in the total number of raised skin ridges forming the fingerprints. What is the broad-sense heritability of total fingerprint ridge count? What is the maximum value of the narrow-sense heritability?

ANS S18.21. The broad sense heritability equals the correlation coefficient between identical twins and so is about 90 percent. This is the maximum value of the narrow-sense heritability because the narrow-sense heritability must always be less than or equal to the broad-sense heritability.

S18.22. In human beings, the correlation coefficient between first cousins in the total fingerprint ridge count is 10 percent. On the basis of this value, what's the narrow-sense heritability of this trait?

ANS S18.22. The narrow-sense heritability equals 8 times the first-cousin correlation coefficient, hence the narrow-sense heritability of total fingerprint ridge count is 80 percent.

S18.23. The narrow-sense heritability of 6-week body weight in mice is 25 percent. From a population whose average 6-week weight is 20 grams, individual mice weighing an average of 24 grams are selected and mated at random. What is the expected weight of the progeny mice in the next generation?

ANS S18.23. The expected average six-week body weight is $M' = 20 + 0.25 \times (24 - 20) = 21$ grams.

S18.24. In the mouse population in the problem above, the selection for greater 6-week weight is carried out for a total of five generations, and in each generation, parents are chosen with an average 6-week weight that is, on average, 4 grams heavier than the population mean in their generation. What is the expected average 6-week weight after the five generations of selection? Make a graph of average 6-week weight against generation number.

ANS S18.24. As calculated in the problem above, after one generation of selection, the average six-week weight is 21 grams. After two generations it is $M' = 21 + 0.25 \times (25 - 21) = 22$ grams. Since the M^* - M term on the right is always 1 gram, it is clear that the average six-week weight is expected to increase by one gram per generation. The graph is:

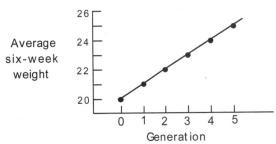

S18.25. Suppose that the selection for 6-week weight in the mouse population above were carried out in both directions for five generations. In each generation, the parents in the "up" selection are, on average, 4 grams heavier than the population mean, and the parents in the "down direction" are, on average, 4 grams lighter than the population mean.

 a. In each generation, how different are the expected means of the "up" and "down" populations?

 b. Draw a graph illustrating the expected course of selection in both populations.

 c. In the "down" population, is the realized heritability of 6-week weight expected to remain 25 percent indefinitely?

ANS S18.25. a. In the "up" population, $M^* - M = +4$ grams, hence the expected average six-weight increases by one gram per generation; in the "down" population, $M^* - M = -4$ grams, hence the expected average six-weight decreases by one gram per generation. The expected difference between the two populations therefore increases by 2 grams per generation of selection, or 2, 4, 6, 8, and 10 grams for the five generations of selection. **b.** The graph is:

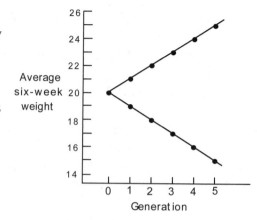

c. The realized heritability of six-week weight must decrease, eventually going to 0, otherwise one would end up with weightless mice.

S18.26. Two inbred lines of maize differ in ear length. In one, the average length of ear is 30 cm, and in the other it is 15 cm. In both lines the variance in ear length is 2 cm^2. In the F_2 generation of a cross between the lines, the average ear length is 22.5 cm with a variance of 5 cm^2. What is the minimum number of genes required to account for these data?

ANS S18.26. The environmental variance is 2 cm^2 and so the genotypic variance in the F_2 generation is 5 cm^2 - 2 cm^2 = 3 cm^2. The difference in average ear length between the inbred lines is 15 cm. Hence, using the formula $n = \dfrac{D^2}{8\sigma_g^2}$, we have $n = 225$ $cm^2/(8 \times 3$ $cm^2) = 9.4$ genes, or a minimum of 10 genes.

S18.27. A threshold trait affects 2.5 percent of the organisms in a population. The underlying liability is a multifactorial trait that is normally distributed with mean 0 and variance 1.

 a. What is the value of the threshold, a liability above which causes the appearance of the condition?

 b. If the underlying liability were normally distributed with a mean of 1 and a variance of 4, what would be the corresponding value of the threshold?

 c. Is there any real difference between these two situations?

ANS S18.27. a. The figure of 2.5 percent refers to the area in the tail of the distribution to the right of the threshold. Because 95 percent of a normal distribution is concentrated in the region between the mean + 2 standard deviations, 2.5 percent of the population have a liability less than the mean - 2 standard deviation and 2.5 percent have a liability greater than the mean + 2 standard deviation. Hence, the threshold must be located at $0 + 2\sqrt{1} = 2$ unit. **b.** The same reasoning as in part (a) yields the threshold as $1 + 2\sqrt{4} = 5$ units. **c.** There is no real difference because the two situations differ only in the scale of measurement of the liability, which is an arbitrary scale in any case. If the liability in the first situation is denoted x and that in the second situation denoted y, the relation between x and y is that $x = (y - 1)/\sqrt{4}$. [More generally, any normal distribution of a variable y with a mean of μ and a variance of σ^2 can be transformed into a normal distribution of a different variable x with a mean of 0 and a variance of 1 by means of the formula $x = (y - \mu)/\sigma$.]

Student Solutions Manual and Supplemental Problems to accompany

GENETICS

ANALYSIS OF GENES AND GENOMES
SIXTH EDITION

DANIEL L. HARTL · ELIZABETH W. JONES
PREPARED BY ELENA R. LOZOVSKY

This essential student resource contains complete solutions to all of the end-of-chapter problems in **Genetics: Analysis of Genes and Genomes, Sixth Edition,** by Daniel L. Hartl and Elizabeth W. Jones, as well as a series of supplemental problems with full solutions.

Written by Elena Lozovsky of Harvard University and the authors of the main text, the supplemental problems provided in this book have been designed as learning opportunities rather than exercises to be completed by rote. They are organized into chapters that parallel those of the main text, and all of the problems can be solved through application of the concepts and principles explained in **Genetics, Sixth Edition.**

Jones and Bartlett Publishers
40 Tall Pine Drive
Sudbury, MA 01776
978-443-5000
info@jbpub.com
www.jbpub.com